FROM THE LIBRARY OF

IMMORTAL WHEAT

Immortal Wheat

BY KATHLEEN WALLACE

*A Personal Interpretation Mainly in Fictional Form
of the Life and Works of the Brontës*

G. P. PUTNAM'S SONS
NEW YORK

Library of Congress Catalog Number: 52-5282

Manufactured in the United States of America
*First published in Great Britain
by William Heinemann Ltd.*

FOREWORD

I would like to say, simply and plainly at the outset, that this book claims to be no more than one individual's personal interpretation of the Brontës, and that I hope it will be read as such, and only as such. There are so many of us to whom the Brontës are peculiarly precious; this book is the voice of one of them, thinking aloud to the others. It is inevitable that we should differ among ourselves, and, on occasion, even aggravate one another. . . . But we are bound by one service; however inadequate that service may sometimes be.

I acknowledge with thanks permission from the Columbia Press, New York, and the Oxford University Press, England, for the quotations from *The Brontës' Web of Childhood*, by Fannie E. Ratchford, used in this book.

K. W.

BOOKS USED

The novels and poems of Charlotte, Emily, and Anne Brontë.

Life of Charlotte Brontë. Mrs. Gaskell, 1857.

The Brontës. Life and Letters. Clement Shorter, 1908.

The Three Brontës. May Sinclair, 1912.

Mrs. Gaskell and Her Friends. Elizabeth Haldane (1932?)

All Alone. The Life and Private History of Emily Brontë. Romer Wilson, 1928.

In the Steps of the Brontës. Ernest Raymond, 1948.

The Brontës' Web of Childhood. Fannie E. Ratchford, reprinted edition, 1949.

CONTENTS

The corn was orient and immortal wheat, which never should be reaped, nor was ever sown. . . . And young men glittering and sparkling Angels, and maids strange seraphic pieces of life and beauty! . . . Eternity was manifest in the Light of the Day, and something infinite behind everything appeared: which talked with my expectation and moved my desire. . . . The streets were mine, the temple was mine, the people were mine. . . . The skies were mine, and so were the sun and moon and stars, and all the World was mine; and I the only spectator and enjoyer of it.

THOMAS TRAHERNE, 1637(?)—1674.

Part One

THEMSELVES

THE room above the front door and the narrow hall was no more than a wedge in space. It was chilly and airless at the same time, that most deadly combination, for there was no fireplace and the window was tight shut. People lived and worked in this room: there was a table pushed under the window with an inkwell and pens and pencils and a colour-box and paintbrushes. There was a narrow cupboard and a set of deal shelves covered by a curtain. A wooden chair, a kitchen chair, was at the table. It was surprising that even so few bare articles of furniture could be established in the small space; it was to be noticed that they were only so contrived by being fitted like the pieces of a mosaic. It was also to be noticed that the room was orderly, bare and tidy as a cell.

The single window looked out upon the square plot of garden, a piece of lawn skirted by currant-bushes and a lilac tree as though a piece of carpet should be shaken from a window and dropped into the churchyard. The flat tombstones thronged to the garden wall set so thickly that there was scarcely room to pass between them and no trees screened them or the house.

The three children scuttled into the room like rabbits darting to their burrow. Their eyes were dilated, their faces intent, with eagerness. Those were not the faces of children arriving at a warm and familiar nursery after some absence; such faces might show relief or satisfaction or merely an inexpressive acceptance, even (quite possibly) boredom. Not ecstasy. Emily drew a deep breath as though she had run a distance, but they had only darted across the landing from Aunt Branwell's room. Her eyes, dark blue-grey eyes, were wide with excited apprehension as though between one door and the other something, someone, could have caught her, snatched her from the haven before she reached the door-handle. Charlotte was breathing fast, she uttered a little, hoarse laugh of exultation which emerged like a bantam crow. For this room, "the children's study", was sanctuary. Here, no one interfered, no one looked in to forbid, to preside, to domineer. They were as safe within its narrow walls as though they turned the key in the lock, which it would never enter any of their heads to do.

Charlotte tugged at the drawer of the table and out came the stacks of minute, neatly-cut sheets of paper. With her wide nose in her small face almost touching the paper and her big myopic eyes concentrated upon it, she is writing directly that the door has closed. Emily is down on the floor with the old box of colours and one of the heavy tomes from the shelves in Papa's study downstairs. The children are allowed to range among those bookshelves as they like. This volume has dark, spotted steel engravings of pictures by the great Italian painters, Raphael, Michelangelo, da Vinci, and others. Emily is copying one of them, minutely and elaborately, and colouring it according to her own fancy, with results which might startle Leonardo. Anne sits on the floor, too, as close to Emily as she can get without upsetting the mug of water, and their voices are a continuous, interwoven murmur.

The chill of the stuffy room is something of a bodily shock because they have been sitting for two hours on end in Aunt's room, first at their lessons, then at their samplers and fine-hemming, and Aunt Branwell has a coal fire and of course her windows are tight shut, too. Anne's tiny teeth begin to chatter. Emily looks up, gets up, and takes a shawl from a peg and folds it round the little girl's shoulders. There is a clatter of thick boots on the stone stairs: Branwell, coming up from Papa's study and his lessons. His red head is put in at the door, he grins at his absorbed sisters, but not as a teasing school-boy about to make trouble. Far from it; his pointed face, where the expressions race like ripples over water, is alight with the same eagerness as theirs.

"Don't jolt the table," says Charlotte absently, bemusedly, as he brings his painting gear and half-finished map to the opposite side.

The passion of high imagination, the ecstatic submersion in achievement, burned in the cold cell of a room. It was sufficient to shatter the grey oblong block of the house, walls and slate roof and draughty stone floors.

Any imaginative children might play the game which they

were all playing: many others did and would always do so. It consisted simply of making a country of their own, and filling it with people, and building a saga of their exploits, their sayings and doings. It began to take shape from nothing more momentous than a box of wooden soldiers brought home for Branwell by Papa, and shared by his sisters. Branwell, the only boy, did not stand aloof from the girls in their game of Let's Pretend; he was a dynamo of activity in it. He and Charlotte, in fact, were the chief if not the only begetters of Glasstown. The game was more voluminous, detailed, and markedly precocious than the same sort of pastime in the hands of other children, because three of these four possessed extraordinary brains, and all four lived in a household where politics were vehemently discussed, and ancient stories of violent north-country life told to them as other children might be told nursery tales. Papa might not see a great deal of his brood of motherless children, but when he did see them, it was no case of children being seen but not heard.

Their young brains were abnormally active, and their memories. This first imaginary world of theirs was over-whelmingly loaded with detail. There were maps, there were histories, there were miniature magazines, there were stories and poems and plays: there were "fancy portraits" of some of the chief personages. Branwell's contributions were of a violence which should have given Papa food for thought—and apprehension—if he had ever set eyes on them: Branwell went in for tortures and massacres in a Big Way. . . . Precocity was the keynote of this all-absorbing game in its beginnings; and Charlotte and Branwell were the master-minds.

But there was no one to perceive what lay ahead, when adolescence took the place of precocious childhood. No one—not the four themselves—was ever to recognise that those children, growing into adolescents, growing into a man and three women, had created something which was to enslave them for life. It was so ecstatic a thraldom that it must be for-ever questionable whether it be a matter to deplore or other-wise. Out of the childish, complicated, and extremely be-wildering world of Glasstown, later Verdopolis, with its characters and its dramatic history, there rose the imagined

worlds which held the four Brontës for life. In the course of
time, the four divided: Charlotte and Branwell created Angria;
Emily built Gondal and Gaaldine, with Anne soldered to her
wrist, Anne's frail wagon inexorably hitched to her meteor.

And it was not only that everything which they wrote in
later life had its roots in the persons and the dramas of these
imaginary worlds: but that the walls of those worlds rose
between them and reality. Their actual lives were phenomenally
enclosed, and arid. And two of the four had genius, and two
had living talent. They might, conceivably, have battled their
way to a wider way of life. Or, equally conceivably, have gone
distraught and pined for lack of it. Instead, they withdrew
behind the ramparts of their self-created worlds. They are,
for all time, the outstanding example of possession-by-day-
dream.

But all this was not yet. For the time being, they are four
children blissfully immersed in play, on a bare floor and at a
bare table.

It would all have been beyond the scope of understanding of
the older persons in the house, who had only a vague notion
of what was going on, in any case. But at least they did not
thwart it, they encouraged; rather as you might encourage a
picnic blaze for convenience and start a forest fire. The
children were out of the way, and occupied, and no trouble,
which was a matter for relief and thankfulness. Papa confided
to a friend that their *"innocent but distressing prattle"* was really
too much for him and he kept well beyond its reach except at
tea-time. When he had given Branwell his lessons and Aunt
had dutifully done the same for the girls, what they did with the
rest of their time was nobody's concern. A release all round
until the summons to tea.

But encouragement there was. Papa was gratified by the
intelligence of his distressing innocents, and fostered it. Fed it,
even, up to his limits, sharing his several newspapers and his
vigorous political opinions with them. Aunt Branwell presented three volumes of Sir Walter Scott as a New Year gift.
Tabby in the kitchen, and the two Garr sisters who were nurse
and maid when the parsonage was brimming over with babies,
were proud of them. Never were such clever little children,

they said. Tabby, who was to live in the parsonage kitchen for upwards of thirty years, told them stories of the strange, violent happenings in the old houses sunk in the moors as they clustered round the kitchen hearth. Strong meat for babes; but these were no ordinary babes. And in the mind of one of them, the atmosphere of those turbulent moorland strongholds was so much the air in which her mind breathed freely that she wrought it into a masterpiece. Charlotte was horrified by *Wuthering Heights* and felt compelled to account for it in some way.

"*. . . what her mind had gathered . . . was too exclusively confined to those tragic and terrible traits of which, in listening to the secret annals of every rude vicinage, the memory is sometimes compelled to receive the impress. Her imagination, which was a spirit more sombre than sunny, more powerful than sportive, found in such traits material whence it wrought creations like Heathcliff, like Earnshaw, like Catherine. Having formed those beings she did not know what she had done . . .*"

Emily was probably the only person who knew, or ever will know, exactly and to the uttermost, what she had done. And old Tabby may be said to have some claim to immortality, in that her gruesome fireside stories had their part in *Wuthering Heights*. As far as the children's busy minds were concerned there were sufficient hands, from study to kitchen, to fan the fires, clumsy hands, some of them, and others groping blindly enough, but there was no banking-up with damp ash.

Their play spread to the cheerless garden. There can seldom have been a patch of ground less like one while bearing the name. In time to come, trees would rise about it and brambles and undergrowth would lock the gate which led from it into tombland, but now it was a bare plot with the tombstones flocking to the wall as a crowd of cattle might do. There were the currant-bushes from which they made jam in the kitchen, and they were so nearly a churchyard growth that the idea is slightly sickening. There was the pallid lilac-bush, where Emily was to sit writing, her sloping rosewood desk on her knee. Emily, tall and spare in an ugly dress with out-of-fashion *gigot* sleeves because Emily had a fancy for *gigot* sleeves and it mattered nothing to her that no one else was wearing them then.

Her dark chestnut hair braided into a tight, heavy coronet with
long curls straggling, and lifting in the slight wind. Her storm-
blue eyes, her strong-featured face, blank as a cast of Emily.
Anyone coming into the garden where she sat, drowned in her
own thoughts, would see her looking almost stupid. So far
withdrawn that the look of ordinary living was drained from
her face. Only, no one suddenly entering the garden would
have seen Emily's face, whatever look it wore, because, at the
first click of the gate, she would have fled into the house or
behind it.

There were a few flowers of spring and summer in the bleak
garden. Anne recalled them in one of her poems:

> *That I might simply fancy there*
> *One little flower—a primrose fair,*
> *Just opening into sight;*
> *As in the days of infancy,*
> *An opening primrose seemed to me*
> *A source of strange delight.*

> . . . .

> *Still wake the golden crocus shine*
> *Among the flowers the most divine,*
> *The glory of the spring.*
> *Still in the wall-flower's fragrance dwell;*
> *And hover round the slight blue bell,*
> *My childhood's darling flower.*
> *Smile on the little daisy still,*
> *The buttercup's bright goblet fill*
> *With all thy former power.*

She wrote her poem, contrasting the lavish gardens of the
house where she was governess with the bare Haworth patch
and its sprinkling of sparse flowers, turning from the cultivated
beauty around her and hungering for the bleak place that was
home.

The crowding tombstones. The grave, and the horrible fact
of the body's decay, were worked into the consciousness of

these children. Hideous but familiar. The tombstones were under their eyes from the house or the garden; they sat among the tablets of their mother and their two sisters, in church, three times every Sunday. And in Charlotte's young mind, at least, the black hymnology, tracts, sermons, of Cowan Bridge School had left a life-long trace. The dead body, ice-cold and decomposing below ground, seeped into their poems, even into the tender love-song and threnody which Emily wrote:

> Cold in the earth—and the deep snow piled above thee,
> Far, far removed, cold in the dreary grave!
> Have I forgot, my only Love, to love thee?

Across the grey garden the stale sense of death lay as it lies across a cemetery, as pervading as the physical smell of it would have been.

But now they were out on the moors. The moorland spread in immensity from edge to edge of the sky under scudding clouds. A limitless dark sea of moor, the summit of the world. The children were scattering and flying like birds let loose. The wild free air was driving over the churchyard and garden and through the grey coffin of a house in spite of its hermetically sealed windows, and the children were free in it. The miasma of death and corruption scattered like broken cobwebs before the splendour and unbounded spaces of the moors.

They held no dread for the children; the moors of home were in their lifestream, not just a familiar setting and so endeared to any child, but blended inextricably with all that they were and did. It was freedom, just as the cramped, fireless "study" was freedom. Other children Went For Walks (and how many generations of children have detested that phrase because of what it stood for: routine, boredom, nursery tyranny); these children spread wings and skimmed the roof of the world, a country of the moon, every day and in all weathers.

Of the four who were darting and scrambling in the wind and the gleams of sunlight under the looming cloud-pinnacles on the sweeping table-lands, Charlotte at least would remember all her life those frozen, torturing walks from Cowan Bridge to an icy church, two miles of marshalled walking in the gang of small prisoners. One item in that massacre of the innocents. When she wrote *Shirley*, she made even that man of iron, Mr. Helstone, arrange on a winter Sunday of snow and ice for the Sunday-school children to wait in a room warmed by a stove until the minute that the service in church began. Now the bitter memory blew across her in an evil gust as she raced over the brown, matted heather, calling to the others. She stood still for an instant, her narrow little chest heaving and her small face dark with a look that no child's face should ever have held, as cruelly disfiguring as a birthmark.

. . . And now the scene shifted, the time slid, and there were young women in place of a group of scampering, calling children. They were dauntless walkers, the Brontë girls and their brother. They walked constantly to Keighley, four miles off, to return carrying loads of books from the Mechanics' Institute, to meet a visitor, to catch a train, as one would walk down a high street. The old woman whose cottage stood alone on one of those unpeopled stretches of the moor cheerfully requested Charlotte to look out for her lost calf, as she would be certain to encounter it in her walks.

These skies were not livid nor heavy with portent and foreboding, there was sunlight, with galleon-clouds racing. And the group was of laughing girls, light of heart in a merry hour, and Emily, the lightest in heart of all and breaking into teasing mischief. Charming Ellen Nussey was one of them, pretty as a miniature, gentle and adoring, and attractive to any male eye in her tasteful, fashionable gowns. Even Papa had a soft spot for pretty, pious Ellen and worried over her love-affairs in case that gentle, sentimental heart should take hurt. Even Emily— whom she so simply and deeply admired and reverenced—liked Ellen; almost the only outsider whom she was ever known to admit across the threshold of her own citadel. Emily was teasing Charlotte, reducing her to little shrieks and shudders, because Charlotte was afraid of strange animals, and Emily amused herself and the others by solemnly assuring her that all manner of wild things of the moors were lurking out of sight just where the girls had been resting in the heather or by the running stream. Emily stretched her long body flat beside the water and played with the minute, flickering creatures of the shallows, happy as a child. And lay in the grass with her face on her crossed arms, relaxed and content.

They have pictured Emily as the Solitary. *All Alone*, Romer Wilson named her when she, who also belonged to the moors and the north, wrote of Emily. And in her essence, her innermost self, she was; as far as human contacts were concerned. But no Solitary in humankind can ever have been less physically alone. She scarcely had a bed to herself, still less a room, until Aunt Branwell died and Charlotte fled back to Brussels.

Were those unchartable ecstasies of hers experienced while a sister breathed beside her in the dark *"of thickest stars"?* Did she move within the fastness of *Wuthering Heights* while she strode over the uplands with a crew of sisters and friends of the sisters? Emily shared the Gondal world with Anne all their lives; did she contrive to slip from her own bodily presence into the life of the brain and the soul, while her body kept company by night and day with her family?

That single year when she had the small place to herself, Charlotte away, Anne away, Aunt Branwell out of the way for ever, and her room free at last: was that Emily's *annus mirabilis?*

The desolate great houses that belonged to the past days of the wool fortunes were dropped like boulders in the folds of the moors. Old Ponden Hall, already falling into ruins and locked in the jungle-hold of its trees. The black cliff of Ponden Kirk. Emily knew them all, and her mind was stored with old Tabby's stories, savage and legendary, of the northern families who had built them and inhabited them. Papa had taken part in the days of riots and mill fights. Miss Wooler told her pupils stories of the Luddite Risings as they took their decorous walks about Roe Head School for young ladies. If Emily was mercifully too small at Cowan Bridge to retain any distinct memory of the deadly walks there, she assuredly remembered Roe Head. Where the entertaining, conducted walks of a handful of schoolgirls with a lady who was a born raconteuse, were prison-misery to a girl who was sick in body and spirit for the freedom of her moors. A girl who could describe the east wind bearing down

upon the house with a freight of influenza and bronchitis as
"a very uninteresting wind . . ."

(ii)

CHARLOTTE was to go to school again.

The girls, sewing in Aunt's room, stitched at the new collars,
the new nightgowns. They were not many, and the time needed
for all the preparations was not long. But it was long enough
for Charlotte's small face to shrink smaller, to whiten, and to
show deep smears under the big brown eyes.

She went about the house in the grip of terror. Emily could
not remember anything very clearly of the months at Cowan
Bridge; Charlotte did not forget an item or a detail. They were
buried alive in the recesses of her mind, overlaid, displaced by
the absorbed contentment of the years which had followed.
Life at home, at Haworth, the freedom and the security in the
small, tight circle of loved and familiar faces.

When the time came that the parsonage at Haworth was a
landmark, a curio, a target for sightseers, one visitor said of it:
". . . joy can never have entered that house since it was built."
But the speaker was wide of the mark. It has been too easy to
see *"that house"* as no more than the bleak and ugly place
which it undeniably was, and childhood in it as something
against nature. Easy, too, to present Papa as a warped domestic
juggernaut. The picture is out of drawing, if only because it is
constantly presented in accordance with the standards and
codes of a later day. There was no warm nursery and no
enveloping tenderness, and from the point of view of health and
hygiene the house was a death-trap, with the churchyard
draining into the water-supply. . . . But if the life at home
lacked physical comforts it held certain elements whose value to
children it would be difficult to exaggerate. There was freedom:
and there was absence of fear. Papa treated his children's minds
as equals of his own, even if he had limited ideas concerning the
care of their small bodies. He had a quick temper—but so have
most Irishmen. Aunt was a trial, and her stuffy, inviolate room
represented dullness and duty, but she was no figure of dread.
And she was, actually, the only figure for whom Haworth

parsonage was the dungeon which too-partial critics have made it out to be for the rest of the household. She relinquished a cheery, chatty existence in the mild climate and beauty of Penzance to immure herself in the bitter north among a population who were little better than savages in her shrinking eyes. She made her three motherless nieces into women who could not do even the homeliest household task other than faultlessly. She loved the wayward nephew and Branwell loved her dearly in return. When she died he could write: *"I am incoherent, I fear, but I have been waking two nights witnessing such agonising suffering as I would not wish my worst enemy to endure; and I have now lost the pride and director of all the happy days connected with my childhood."* She lent them money, left them her savings and her little personal treasures, and, being no fool, left her favourite nothing, since Branwell had by this time proved himself a spendthrift. (Which was an unpleasant jar for Miss Branwell's warm-hearted nephew . . .) They found her a nuisance and sometimes a bore; but they were never afraid of Aunt. Even Anne could be pert to her. Aunt, sailing into the kitchen where Anne sat toasting her toes at the hearth, an unladylike habit much strictured by the good lady, asked pointedly: *"Where are your feet, Anne?"* And Anne returned in her soft, imperturbable tone: *"On the floor, Aunt . . ."* which Emily found so good a joke that she put it on record. . . .

The kitchen, with its good, glowing range. There was comfort and warmth for them all, and Tabby, sparing of fondness and ready enough to order her children about, but faithful through a long lifetime and most certainly to be numbered among *"the loved and the loving"* of whom Emily sang. So loved that when she broke her leg and Aunt wished her to be nursed in the village by a sister or niece, the girls coolly went on hunger-strike until she was allowed to remain and to be nursed by themselves while they did her work in the house. So loved that when Charlotte, in her time of fame, went shopping in Manchester under the wing of beautiful and sociable Elizabeth Gaskell, her principal anxiety was to find a kerchief, or little neck-shawl, for old Tabby, something gay enough for a surprise and yet sober enough to suit the old woman.

A household of freedom and no fear. There have been children in comfortable homes who did not have those privileges. . . .

And home meant, also, that vehement life of the imagination, that laborious, intoxicating delight. Charlotte sits in the parlour window-seat compiling a list of written works only covering the space of one year and four months:

"*The Adventures of Edward de Crack. The Adventures of Ernest Alembert. Tales of The Islanders in four volumes.* . . . *The Young Men's Magazine in six numbers* (with a double number for Christmas in the approved style of such publications). *The Poetaster. A Drama in two volumes. A Book of Rhymes. Miscellaneous Poems* . . . *Emily's and my best plays were established the 1st of December 1827; the others March 1828. Best plays mean secret plays; they are very nice ones. All our plays are very strange ones. Their nature I need not write on paper, for I think I shall always remember them.* . . ."

The list rolls on dizzily. And in those last sentences, Charlotte, aged fifteen, was putting into words the main-spring of their existence without an inkling of what the abrupt, childish phrases implied. Her eyes smarted and watered as she wrote, in her microscopic script. There rose from the tiny pages that overpowering sense of enrapt achievement, of minds so dynamically occupied and active that the room with waver-ing firelight and the last of daylight at the window for a child's straining eyes was a crucible.

Rather more than five years of home, and all that home contained, implied, and fostered, to bury the horror of Cowan Bridge and set live plants shooting, spreading, and flowering above its tomb. And now, school again: and the ghosts sat up, and burst through the covering gravestone and the screening fresh growth. Maria, the little saint, the child who spread the wings of a dove over the motherless small sisters and brother. Who was, at ten years old, Papa's favourite companion because "*he could converse with her on any of the leading topics of the day with as much freedom and pleasure as with any grown-up person.*" Done to death by the cruelties at Cowan Bridge. And Elizabeth, too, coming home to die. Elizabeth is no more than a shadow. But how characteristic of herself and of Cowan Bridge that she was remembered for only one thing: her courage when she cut her small head so badly that her bed had to be moved into the room of the headmistress for care and supervision. *I suffered to see my sisters perishing.* That was Charlotte's ineffaceable memory of her first school. Now, there was to be another school.

Could no one in the house see what was in the girl's mind? For all that she knew, she was being driven back to a torture-chamber, and by Papa and Aunt of all people, who were never knowingly unkind. Branwell, as a little boy, saw Elizabeth in her coffin: had he no idea of Charlotte's dread?

In bed, Emily felt Charlotte's small frame shaking beside her.

"You could run away——" said Emily in her odd, deep voice. "You could get home somehow. Twenty miles . . ."

"No, I will not do that. I must go to school, Em. I want to *learn.* If I can learn—I think I can bear it. I must. Aunt cannot teach us anything more than sewing and the housework, now. That I do know. There'll be books . . . it's like being hungry and parched, sometimes I want books so *badly.* I must go; and I mustn't die. . . . Perhaps, later, you'll come too——"

"That I never will. No books and no schooling would be worth it. I cannot see why one should forever be reading what other people have written. As for school—I would as soon be put in my coffin and nailed down alive."

"That is a silly way to talk. Wicked, too——"

"It's the truth, wicked or not. I couldn't breathe anywhere else, anywhere but here."

And after all; after the agony and apprehension endured in the paralysed dumbness of the child whose head it does not enter to question the decisions of the elders; after the winter journey all by herself in the covered cart; school turns out to be Roe Head. The comfortable country house in the green countryside of meadows and parkland and hanging woods. And plump, kindly Miss Wooler with her gentle ways and her gift for telling enthralling stories in a memorably sweetspeaking voice, in place of the nightmare figure of Cowan Bridge, the "Scourge-mistress" whom Charlotte named Miss Scatcherd (and there is little to choose between the ugliness of the names . . .) No crowd, either, to overwhelm Charlotte: only seven or eight girls in all. Charlotte at school again would suffer home-sickness, and all the prods and pricks of school-girl dealings, but never fear, and never the spectacle of cruelty.

And now there were friends for Charlotte: the two who were to be her close friends always. And much more like a story-book than real life is the fact that she encountered both in her first hour at Roe Head. If the scene of her arrival belonged to fiction, it could be criticised as too much of a manipulated coincidence. Here was Miss Wooler in her well-fitting dress and with her long, pretty ringlets, sailing out to welcome the new pupil who arrived in the covered cart. And hovering about the shrubbery in curiosity was Mary Taylor. This blunt, indomitable girl was the one who told Charlotte that she was *"very ugly"*; and who uttered the unforgettable phrase describing the Brontës as *"like growing potatoes in a cellar."* Charlotte answered sadly: *"Yes! I know we are!"* in her low voice with its marked Irish brogue. The murmured words are more poignant than any which she was ever to write. No woman had a greater mastery of words in which to express suffering than she came to achieve; but that schoolgirl sentence surpasses them all.

All through Mary's life, she was to befriend Charlotte with an impatient, exasperated affection. Urging her to revolt, to the bursting of bonds; blaming everyone but Charlotte herself because Charlotte was intrinsically incapable of doing any such thing on her own behalf. Elizabeth Gaskell saw with deeper penetration there, for all her limitations and impetuous errors; saw the more clearly, perhaps, because she so honestly and with such dignity of mind admitted some of those limitations.

"The family with whom I have now to do shot their roots down deeper than I can penetrate. I cannot measure them . . ."

But she could measure the dreadful acquiescence in fate which Charlotte named God's will.

"I am struck afresh by the absence of hope which formed such a strong characteristic in Charlotte . . . she never dared to allow herself to look forward with hope . . . it must have been, so to speak, constitutional . . ."

". . . She said, in her own composed manner, as if she had accepted the theory as a fact, that she believed some were appointed beforehand to sorrow and much disappointment . . . that she was

trying to school herself against ever anticipating any pleasure; that it was better to be brave and submit faithfully."

Charlotte herself, after reading Matthew Arnold's Life: *"I was struck by the almost unbroken happiness of his life. . . . One feels thankful to know that it has been permitted to any man to live such a life."*

Thankful; but almost incredulous. And with something far deeper and less ignoble than envy.

As though a trick of light from more than one lamp should throw a double shadow, there were two Marys in the person of the one girl who stole from the path which skirted the Portuguese laurels, wrapped in her winter cloak, drawn by the noise of creaking wheels on the dignified drive. (That covered cart was surely a vehicle for the back door, not the *porte cochère?*) There was the appallingly outspoken schoolgirl; and there was the shrewd, untramelled young-woman-to-be. Mary who went on strike for a fortnight against even Miss Wooler's mild rules because Charlotte had suffered some injustice in the matter of marks, for which, incidentally, the kind little headmistress had apologised. Mary who, later on, told Charlotte that *"to spend the next five years at home in solitude and weak health would ruin her; that she would never recover it. Such a dark shadow came over her face when I said 'Think of what you'll be five years hence!' that I stopped and said 'Don't cry, Charlotte!' She did not cry, but went on walking up and down the room, and said in a little while 'But I intend to stay, Polly.' "* Mary's bludgeoning use of a blunt instrument invariably brought in answer some of the most poignant words spoken by Charlotte. Mary cut loose, went free, went pioneering to New Zealand and set up a shop there when no young lady ever kept a shop. And wrote home such letters as might be written by a girl a century later. She had forgotten what it felt like to sit down to dinner, wrote Mary. She was too busy; she cooked some eggs and brewed some tea when she felt the need of a meal. She fairly launched a burst of grapeshot at Ellen Nussey, when Ellen wrote fluttering with apprehension over Charlotte's marriage.

"You talk wonderful nonsense about C.B. in your letter. . . . What do you mean about 'bearing our lot, whatever it is'? If it's Charlotte's lot to be married, shouldn't she bear that too? Or does

*your strange morality mean that she should refuse to ameliorate her
lot when it is in her power?"* She goes on to pepper Papa as *"that
selfish old man"*, which no one could deny that he was. But
Mary, firing off round after hearty round, missed Ellen's
nebulous point, implied, hinted-at, no more: that even
Charlotte's *"lot"* would have been better than such a marriage.

Charlotte spoke pityingly of Mary, facing seasickness and the
danger of shipwreck. Charlotte depicted her in *Shirley*: *"The
quiet Yorkshire girl is a lonely emigrant . . . no European river,
this on whose banks Rose sits thinking."* But Mary did not sit
thinking on the banks of her New Zealand river; she was far too
busy . . . Charlotte's compassion was envy of the blazed trail
which she could never follow.

Another new girl was ushered into the schoolroom and was
startled to find Charlotte crying her heart out in the big bay
window, partly hidden by the curtains and partly by the long
table with its cheerful crimson cloth. Dear Ellen Nussey! with
her pretty face, her copious brown curls, her black dress and
white scarf of Charlotte's fond word-picture. Gentle, and
pious, and very loving; sentimental if you like. What tender,
innate courtesy of the heart she showed in this first embarrassing encounter (and how few schoolgirls of any period would
have possessed such a trait). She did not beset the diminutive,
bitterly weeping stranger with words or questions or even
sympathy but *"went to the far end of the room where the bookshelves were,"* though she herself was *"touched and troubled at once
to see her so tearful."*

Warmth stole into the air with the sight of Ellen's pale, fair
face. Hearthstone warmth and the liquid light of a virginal
lamp. Here was Charlotte, headlong into a fervent schoolgirl friendship with someone as great a contrast to masterful
Mary as could well be found. But it lasted for their lives and
beyond Charlotte's. Ellen had no part in the pillar of fire,
pillar of cloud, of her friend's mental life. She simply supplied
warmth and light. And a love that was greater than she was
herself; great enough to dispense with understanding.

Charlotte was at school; and happy. Happy in all the
momentous, trivial ways of a schoolgirl. Hopeless at games of
ball but outstripping all the others to vanishing point in the

matter of book-learning. Famous for telling such bedtime stories
that she could reduce the dormitory to screams of terror.
. . . Important, in a small school world; and loving, and loved.

One fine day, Branwell came trudging the twenty miles from
home, just to visit his sister. Appeared at the pillared front
door with dusty boots and pale, handsome face, and red hair
blowing. And Charlotte's importance shot still higher. You
may be an ugly little thing (though Ellen says you have beautiful
hair, fancy that?) but you have a very good-looking brother of
distinguished and unusual appearance. And it is not everyone
whose brother walks twenty miles over hill and dale to see her.
The young ladies of Roe Head School are local girls; your home
is more distant than the home of anyone else, and yet it is your
brother who comes. And on foot.

There is a buzz of whispered talk in the dormitory that night
and no stories. Charlotte is, as usual, the centre of the
dormitory chatter but for quite a new reason.

"He isn't at all like you, is he?" That, of course, is Mary,
wielding the blunt instrument, as always. But Charlotte, so
passionately sensitive and so morbidly conscious of her own
defects, does not mind. Plumes herself, indeed.

"No, is he? Branwell is far the best-looking of us all."

The sister's tone is complacent and taking-for-granted. She
will voice her conviction in other words, in a later day:
". . . nature had favoured him with a fairer outside, as well as a
finer constitution, than his sisters." That was Charlotte, standing
beside the bed where Branwell's wrecked body lay, when the
process of death had completed the transformation which is
sometimes the consoling miracle. "I looked on the noble face of
my dead brother . . . when a marble calm began to succeed the last
dread agony." She was looking down at more than the physical
transformation of rigor mortis; seeing the bright, mercurial
face and the beacon hair of the boy who had been her boon
companion and her pride in the days long before he destroyed
himself.

"Is your brother clever, Charlotte?"

"Much better than clever. You don't know the meaning
of that word. Sheridan was clever—scamps often are; but Johnson
hadn't a spark of cleverality in him——"

Silence. Ellen is dubious about the word; but if Charlotte, who is mistress of words, uses it, it must be all right?

"I suppose," Ellen ventures softly, "that he will follow your papa's calling? Will be a clergyman?"

"No. Branwell is to be an artist," says his sister grandly. "He could be anything. He writes poetry, he *makes out*, you wouldn't believe how wonderfully he *makes out*." (The Brontë phrase for making up stories, but it was Mary who first supplied it.) "But he will be a painter. Papa talks of sending him to London to study——"

"Charlotte must bring him home to meet *our* papa, mustn't she, Polly?" Martha Taylor, Mary's lively, engaging younger sister is speaking. "Papa dotes on pictures. He made the Grand Tour when he was a young gentleman, and our house is *full* of pictures. Isn't it, Polly?"

There is Briarmains, the mansion of the Yorke family from *Shirley*, the Taylor household brought to fame (for which, not unreasonably, they were more indignant than appreciative. Mrs. Taylor did not relish being portrayed as a female dragon and repudiated the idea that her husband was such a rough diamond). There was *"the matted hall, lined almost to the ceiling with pictures."* The *"large parlour"* with its *"series of Italian views to deck the walls,"* its *"cameos and beautiful miniatures,"* its *"set of Grecian-looking vases on the mantelpiece."* And the back parlour, *"the usual sitting room of an evening,"* with its astonishing combination of stained-glass windows containing medallions of Shakespeare and Milton with *"Canadian views of green forest and blue water scenery—and in the midst of them blazes a night-eruption of Vesuvius."* Charlotte wrote: *"There was taste everywhere—unusual taste—the taste, you would have said, of a travelled man, a scholar, and a gentleman . . ."* Unusual taste, it may be hoped?

Branwell never came to Briarmains. Never saw the stained glass, the shattering juxtaposition of the Canadian scenes and Vesuvius in eruption while Hiram Yorke, otherwise Mr. Taylor, enlarged to him on art and travel. Branwell would have been enraptured and Mr. Taylor would have had the most receptive audience of his life. A pity. Charlotte should have contrived that he went there. She went there, many times; and

only the pages of *Shirley* reveal how her hunger for the unknown and her passion for painting devoured Mr. Taylor's
fearsome collection. And perhaps it was not only his pictures
and medallions and volcanoes that enthralled her, but his
merchant-adventuring. He did the Grand Tour; in early
middle life his spinster daughter, her friend, made her way to
New Zealand and opened a shop. . . . Charlotte would have
been glad to do either.

> . . .   .

At home, they were proceeding very peacefully and con-
tentedly without Charlotte. There was no one, now, to be
somewhat overpowering in administration of the play-world,
somewhat exhausting, while inexhaustible, in creative energy;
and at the same time, in a very inconsistent and baffling way, to
swoop down, just now and again, with uneasy hints that it was
all rather—foolish, somehow, and even—wrong, in some
way. . . . That make-believe continents and teeming peoples
were, perhaps, childish things to be put away. . . . And yet,
Charlotte *didn't* put them away. So why make such a fuss,
even just now and again? . . .
Left to themselves, Emily and Anne were creating them with
an energy that was naïve and pristine and god-like. Dynasties,
heroes, heroines; histories, sagas, ballads. None of the involved
and tortuous politics which were Charlotte's delight, and less of
the bloody frays that were Branwell's. "*To the Horse Black
Eagle That I Rode at the Battle of Zamorna*", has been quoted as
the title to one of Emily's later poems: but the title is open to
query, for Zamorna belonged to the domain of Charlotte and
Branwell, not to hers and Anne's. She may have borrowed it?
It does not greatly matter. Nothing can challenge or take from
the central fact: that Emily's entire life, from the time when she
could think at all, was lived in the world of her own creation.
The two younger girls were inseparable in mind, in spirit, and
in heart, as Siamese twins in body, and the unity appears as
much of a phenomenon. Emily, a gawky overgrown being of
fourteen with glorious eyes; Anne a very pretty little creature of
ten with geranium colouring, too bright, too transparent, and
soft curls, and mild eyes the colour of violets. Power of

character, force of personality, emanated from the spindling older girl, but even more amazing was the self-contained, self-sufficient reserve which she wore, a veritable coat of mail and vizor. Anne, Aunt's favourite among the girls, after Branwell, was docile and very gentle. But she was Emily's chosen company. Anne in Gondaland: it sounds like a wide-eyed Alice; and that has been for too long the accepted portrait of Anne. But the Gondal saga was one of love and hate, tyranny and bitter savagery; and Emily was not one to stride through that fabulous and turbulent world of passions with an Alice clinging to her skirts. Anne was her heart's and her mind's companion.

(iii)

THERE was a sense of mild and temperate sunlight slipping through the bare rooms, shedding faintly warm pools on the stone floors. Charlotte was home from school for good; the three did their lessons together in the morning. "*I instruct my sisters,*" Charlotte was informing Ellen grandiloquently. My sisters were not always amenable, it would seem, from one of the infinitesimal diary-papers written by Emily and Anne on their birthdays for no one but each other. They were folded into the size of a sixpence in a tiny box, and how or why they survived, in the holocaust of dissemination, loss, and destruction, which wiped out so appalling an amount of the written words of the Brontës, suggests the quotation from Lewis Carroll's *Sylvie and Bruno:*

"Once there were a teeny weeny mouse."
"Go on, Bruno. What happened to it?"
"Nothing happened to it. It were too teeny-weeny."

In one of these birthday papers Emily writes:
"*It is past twelve o'clock. Anne and I have not tidied ourselves, done our bed work, or done our lessons and we want to go out to play. . . . The Gondals are discovering the interior of Gaaldine. Sally Mosley is washing in the back kitchen.*"
The Gondals were as all-pervading as the steam of Sally

Mosley's washing and as much a part of the day's taken-for-granted pattern.

There were happy visits between Charlotte and Ellen, and a perpetual stream of letters: the going-to-stay, the having-to-stay, and the tremendous outpourings on paper, that are the rightful heritage of the schoolgirl. Papa indulgent, Aunt approving, even Tabby, the matriarch in the kitchen, bewitched by gentle Ellen. And *"Emily and Anne say they never saw anyone they liked so well as you."* Ellen was so happily at home in her friend's extraordinary household that she could make a later word-picture of Emily which supplements all Charlotte's burning words of baffled devotion. Ellen's simplicity had singleness of vision for something which went beyond her understanding. There was no strain of stupidity in her. And she never made the mistake, which Charlotte made, of insisting on explaining Emily, who was beyond the comprehension of either.

"She had acquired a lithesome, graceful figure. Her hair, which was naturally as beautiful as Charlotte's, was in the same unbecoming tight curl and frizz, and there was the same want of complexion. She had very beautiful eyes—kind, kindling, liquid eyes, but she did not often look at you; she was too reserved. . . . Few people have the gift of looking and smiling as Emily could look and smile. One of her rare, expressive looks was something to remember through life, there was such a depth of soul and feeling, and yet a shyness of revealing herself—a strength of self-containment seen in no other."

There are so many voices to speak of Emily, with assertion and surmise and contradiction, and some with words that had been better left unsaid. It is left to Ellen, as unconcerned with titanic forces as with theories, to leave a picture of a girl emerging from the chrysalis of coltish ungainliness into that grace which is a perpetual surprise. Emily's freedom of limbs on the moors contributed something to that transformation. A girl with beautiful hair and eyes; and the same want of complexion which Frank Churchill deplored in Jane Fairfax. Ellen saw the kindness in Emily's eyes and remembered how she smiled. And the village stationer at Haworth, who was hard put to it to keep the parsonage young ladies supplied with paper for their perpetual writing, had the same words:

"*I did so like them to come . . . they were so different to anybody else; so gentle and kind and so very quiet.*"

In its beginnings, Charlotte's friendship for Ellen was a schoolgirl *schwärmerei*. When she herself had reached her peak of fulfilment and fame Charlotte could write of Ellen with a touch of condescension: "*A calm, steady girl—not brilliant, but good and true. She suits me and has always suited me well*". . . "*. . . a simple Yorkshire girl. But I love her.*" Charlotte wrote thus in a time when the craving for intellectual parity in companionship was a driving hunger within her rendered the more excruciating by one short interlude of satisfaction followed by starvation. But however simple was the Yorkshire girl, throughout Charlotte's life she turned to Ellen, called to her, cried aloud to her, desperately, in all times of her own direst need. And Ellen could say in her own unvarying and un-declamatory truth: "*She told me things she never told anyone else. And I had her heart.*"

There is hardly a term of endearment in any love-passage in the sisters' books. They could not bring themselves to make free use of that currency of the emotions small or great. Which is understandable in Emily; the dæmonic loves of Heathcliff and Catherine could have no use for tenderness. But Charlotte, writing in a lesser key and of lesser loves, shrank and steeled herself, retreating into harshness or into blank aridity. Only in her earlier letters to Ellen the hankering need broke through. "*Good-bye, my darling Ellen——*" and then the instant post-script: "*Strike out that word 'darling'; it is humbug. Where's the use of protestations?*" Another letter ended "*dearest, dearest*"; and once only, in homesickness a cry burst from her un-controllably: "*Talk no more about my forsaking you, my darling. I could not do it.*" These were letters belonging to girlhood and young womanhood; the steadfast friendship needed no such demonstration through the years. But the sisters, who were north-country women, lived all their lives with an Irish father, and Charlotte, as a schoolgirl, even spoke with Papa's Irish brogue; it was part of the conflict which rent her through all of her life that a half-Irishwoman should flagellate herself for calling her best friend "darling". . . .

Branwell escorted his sister to stay at the Nussey home, The Rydings, with its garden which was a small park, its orchard, its gracious and comfortable interior. He told Charlotte that he was leaving her in Paradise. He came home and talked about it, excitedly, to the others. And bye-and-bye, Cathy and the boy Heathcliff stared through the windows of the Linton mansion into just such a paradise and Cathy sold her young soul to gain it.

There is a drawing-master at Haworth now, and all the young people are drawing and painting for dear life. Papa encourages their talent and their zeal, at considerable sacrifice and two guineas a lesson; while his hopes and theirs are concentrated on Branwell. The peeling and cracking canvases of his pictures of his sisters are in the peopled silence of the National Portrait Gallery for all to see that truth spluttered through Mrs. Gaskell's tact and decorum when she said that they were more like sign-painting than anything else. But the separate, unfinished sketch of Emily is fit to stand beside the word-paintings of her made by Charlotte and by Ellen. In such a gown as Emily could never have owned and would not have worn if she had, her beautiful shoulders and long neck bare, her face eagerly smiling, her curls loose, and the whole head poised for flight. Somehow, in an hour of genuine inspiration, Branwell caught and put her on canvas, Emily straining towards Infinity.

You hear spectators murmur "What frightful daubs!" and with equal candour and more universal regret "Isn't it maddening that it should be Branwell who painted them? . . ." The Richmond portrait of Charlotte hangs beside poor Branwell's daubs, and makes it possible to feel something other than regret, since it makes her into something from a Ladies' Journal of Modes. Charlotte burst into tears during one of the sittings because, she said, it had such a look of Emily . . . but her desolate heart saw Emily everywhere: from a tepid portrait of herself done in true Winterhalter-court-style, to the handsome, foppish features of George Lewes.

They all left fragmentary records of their drawing and painting. Emily's pictures of her dog and her bird, painted with skill and with strength; what could she do that had not strength in it? Charlotte's rigid picture of Anne and her fancy portraits of Angrian figures. They were very happy, painting.

And Emily was a musician as well. There was a cottage piano in the scoured shell of the parlour, bare of every Victorian ornament. And Emily taught music when she went to Brussels to the Pension Héger. Every girl of her time pounded and tinkled at a piano and pored over sketching-blocks. These were Accomplishments. But Emily could never trifle with accomplishments.

Now Branwell is away to London and to be made into an artist of distinction and renown. They saw him off, at the gate, and he turned to wave his hat as he went down the steep street and swung on to the road to Keighley. His red hair was to be seen for a few moments, blazing its way like a comet to the great world and the future and to fame. There was something of Dick Whittington in this departure.

He came back a few days later. And he never went to London again.

Elizabeth Gaskell was tactfully to suggest that the London plan fell through for lack of money. Other writers have left the matter an admitted mystery. But among Branwell's haphazard, unfinished writings is a word-sketch of a young man, Went-worth, who made that Dick Whittington journey and spent a day or two at an inn, stretched on a sofa and tippling noggins of rum. And, unable to face the wider world, went home again.

Branwell had so dreamed of London and freedom and fame that, before he ever set foot in it, he pored over maps until he could even set right a traveller at the "Black Bull" on the other side of the parsonage wall, on the question of the whereabouts of an obscure alley in the City. He would not be, as Charlotte was to be, daunted and petrified by the traffic and the maze of seething streets. Something less tangible and far more powerful overcame him and sent him scurrying back to obscurity and defeat and decay. He trudged up the hill again, whistling as he came, with an air of piteous bravado. And it is the shadow-in-advance of another scene: when Charlotte, established in fame, paced up and down a quiet Manchester terrace, struggling to muster sufficient poise, and quietude of nerves, to enter the

house where two affable girls had cordially invited her to hear
the Scottish duets which she loved. There was to be no party.
It was a morning call, and two young women who would sing
to give her pleasure, and perhaps a third sister would listen as
well. But Charlotte could not face it after all. She turned away,
her tiny hand shaking in Elizabeth Gaskell's arm, and skimmed
back to the shelter of the Gaskell house.

Psychiatry might have diagnosed and prescribed for the
brother and the sister. Would surely have detected a kindred
flaw in each? But these were before the days of psychiatry.
The world which each so desperately craved was too much for
them when they stood on its brink. They shrank and shivered.
Branwell hid himself in a tavern and sipped rum to fortify
himself. Charlotte was deathly sick, and prostrated by
migraine. They both winged back to the parsonage walls and
to the inner keep of the imaginary world which held no terrors
because they built it. The boy went back to his village cronies
and to the "Black Bull" and to be the big frog in the small
puddle. His flaming head and white face gleamed murkily
through the fug of churchwarden pipes and his lilting Irish
voice sounded through the roars of laughter and the clinking of
bottles and glasses. The little maid-of-all-work at the "Bull"
remembered Branwell's beautiful speaking-voice and his
beautiful and courteous manners, extended even to her. "Good-
morning, Ann," and his hat swept off. All the Brontës were
courteous to servants, in a period when courtesy to underlings
was far from universal. It is a part of the family's hall-mark. It
is marked in every one of their books. When Charlotte set out
to draw the picture of an atrocious young woman in Blanche
Ingram, she makes Blanche address her host's footman with
"Cease chattering, blockhead, and do my bidding . . ." and that
incredible remark is, quite justifiably, a source of amusement to
everyone who reads Jane Eyre. It is constantly quoted to show
that Charlotte, like Dickens, failed ignominiously to draw the
fashionable world with any true likeness. (Well—Jane Eyre
was written before Charlotte knew anything of the fashionable
world. The households where she was governess did not
belong to it.) But it shows something of more fundamental
importance; especially when contrasted with any or every scene

in the same book where Jane is in contact with servants,
including the "blockhead", Sam. Anne, too, makes every
character whom she wishes to show as objectionable rude and
inconsiderate to the servants. Everyone who served the
Brontës loved them, and not only the girls but Papa.

Papa had something in common with his son. Behind
Branwell in the smoky shadows were other shadows of the Irish
peasants who were his forebears: one of the shadows, Patrick
Brunty, had trudged away from the mud cabin and worked and
dreamed and forced his way through the courts and river-
reflections of Cambridge to the parsonage and the wide,
scattered parish which included Haworth. There the impetus
failed him: he went no farther. But his son's impetus failed at
the first citadel to be scaled and he dropped back to the level
of the mud cabin.

(iv)

THE warmth of a pale sunlight lying on the stone floors and
the dark stretches of the moors; because they were happy
there. A sense of sunlight apart from the splendour and awe of
the skies above the desolate heights and empty levels. But over
the pleasant green gardens of Roe Head and the woods and
calm fields of the Calder Valley, *malaise* hung in a miasma.
Emily and Charlotte are both at school, Emily as pupil,
Charlotte as teacher. And Emily is literally sick unto death,
because the kindly place is a dungeon to her. While Charlotte
is frantic with anxiety for her sister, and succumbing on her
own account to the nervous depression which was as near to
religious melancholia as makes no matter.

In *Shirley*, Charlotte wrote, in a burst of rhetoric and
ignorance, of air "*commissioned to bring in fog the yellow taint of
pestilence, covering white Western isles with the poisoned ex-
halations of the East, dimming the lattices of English homes with the
breath of Indian plague.*" She was to write those lines, the first
that she could drive herself to write, immediately after Emily's
death, to account for Caroline's illness in the book. They were
as absurd as they were grandiose; but they can take shape in a

poisoned mist of misery wreathing through the comfortable rooms and flowering gardens of Roe Head, where Emily was undergoing her first intolerable ordeal. Homesickness; yes, any girl may be homesick at school. Charlotte cried with homesickness there. But with Emily it went immeasurably deeper. Charlotte could understand a great part of it, though only a part. Enough to feel terror of the consequences, and to see in her mind's eye Maria dying by inches before her eyes of a nine-year-old child at Cowan Bridge, and the little ghost that is Elizabeth. Enough to recognise that there was only one cure for Emily.

"My sister Emily loved the moors. Flowers brighter than the rose bloomed in the blackest of the heath for her;—out of a sullen hollow in a livid hill-side, her mind could make an Eden. She found in the bleak solitude many and dear delights; and not the least and best-loved was—liberty. Liberty was the breath of Emily's nostrils; without it she perished. The change from her own home to a school, and from her own very noiseless, very secluded, but unrestricted and unartificial mode of life, to one of disciplined routine (though under the kindest auspices), was what she failed in enduring. Her nature here proved too strong for her fortitude. Every morning, when she woke, the vision of home and the moors rushed on her, and darkened and saddened the day that lay before her. Nobody knew what ailed her but me. I knew only too well. . . . I felt in my heart she would die, if she did not go home, and with this conviction obtained her recall. She had only been three months at school."

Charlotte was fighting for Emily's life, and fighting an array of people who wanted nothing but Emily's good: Papa, Aunt, kind Miss Wooler. A brave, complex battle. And she was fighting for an issue which she did not completely understand, then, nor, probably, ever. Emily was sick for home, for her moors, for the free, unconventional life where the only bonds were a matter of sewing under Aunt's eye for a period of each day. (And you can think while you sew. You can think better while your hands are occupied mechanically and rhythmically.) Aunt might be tiresome, and Tabby summon you to "pillo-potate" when you were lost in writing, but neither could intrude on the spell which locked you into the world of your own imagining. You barred the gates and remained behind

them while you sewed Branwell's shirts and the yards of Papa's
white stocks and your own drawers and petticoats. You tickled
Tabby's cheek with your quill pen (*"Tabby said on my putting a
pen in her face Ya pitter pottering there instead of pilling a potate"*),
and you peeled the potatoes, and the spell was unbroken.

At Roe Head, the company, the voices, the routine shattered
the spell. The Gondals or their precursors were as good as dead
while Emily was at school. Charlotte could transfix a dormitory
by her wild stories, but Emily could no more have shared her
dream-world with other than Anne than she could have
stripped herself of her layers of clothing before those schoolgirl eyes. She was an exile from her own country as from home.
They took it away from her at school without knowing of its
existence.

Everyone admitted Emily's "reserve" and either censured it,
aggravated it to torment, or accepted it. But not even Charlotte
knew sufficient to recognise that Emily found no place for the
sole of her foot in a world of everyday human contacts. She
could not endure strangers. The words are not a phrase, they
state a physical, a physiological fact. Emily flew from the
kitchen if the baker's boy appeared. Emily retreated to Tabby's
bedroom and shared the old woman's bed when some visiting
friend of Charlotte's must share the girls' bedroom. Emily, as
Ellen put on record, could seldom bear to turn her beautiful
eyes full on a stranger's face. (And Charlotte never lost that
paralysing incapacity.)

Charlotte's dread was no exaggeration. Emily, in three
months, was ill in body and mind, of that excruciating malady,
compulsion to live utterly out of your own environment. Not
boredom nor loneliness but the successive and unrelaxing
torture of the trivial and inevitable, all day long. *Every morning,
when she woke, the vision of home and the moors rushed on her.* No
doubt: but what rushed on her more immediately and sickeningly
was the sight of the seven or eight strange faces on adjoining
pillows to her own. Those strangers would wake and chatter
and wash and dress, all around her. Sit beside her at meals that
she could not eat, walk with her in the green valley while Miss
Wooler's charming voice prattled on and on relating stories of
the past which fell on deaf ears where Emily was concerned.

The past, for her, lay on the savage and haunted heights of the black moors, not in these tranquil fields.

Privacy and solitude were denied her. And most destroying of all, her secret world perished for her. The voice of Emily's spirit was the cry from the Song of Songs: "They took away my veil. . . ."

Something of her intrinsic and unconquerable suffering was acknowledged by the time that she was persuaded to go to Brussels with Charlotte. She went, to acquire the learning which she did not want and would never use since her gift was absolute and self-sufficient, preferring its own flaws and short-comings to whatever it might have assimilated from the output of other men's minds. *"I considered it kind in Aunt to consent to an extra sum for a separate room,"* Charlotte told Ellen. *"We shall find it a great privilege in many ways."* Charlotte might. But for Emily it would mean the difference between the intolerable and an existence which could just be endured.

So, Emily went home. Roe Head was comfortable and full of amenities of living; Miss Wooler was certainly one of the most indulgent and attractive of headmistresses; the Calder Valley was a region of green beauty. The parsonage at Haworth was a grey stone tomb and the kitchen, with Tabby's glowing range, the most comfortable spot within it. The moors were the very spirit of desolation. But what it all meant to Emily she made Catherine Earnshaw utter:

"I was only going to say that Heaven did not seem to be my home; and I broke my heart with weeping to come back to earth; and the angels were so angry that they flung me out into the middle of the heath on the top of Wuthering Heights; where I woke sobbing for joy."

Emily only had a few months at home in free air. And even so, she was without Anne, the rest of herself, who was sent to Roe Head in her place. For a few months she knew the deep, unvoiced relief of coming back into her own. The house was very still. The father and aunt kept to their own rooms, Bran-well spent much of his time at the "Black Bull", where he found the only company available to him. She had "the children's study" to herself for a bedroom now. She did a great deal of the housework and the washing and the ironing; she studied

German with a book propped up against a mixing-bowl on the kitchen table. For which no one need pity her. It is, of course, easy to see her as genius fettered to household chores and to forget that her driving energy for homely tasks was balance for the creative labour of her inscrutable mind and brain. Anyone who makes gigantic demands on his brain uses his hands in compensation. And Emily was a Yorkshirewoman, house-proud to the bone. Elizabeth Gaskell described the parsonage: *"I don't know that I ever saw a spot more exquisitely clean; the most dainty place for that I ever saw."*

The flame crept and rose through the silent house again. It will never be known, and it need never be known, precisely when Emily wrote down each of the poems which broke into the flame from a morass of indifferent verse and the accumulation of Gondal's writings. Nor when *Wuthering Heights* first began to stir and take life within her mind. Emily at eighteen, in the house where three elderly people were sunk in somnolence or petty parochial activities or old age, and where an erratic boy was madly dreaming and drinking, was living her own life. *"You will write . . . that you may give your soul its natural release."* They are Shirley's words in Emily's voice.

There is Emily coming down from the moors, colour whipped into her sallow face and her blue eyes dilated with fulfilment, and Keeper plunging beside her. And there is Branwell at the club table of his tavern, with John Brown, his father's sexton and the landlord and a traveller whose bottle he is sharing. Not soused and not besotted; wildly excited and talking, holding the stranger in wondering thrall to his brilliant charm. One is beset by the helpless desire to question Emily: to ask her, Why did you not share the dream with *him?* He was writing too; he was always writing when he wasn't painting or drinking. He had more of you in him, that unstable lost boy, than either of the other two ever had or could have. What happened, that you could share your soul with little Anne instead of with him? He was wrestling with Blackwood's and pummelling Wordsworth with a blind vehemence which would be comic if it were not pitiful, when Charlotte was decorously pleading with the Poet Laureate for a word that should give her

life in place of a living death. Why was it Charlotte to whom
he turned, and not you? The seed of an Irish wastrel was born
in him, and the father who believed in him and nourished his
talent was wrapped up in dyspepsia and seclusion. But how
could it come to pass that you and Anne paired instead of you
and Branwell? . . .

Presently Emily is away from home again. Making another
shattering effort, because, with Branwell's drawing fees and the
hire of a Bradford studio and Papa's limited stipend, the girls
must earn. *"Hard labour from six in the morning until near eleven
at night, with only one half-hour of exercise between. This is slavery.
I fear she will never stand it."*

But this is also a panic of exaggeration on Charlotte's part.
Something at least is known of the school above Halifax; it was
fashionable, expensive, and the headmistress was a woman of
culture and also something of a sportswoman. A situation less
suited to Emily could hardly be imagined, but it is probable that
the *"slavery"* was mental rather than physical and that the whole
circumstances, rather than the lady, loaded Emily with chains.
Charlotte had closed with her family and Miss Wooler to
rescue Emily from Roe Head where there was nothing but
kindness. It is less than likely that she would sit down, supine
and inactive, before a spectacle of Emily being done to death
by a seventeen-hour day of unremitting toil or dismiss it with
the fear that she could not stand it.

A strange setting for a fashionable school, the hill-tops above
the chimneys and smoke of Halifax. But a better setting for
Emily than the parklands and pastures about Roe Head. The
neighbourhood alive with dark tales of the families which
once lived on those moors. And the stronghold of High
Sunderland Hall only a mile or two away, rising starkly and
suddenly from a slope with bare country spread all around it.
A fifteenth-century house with battlements and spearhead
pinnacles high above the surrounding walls, which might be the
walls of a Chinese compound; nothing about it but level
moorland and tremendous, empty sky. The tenants or owners
were a family of a famous Yorkshire name and acquaintances of
Emily's headmistress. Here is Emily, seeing High Sunderland
Hall first as a reluctant visitor in her employer's wake; a

morning call, possibly, with cake and wine; or a tea-drinking, with the ample Yorkshire spread of cakes and wafer-thin ham and preserves. Emily, dumb as a statue, frozen in unease and dismayingly indifferent to the hospitable fare (though she was a prime cook and a meticulous housekeeper).

Emily coming back to High Sunderland Hall alone (in spite of the fabulous half-hour for all relaxation), standing on the uplands in the raking wind, never lifting the knocker or pulling the iron bell-rope. Standing there, outside the eastern compound wall of a north-country property: while the walls and roof of Wuthering Heights rose behind it. . . .

(v)

CHARLOTTE was bending her short-sighted eyes over the letter in which Southey, with so much gentle courtesy and feeling, discouraged her writing of poetry. The paper shook and rustled in her hands.

"Literature cannot be the business of a woman's life, and it ought not to be. The more she is engaged in her proper duties, the less leisure will she have for it, even as an accomplishment and a recreation. . . . The daydreams in which you habitually indulge are likely to produce a distempered state of mind. . . . Write poetry for its own sake . . . so written it is wholesome both for the heart and soul . . . soothing the mind and elevating it."

She had to write: driven by the gift that filled her. And Southey, carefully and with marked consideration, bade her bury the gift, and laid a flat tombstone upon it.

Charlotte folded the letter and put it away, and her big, protruding eyes were swimming and her lips set tightly. *"It did me good,"* she told Elizabeth Gaskell in time to come. The same words as she used to Mary Taylor, who told her that she was very ugly: Charlotte's set phrase for the turn of the screw. Presently, she was writing her reply, with a quill pen which was almost noiseless because Charlotte could never endure the squeak and scratch of the usual quill. She was a terrific letter-writer; she wrote some of her copious letters with venom and some with a sharp-edged humour and some which were such an uncontrollable cry of passion and sorrow that when you read them, you do not so much follow the lines as hear them uttered by a hoarse, torn voice. And among them, she hardly surpassed for dignity and poignancy the reply that she sent to Southey in return for a death-sentence.

"*At the first perusal of your letter, I felt only shame and regret . . . I felt a painful heat rise to my face . . . but after I had thought a little and read it again and again, the prospect seemed to clear. You do not forbid me to write; you do not say that what I write is utterly destitute of merit. You only warn me against the folly of neglecting real duties for the sake of imaginative pleasures; of writing for the love of fame; for the selfish excitement of emulation. . . . You kindly allow me to write poetry for its own sake, provided I leave undone nothing that I ought to do, in order to pursue that single, absorbing, exquisite gratification. I am afraid, sir, you think me very foolish. I know the first letter I wrote to you was all senseless trash from beginning to end; but I am not altogether the idle dreaming being it would seem to denote. . . . I find enough to occupy my thoughts all day long, and my head and hands too, without leaving a moment's time for one dream of the imagination. In the evenings I confess I do think but I never trouble anyone else with my thoughts . . . I have endeavoured not only attentively to observe all the duties a woman ought to fulfil, but to feel deeply interested in them. I don't always succeed. . . .*"

She sat at the square parlour table, writing her letter, and she was quite dry-eyed now. A tiny figure, rigid and tense with an effort at renunciation, like a reluctant novice striving to accept the veil:

"I was not good enough for man
And so am given to God."

Charlotte's baroque possession by rhetoric and allegory led her, at times, to bouts of shocking verbal inebriation. She could become as drunk on words as Branwell on gin, and on much the same unseemly and disastrous occasions. Those outbursts would flaw her work to the last book, and the last reader will squirm before them. But Charlotte in deep pain was compelled by a perfection of simplicity. No written word will ever convey the wrenching turmoil of the woman torn between her life of the mind and her life of the besetting functions integral to being a woman, with more piercing integrity than Charlotte used in her reply to Southey. He answered it because he could not help himself, and with equal simplicity and sincerity, if a tinge of smugness.

"Your letter has given me great pleasure and I should not forgive myself if I did not tell you so. You have received admonition as considerately and kindly as it was given. . . . And now, Madam, God bless you!"

One self must be buried alive, then? But the other self rose, loomed, took possession, grew, for a time, into a tyrant-genie. Charlotte the churchwoman, the very narrow Christian, the parsonage-daughter, took control, until all other control snapped. She lived and moved in a state of religious depression which veered between melancholia and mania. She was obsessed by Duty to the end of her life; now, Duty took the form of refusing any alleviation of her lot whatever.

The daydreams in which you habitually indulge are likely to produce a distempered state of mind. Southey never knew what he did when he pronounced that sentence upon Charlotte. It was not the daydreams which all but wrecked her: it was her fearful and ineffectual struggle to renounce them. Her secret world was all that she had. And now she was coming to see her high-wrought and fantastic imaginings as a secret sin. . . . She could not live without them. But she saw herself as a drug-addict might see himself. Duty; a horror of her own soul as she saw it in the glass darkly; and the snare of the imagination which she could not wholly forgo: these made the deadly pattern of Charlotte's life at Dewsbury Moor, the new establishment of Roe Head. *"She could not help thinking,"* said forthright Mary, describing an evening when Charlotte sat solitary in a dressing-room lost in her dreams, until she realised that darkness had set in, and *"took sudden fright."* (*In the evening I confess I do think* . . .)

Charlotte is writing to Ellen, plying the continual quill pen.

"If you knew my thoughts, the dreams that absorb me and the fiery imagination that at times eats me up, and makes me feel society as it is, wretchedly insipid, you would pity and I dare say despise me."

An overpowering sense of sin: a dread of being eternally lost to God. A blackness of depression, and throughout the darkness a reiterated and echoing cry to Ellen, whose simple piety and gentle affection shone like stars in the terrifying gloom.

". . . *If you love me, do, do, do come on Friday: I shall watch and wait for you and if you disappoint me, I shall weep.*"

"*I have some qualities that make me very miserable, some feelings that you can have no participation in—that few, very few people in the world can at all understand.*"

"*What shall I do without you? How long are we likely to be separated? Why are we to be divided? Surely, Ellen, it must be because we are in danger of loving each other too well—of losing sight of the Creator in idolatry of the creature? . . . I forget God, and will not God forget me? . . .*"

Ellen, bewildered and loving and faithful, could only offer to Charlotte's veiled and chaotic appeals her own simple religious faith and assurance. Charlotte strove to cling to them, but they were not the answer to her need. Gentle Ellen has been blamed for encouraging Charlotte in her welter of religious depression: the greatest and most intuitive of all writers on the Brontës since Mrs. Gaskell referred with her own impish humour to "the dance Miss Nussey led her (Charlotte) round the Throne of Grace . . ."* But she was wrong there.

Poor Ellen! utterly puzzled and distressed by her friend's wild outpourings, and without any knowledge of the very different dance, the frantic bacchanalia, of Charlotte's fevered brain. Everyone who had been at Roe Head knew that Charlotte "made out"; but no one had any idea of the scope and power of those imaginings nor of their obsessing hold upon her. She could not reveal herself to Ellen, she could only call piteous hints. Some fragments of her private diary remain, which supplement her letters to a really harrowing extent.

. . . There is something exasperating about these diary-fragments; embarrassing; and disappointing. Not because they reveal, as many journals do, thoughts and feelings which the writer never intended to be seen by other eyes and which leave one feeling contrite for having read the pages at all: but for the

* *The Brontës' Web of Childhood.* Fannie K. Ratchford.

opposite reason. This diary of Charlotte's smacks rather
horribly of the writer writing for effect. . . . It is Charlotte at
her worst. It is painfully artificial. Charlotte sits plying that
ruthless quill with something on her sick face of a bitter smirk
of satisfaction. She sits back in her chair and scans a finished
entry, and the "finish" is on a very good exit-line; and she
knows it. . . . There is nothing of the desperate and wild
sincerity which rings in her letters to Ellen.

But perhaps the answer to Charlotte's rather painful diary-
pieces is, simply, that no writer of fiction should write a diary.
It is infernally difficult (the word is used deliberately) for such
to avoid standing at their own shoulders, reader and writer in
one.

"And now once more on a dull Saturday afternoon I sit down to
try to summon around me the dim shadows, not of coming events,
but of incidents long departed, of feelings, of pleasures, whose
exquisite relish I sometimes fear it will never be my lot again to taste.
How few would believe that from sources purely imaginary such
happiness could be derived! Pen cannot portray the deep interest of
the scenes, of the continued train of events, I have witnessed in that
little room with the low narrow bed and bare white-washed walls
twenty miles away. What a treasure is thought! What a privilege is
reverie! . . . Remembrance yields up many fragments of past twilight
hours spent in that little unfurnished room. There have I sat on the
low bedstead, my eyes fixed on the window, through which appeared
no other landscape than a monotonous stretch of moorland and a grey
church tower rising from the centre of a churchyard so filled with
graves that the rank weeds and coarse grass scarce had room to shoot
up between the monuments. . . . Such was the picture that threw its
reflection upon my eye but communicated no impression to my heart.
The (mind)? knew but did not feel its existence."

This doesn't sound like Charlotte. It sounds like any and
every commentator who has written on the Brontës: we are all
impressed and horrified by the dreariness of the parsonage and
the pervasion of the churchyard—even into the scullery sink.
But they took it for granted.

But to resume:

"Well, here I am at Roe Head. It is seven o'clock at night; the
young ladies are all at their lessons; the schoolroom is quiet, the fire is

low; a stormy day is at this moment passing off in a murmuring and bleak night. I now assume my own thoughts: . . . I now, after a day of weary wandering, return to the ark which for me floats alone on the billows of this world's desolate and boundless deluge . . it is the still small voice alone that comes to me at eventide . . . over the deeply blue hills and out of the now leafless forests and from the cities on distant river banks of a bright and far continent; it is that which takes up my spirit and engrosses all my living feelings, all my energies which are not merely mechanical. . . . Haworth and home wake sensations which lie dormant elsewhere."

". . . stupidity the atmosphere, schoolbooks the employment, asses the society! What in all this is there to remind me of the divine silent unseen land of thought, dim now, and indefinite as the dream of a dream, the shadow of a shade? . . ."

There follows a description of a storm of wind:

". . . that wind I know is heard at this moment far away on the moors of Haworth. Branwell and Emily hear it, and as it sweeps over our house, down the churchyard, and round the old church, they think, perhaps, of me and Anne! Glorious! that blast was mighty; it reminded me of Northangerland. . . ."

". . . Then came on me, rushing impetuously, all the mighty phantasm that this" (i.e. the sound of Huddersfield church bells), "had conjured from nothing—from nothing to a system strange as some religious creed. The spirit of all Verdopolis—of all the mountainous North—of all the woodland West—of all the river-watered East, came crowding into my mind. . . . But just then a dolt came up with a lesson."

There is also an account of a trance of dreaming when she "saw the Duke of Zamorna leaning against that obelisk. . . . I was quite gone. I had really, utterly, forgot where I was, and all the gloom and cheerlessness of my situation. . . . 'Miss Brontë, what are you thinking about?' said a voice that dissipated all the charm, and Miss Lister thrust her little rough black head into my face. . . ."

At the end of another and even more vehement vision, ". . . while this apparition was before me, the dining-room door opened, and Miss W. came in with a plate of butter in her hand. 'A stormy night, my dear!' said she."

And presently, still in her diary, Charlotte states her resolve to write with less scaring excitement and of themes which

D

would not belong to the exalted fantasy of her dream-world.

"*. . . I long to quit for a while that burning clime where we have sojourned too long—its skies aflame—the glow of summer is always upon it—the mind would cease from excitement and turn now to a cooler region where the dawn breaks grey and sober, and the coming day for a time at least is subdued by clouds.*"

She was propelled to this decision by the fact that she had sent one of her romances to Coleridge, and he had censured its flaming tone and atmosphere. But here, in her diary, Charlotte addresses her "readers", and petitions their patience. What readers? She had none, so far. This pompous key suggests, at the very least, that Charlotte the diarist was not writing in the unmasked sincerity which is, after all, the only excuse for keeping a discursive diary at all.

It does not greatly matter. The chief disappointment of these diary-fragments lies in that single fact: they do not really matter; and they *should* have mattered almost beyond anything else which Charlotte ever wrote. They should have been even more valuable, and to the world of Brontë readers more precious, than all. And they are nothing of the kind. . . .

They are Charlotte as anyone who loves and reveres her must deplore to see her. Making conscious copy—or hay—of her supreme gift and her misery. . . . But, to repeat, they do not matter. Her spontaneous letters to Ellen, and Mary's stark, unimaginative account of her at this time, are sufficient to give her as she was, battered in conflict and sinking in body and mind.

The two staunch friends who could not enter into the secret world of her tortured mind; who have been dimissed as negligible by commentators who felt that they knew Charlotte better than these two; have saved Charlotte in her torment for posterity.

(vi)

THERE is upheaval at Dewsbury Moor. Miss Wooler is in tears, and the girls are whispering together, and the doctor, who has paid several visits lately, comes from the parlour rather red in·

the face, his lips pursed grimly, and shaking his head. There is
another side to the picture of Charlotte in distraught unhappiness there. *"Dewsbury Moor is a poisoned place to me,"* she
said: remembering nothing but her wretchedness. It was no bed
of roses for anyone else, through that black period. Poor Miss
Wooler, full of kindness and anxiety, would have made
Charlotte relax, urged her to visit Ellen and Mary, who lived
within easy distance: she refused in a dogged fervour of self-
denial and self-immolation. Anne was ailing and coughing:
Charlotte accosted Miss Wooler, who, not perhaps unreasonably, told her that she was seeing everything, Anne's
health included, in exaggerated gloom. There was a shattering
scene, which reduced the poor lady to prostration, and a letter
to Mr. Brontë. Anne was sent home. And the fracas was
patched up.

And what about the luckless pupils, whom Charlotte called
"asses" and *"bulls of Bashan"* and only saw as cumbersome
bodies standing between herself and the light that never was on
sea or land? To be taught by a mistress in the grip of a nervous
breakdown is not a salutary experience. . . .

The doctor and Miss Wooler prevailed at last. The haggard
little wreck which was Charlotte went home. And it may be
surmised that Miss Wooler, pressing a handkerchief steeped in
eau-de-Cologne to her throbbing temples, felt nothing quite so
much as relief. Really, these Brontë girls . . . first Emily, then
Anne, and last (and worst), Charlotte. . . . One did one's
utmost, one was patient and forbearing and indulgent; but to
listen to Charlotte, one might as well be a murderess.

It speaks considerably both for Miss Wooler and for
Charlotte that when this painful interlude was over and done
with, their friendship remained unstrained, unbroken, and that
Charlotte, recovered, was swift to acknowledge Miss Wooler's
constant if unavailing kindness.

They were all at home and together again. And very quickly,
the crushing darkness lifted. The healing satisfaction of being
where she would be, among the people for whom she craved,
was at work in Charlotte.

"A calm and even mind like yours," she was presently writing to
Ellen, *"cannot conceive the feelings of the shattered wretch who is*

now writing to you, when after weeks of mental and bodily anguish not to be described, something like peace began to dawn again."

Papa, who'd had a fright, encouraged visits from Charlotte's friends, not only Ellen whom he liked and approved but Mary of the rough tongue from the *"fierce Radical"* household of the Taylors, and her sprightly younger sister.

"They are making such a noise about me that I cannot write any more. Mary is playing on the piano; Martha is chattering as fast as her little tongue can run; and Branwell is standing before her, laughing at her vivacity."

It was June, and there was summer in the parsonage parlour. Mary pounding the piano with the vigorous fingers that were to hammer nails and rend packing-cases apart in a New Zealand settlement. Martha, who was piquant and daring, flirting with Branwell. And Branwell bending over her in the approved gallant-Napoleonic attitude and spoiling his pose by going off into laughter at her sallies. Emily, coming down from a walk, put her tawny head round the door and retreated. She went upstairs with a lowering look on her face and her lip thrust out. It was her piano . . . and Mary's parlour-playing owed far too much to the loud pedal. She might as well be thumping Tabby's iron. . . .

The sickness of spirit was over, for Charlotte. But the conflict would continue for all of her life. The friends who loved her and the strangers who acclaimed her would see her as for ever beset by loyal duty and filial piety, a slave to Papa and a prisoner in the parsonage. One of them wrote: *"A field had evidently been set apart, and the founders of the Church had said 'In three-fourths of it we will inter the dead, and in that other fourth we will bury the living'."* *

They were wrong. Charlotte was her own prisoner, no one else's. The straitness of the parsonage walls and the church that was a mausoleum were as necessary to her as her stays. A part of her nature chafed and strained and struggled to soar; the rest of it clung, soldered, to the narrowness of dogma, of codes, of rectitude.

There was no conflict for Emily, and Anne knew none. There is something fantastic in the sight of Emily sitting bolt

* J. Storrs-Smith, 1868.

upright in the parsonage pew three times on Sunday while Papa
boomed from the pulpit. Still more, to watch her hearing her
Sunday-school class their catechism. But there was no rebellion
for Emily, who could go through the motions of conformity
like a tall ghost gliding through church and Sunday-school,
exactly as she had once gone through the motions of hemming
the sheets and working a useless sampler in Aunt's bedroom.
Her body was the ghost. Emily's spirit was elsewhere: so
enfolded, so totally withdrawn, that even Papa and the
catechism could not intrude. A curate's voice reading the
lesson would utter the tremendous words "Absent from the
body, present with the Lord"; but Emily knew their meaning in
life, not in death. Daughters and sons of clerical houses were
kicking against the pricks, breaking away in revolt, or dropping
into a smouldering submission. The transcendent power of the
experience that was Emily's life burned up such pitiful efforts
like weeds on a garden bonfire.

Still—it remains a fantastic spectacle: Emily striding across
the churchyard as the bell rang, and Emily seated on a wooden
bench with a row of Sunday-school children before her. And
no one except Emily would know just where Gondal ended and
God began. The organ is sounding in church, but the chords
form themselves into the words of Emily's greatest and most
incomparable poem:

He comes with western winds, with evening's wandering airs,
With that clear dusk of heaven that brings the thickest stars. . . .

Immortality for any achievement in whatsoever form is
in so far as it becomes a part of human consciousness and
endurance. "After the singer is dead And the maker perished."
And those verses are in the conscious memory of every soul
that has ever read them with seeing eyes. But they were uttered
by a captive in one of Gondal's dungeons. While Emily sat
upright and without fidgeting through Papa's sermons, the
rapines and massacres, the passions and vengeances of Gondal
were surging behind her straw bonnet. None of Papa's children,
except Branwell, gave him any trouble. ("*The poor old man and
I have had a terrible night of it. He does his best, poor old man.*")

But the poor old man would have been shattered if he had any idea that his boy's delirious ravings were a thin piping compared to the passions let loose in the world created by one of his girls: and that one the home daughter, the diligent housekeeper, the good cook.

No conflict for Anne. The soft, drooping melancholy of her religion might burden her most innocent spirit with a sense of perpetual shortcoming, a fear of damnation, and Charlotte said that "*a tinge of religious melancholy communicated a sad shape to her brief, blameless life,*" and found a strain of Cowper in her verses. But Anne was all of one piece. Two forces did not wrestle in her delicate frame.

There was a streak of imagination in her—how, otherwise, could she have been Emily's mind-companion for all of Emily's life?—an appetite for drama, very often found in people of gentle temperament and retired lives. The Gondals satisfied it, for Anne.

The figures of the two younger sisters are to be seen, on an excursion to York when Emily was twenty-seven and Anne was twenty-five.

"*And during our excursions we were———*" (here follows a list of eight romantic Gondal names, both of men and women). "*The Gondals still flourish as bright as ever. I am at present writing a book on the First War. Anne has been writing some articles on this, and a book by Henry Sophona. We intend sticking firm by the rascals as long as they delight us, which I am glad to say they do at present.*"

The tall figure and the slighter figure, side by side, paced the aisles of the Minster. Did a little shopping. Retired early to a bedroom in a modest lodging. And it was Ronald Macalgin who strode between the pillars, and Cordelia Fitzaphnold who purchased a length of merino at the draper's. And Henry Sophona who discussed his new book.

The same streak or urge in Anne went to the writing of *The Tenant of Wildfell Hall*. Charlotte was to sit at the parlour table in the desolate house, fervently writing her apologia for Anne. But Anne's shadowy ghost-figure slides into Charlotte's place at the table, writing, writing, with her pretty gold-brown curls falling across her flushed cheeks and an un-

conscious smile of absorbed excitement hovering on her mouth.
Charlotte edited and explained her sisters in an anguish of
loss and loyalty. Doing them only a lesser disservice than when
she destroyed every available paper that they left which she
felt they would wish to perish unseen by other eyes. Charlotte's
conflict would have obliterated everything of them which the
parsonage daughter could not explain away. . . .

But Anne's mournful serenity held an ember of clearer truth:
she was not, like Charlotte the afflicted and tossed with
tempest, afraid to be herself.

.   .   .   .   .   .

Emily has the house to herself again. Charlotte and Anne
are away from home in situations as governesses; Branwell is
in a studio at Bradford, painting portraits and finding some
society among a few men who were to remain his friends and his
adherents through thick and thin to the last days (literally)
of his turbulent life. It seems that Anne makes a good
governess. Her employers are kind even if the children are out
of hand and her older pupils love her. Charlotte is in feverish
revolt. Her ordeals are short and successive, she cannot keep a
situation for more than a few months.

To be a governess was the sole form of work for respectable,
middle-class young women who had to earn a living and who
were not sufficiently accomplished to teach in a school. They
had to "go out"; that was the current phrase, and it has a ring of
doom about it. . . . You meet it in all fiction of the early and
middle Victorian era. Noble-minded young men in the books
of Charlotte Yonge cripple their own careers in order that their
sisters shall not "go out" and so drop a whole octave in caste
for ever. An inexperienced damsel is described as "not having
gone out before, I think?" Another fears that she has en-
dangered her sister's marriage because she herself has "gone
out", and even the devoted lover may recoil before the thought
of a sister-in-law who has been a governess. But no one except
Charlotte and Anne has presented such a grim picture of
servitude; and it comes rather strangely from Anne, who was so
dearly loved by her pupils that those young ladies made a
journey to visit her after Branwell's scandal in their household

had caused him to be dismissed and Anne herself to resign her post. And her memories of Scarborough holidays with them were so happy that she went back there to die by the beloved sea.

Charlotte is writing in the schoolroom by a single candle, pouring out to Ellen the torment of the human being bound on the wheel of incongruous and uncongenial work.

". . . *no one but myself is aware how utterly averse my whole mind and nature are for the employment.*"

". . . *Write whenever you can. I could like to be at home. I could like to work in a mill. I could like this weight of restraint to be taken off.*"

They said that she was peevish and hypersensitive and difficult, her bewildered employers. They could not know—and what was far worse, she herself did not fully know—that the powers pent within her were raging at the preposterous groove into which she was straining to thrust them. A shrinking, eccentric near-genius struggling to make herself into a governess. When Charlotte came to write her novels, she appeased herself for every pent-up and rankling sense of wrongs done to her by exchanging ink for acid—you may say venom and not be very far wide of the mark—and etching an enduring picture. But as far as her governess-apprenticeship is in question, some sympathy may be spared for the people who employed her and for her unlucky little pupils . . . Charlotte in revolt, whether at Dewsbury Moor or Stone Gappe, was no restful addition to any household.

But Emily is at home, and the "study" is her bedroom now, and she has moved the bed under the window. She can see the moor from her pillow. And she is writing at the little desk on her knee or on the table. You see those little desks occasionally in junk-shops or at auctions; a writing-box with a sloping lid and a sunken ink-well. Every young woman of any education possessed one. They play so pervading—and in one instance so dramatic—a part in the lives of these girls that one cannot see one of these little desks without instantly seeing Emily. She is writing poems: Gondal poems, uttered by Gondal personages, and the mass of them is indifferent verse; but a few break forth, elemental as thunder rolling above the moors or tender and rhythmic as a strain of music. Her greatest poem breaks into white-hot flame in the middle of a species of doggerel ballad; a narrative poem so poor that it was unimaginable how one and the same brain could have created both elements. Papa comes out from seclusion now and then to peer in passing at his tall and very silent daughter, not curious but vaguely gratified and a trifle amused. The girl keeps up her childish scribbling . . . well, well! Patrick Brontë is caught by an unexpected, short sigh. The happiest time of his own life was the period when he was writing poetry, writing all day long except when interrupted by his duties as a clergyman who did not believe in visiting. Perfectly atrocious poetry, little as he knows it; he only knows that he was supremely happy in the writing of it. . . .

The Gondal prisoner's challenge to jailer and tormentor; Emily's challenge to life, who had passed beyond the need for almost any human contacts and equally beyond the capacity to sustain them, into the region where her soul entered into a union which should be absolved from the touch of words other than her own.

"He comes with western winds, with evening's wandering airs,
With that clear dusk of heaven that brings the thickest stars:
Winds take a pensive tone, and stars a tender fire,
And visions rise, and change, that kill me with desire.

Desire for nothing known in my maturer years,
When joy grew mad with awe, at counting future tears:
When, if my spirit's sky was full of flashes warm,
I knew not whence they came, from sun or thunder-storm.

But first, a hush of peace—a soundless calm descends;
The struggle of distress and fierce impatience ends;
Mute music soothes my breast—unuttered harmony
That I could never dream, till Earth was lost to me.

Then dawns the Invisible; the Unseen its truth reveals;
My outward sense is gone, my inward essence feels;
Its wings are almost free—its home, its harbour found,
Measuring the gulf, it stoops, and dares the final bound.

Oh! dreadful is the check—intense the agony—
When the ear begins to hear, and the eye begins to see;
When the pulse begins to throb, the brain to think again,
The soul to feel the flesh and the flesh to feel the chain.

Yet I would lose no sting, would wish no torture less;
The more the anguish racks, the earlier it will bless;
And robed in fires of hell, or bright with heavenly shine,
If it but herald death, the vision is divine!"

What, one ventures to wonder, would Emily feel if she could
see the fate which lay ahead for her poems? She was furious for
days when Charlotte so much as discovered and read them; what
would she feel if she could see the future and see Charlotte
editing, annotating, explaining, chopping, and snipping; and
even Charlotte's most unliterary husband, Arthur Nicholls,
leaving his pencil marks on her pages? No poet who ever wrote
has suffered such loyal and destructive and misleading treatment as Emily. She would, one suspects, have torn every line
she had written into very small pieces and burned the scraps in
Tabby's kitchen fire for greater surety.

In the long, involved ballad from which that beautiful
fragment has been taken, Julius of Gondal falls in love with his
prisoner, releases and guards her in secret, and, to protect her,
refuses to go to the wars, thereby bringing down the scorn of
his family on his head.

With this *motif* Emily, strangely, starts her whole poem; in
three verses of lilting music that speak the challenge in a
lighter key: Emily could afford to laugh at the world in her own
unassailable surety. There is a chuckle of malice, of defiant
mischief, in these opening lines, and no chord of intensity at all.

"Silent is the house; all are laid asleep:
One alone looks out o'er the snow-wreaths deep,
Watching every cloud, dreading every breeze
That whirls the wildering drift and bends the groaning trees.

Cheerful is the hearth, soft the matted floor;
Not one shivering gust creeps through pane or door;
The little lamp burns straight, the rays shoot strong and far
I trim it well to be the wanderer's guiding star.

Frown, my haughty sire! Chide, my angry dame!
Set your slaves to spy; threaten me with shame!
But neither sire nor dame nor prying serf shall know
What angel nightly tracks that night of frozen snow.

What I love shall come like visitant of air,
Safe in secret power from lurking human snare;
What loves me no word of mine shall e'er betray,
Though for faith unstained my life must forfeit pay.

Burn then, little lamp; glimmer straight and clear—
Hush! a rustling wing stirs, methinks, the air,
He for whom I wait thus ever comes to me:
Strange Power! I trust thy might; trust thou my constancy."

In a glass case in the manuscript room of the British Museum, the small, maroon-covered notebook headed "Gondal Poems" in a rather shaky garland of arabesques is kept open at the pages covered with this ballad, because it is the best-known of Emily's poems. But if it is taken out, at your request, and left in your hands to read, you see that the two last verses here quoted do not appear at all. They appear in every printed version of this part of the ballad, which has invariably been printed as a separate poem. Did Emily add them later? Did Charlotte add them for some reason of her own? If Emily added them, it is to be seen that her pen wavers and halts; the last two lines are weak, inadequate, a petering-out of the lamp's wick; and she knows it. The Gondal maiden is lost, for a moment, in the rise and peal of the voice that is the voice of Emily's own soul. She herself is confused between the two elements: and so is her poem . . .

"Sweet Love of youth, forgive if I forget thee,
  While the earth's tide is bearing me along;
Other desires and other hopes beset me,
  Hopes which obscure but cannot do thee wrong!

No later light has lightened up my heaven,
  No second morn has ever shone for me;

All my life's bliss from thy dear life was given,
All my life's bliss is in the grave with thee.

But when the days of golden dreams had perished,
And even Despair was powerless to destroy,
Then did I learn how existence could be cherished,
Strengthened and fed without the air of joy.

Then did I check the tears of useless passion,
Weaned my young soul from yearning after thine;
Sternly denied its burning wish to hasten
Down to that tomb already more than mine!

And even yet I dare not let it languish,
Dare not indulge in Memory's rapturous pain;
Once drinking deep of that divinest anguish
How could I seek the empty world again?"

A writer whom Charlotte was to read and despise, and Emily
never to read at all, spoke the same theme in words whose
echoes linger:

"All the privilege I claim for my own sex (it is not a very
enviable one, you need not covet it), is that of loving longest
when existence or when hope is gone."

That is Anne Elliott speaking, in Jane Austen's *Persuasion*.
It is Emily the musician who writes:

"*The linnet in the rocky dells,*
The moor lark in the air,
The bee among the heather bells
That hide my lady fair . . ."

.   .   .   .

"*Blow, west wind, by the lonely mound,*
And murmur, summer streams—
There is no need of other sound
To soothe my lady's dreams."

She sits, not with her desk on her knee, but at the upright
cottage piano, and her hands, which are the hands of a pianist,

with force but without grace, weave the words into the notes.
And it is Emily, who could lie for hours in the grass, who
writes of willow trees in the two flawless lines

> *"Though years ago the woodman's stroke*
> *Laid low in dust their Dryad-hair."*

While, welded into the life of her brain by day and night; an
integral part of the splendour and the tenderness of certain of
her poems; an integral part, even, of the soul's experience which
swept and held her apart in her sufficing, god-like quality of
being, beyond human reach; the dark tapestry of *Wuthering
Heights* was weaving itself.

The figure of Emily merges into the core of the stupendous
allegory which Charlotte wrote in *Shirley*, disguised as a schoolroom *devoir* under the preposterous title *La Première Femme
Savante*. Because Shirley herself was an idealised and inadequate portrait of Emily, the power of Charlotte's devotion
flowed in her words. She had a weakness for allegory in and
out of place which reminds one of the painted ceiling of Mr.
Tulkinghorn's chambers in *Bleak House*. "Allegory, in Roman
helmet and celestial line, sprawls among balustrades and
pillars, flowers, clouds, and big-legged boys, and makes the head
ache—which would seem to be Allegory's object always, more
or less."

But, for once, it is complete in itself and in beauty. The air is
filled with a rushing of winds that is the surge of titanic wings.
"*This was in the dawn of time, before the morning stars were set
and while they yet sang together.*" Woman, in the form of a
solitary woman, stands alone on the earth. "*Slow and grand the
Day withdrew, passing in purple fire. . . . The Night entered, quiet
as death: the wind fell, the birds ceased singing. . . . The girl sat,
her body still, her soul astir. . . . Of all things, herself seemed to
herself the centre—a small, forgotten atom of life, a spark of soul,
emitted inadvertent from the great creative source, and now burning
unmarked to waste in the heart of a black hollow. . . . Yonder
sky was sealed: the solemn stars shone alien and remote. . . .*"
"*Again—a fine, full lofty tone, a deep soft sound, like a storm
whispering, made twilight undulate.*"

"Once more, profounder, nearer, clearer, it rolled harmonious."
The voice of the god descending calls her by name, summons
her and possesses her.

*"Eva, I have brought a living draught from heaven. Daughter of
Man, drink of my cup!"*

*"I drink . . . and the night changes! the wood, the hill, the
moon, the wide sky—all change!"*

*"All change, and for ever. I take from thy vision darkness. . . .
I claim as mine the lost atom of life. I take to myself the spark of
soul—burning, heretofore, forgotten!"*

"Oh, take me! Oh, claim me! This is a god."

*". . . I saw thee that thou wert fair: I knew thee that thou wert
mine. . . Acknowledge in me that Seraph on earth, named Genius."*

*"My glorious Bridegroom! True Dayspring from on high! . . .
The dark hint, the obscure whisper, which have haunted me from
childhood, are interpreted. Thou art He I sought. Godborn, take
me, thy bride!"*

*". . . I can take what is mine. . . . Come again into the heaven
whence thou wert sent."*

*"That Presence, invisible but mighty, gathered her in like a lamb
to the fold; that voice, soft but all-pervading, vibrated through her
heart like music. . . . A sense visited her vision and her brain as of
the serenity of stainless air, the power of sovereign seas, the majesty of
marching stars, the energy of colliding elements, the rooted endurance
of hills wide based, and above all, as of the lustre of heroic beauty
rushing victorious on the Night, vanquishing its shadows like a
diviner sun.*

"Such was the bridal-hour of Genius and Humanity."

Charlotte was inspired here. She wrote, with tears and
heart's blood, in a single allegory, her tribute to Emily. And,
being Charlotte, flawed it with grotesque limitations, flying in
panic before the ungovernable flood of her own power before it
carried her away. She had to quote the Bible. She had to call
the woman who was Woman, Eva—(*"If Eva were not this
woman's name, she had none"*)—because, to name her Eve would
have been to take liberties with Genesis. She had to name the
whole chapter *The First Blue-stocking* and shut her ears to the
bathos. (But that was hardly necessary, Charlotte was tone-
deaf when it came to bathos.) She had to make Shirley remark

airily, on the last echoes of those thunders, "*I never could
correct that composition. . . .*"

And above all, she did not realise what she was writing. The
allegory, with its shocking title, stands beside Emily's "*He
comes with western winds*" and speaks with Emily's voice. But
Charlotte had to label it, very firmly, a picture of the espousals
of Genius and the Human Mind. Covering her eyes—as well
she might—before the blinding vision of a more ineffable
Espousal.

(vii)

THE interludes of homely enjoyment and happiness pierce in
shafts of everyday sunlight through the moving pillars of cloud
and fire, through the murmurous swarm of petty miseries away
from home. There are holidays; they are together again. Life
at the parsonage takes on the shape and colours of a story by
Charlotte Yonge, not the Charlotte of Haworth. When
Elizabeth Gaskell wrote her book she wrote one which must
stand above anything written on the Brontës, not so much
because she was an expert novelist as because she, alone, of all
who have written on them, knew Charlotte personally. Her
sins of omission and commission as a biographer are grotesque
enough; but she had two invaluable assets, neither of which has
been possessed by any other writer on the Brontës: she knew
Charlotte in life; and she had the mental grace to admit that her
subject was greater than she could handle. . . . But Ellen
objected so strongly to the book that she considered writing
one herself; and the ground for her objection was this: that
Mrs. Gaskell drew too sombre, too unrelieved a picture of the
life at Haworth. She had never known it when it was full of
young people, and happy.

It is to be wished that Ellen had kept to her half-formed
resolve. Constantin Héger headed her off from it very
courteously, very strategically; and no wonder; what might not
that brilliant and most upsetting pupil have confided to her best
friend? (*She told me things which she told to no one else.*) His
most reasonable self-protection and Mrs. Gaskell's heartfelt

commiseration for the famous little creature to whom she privately referred as *"poor soul"* have postulated a Haworth scene of inhuman gloom. Whereas, until Branwell came home to be an unconscionable time a-dying in mind and character before his spent body died, there was much simple, homely, and natural happiness within the stone walls of the parsonage. The picture is thrown out of focus if this is unacknowledged and overlooked.

They are not always and perpetually obscured by the ferment of their high-wrought brains, these three girls. Nor ailing; nor sunk in trouble. The Brontës had fun. . . .

Now Charlotte received two proposals and refused them. Even though the first was from Henry Nussey, the handsome, correct clergyman who was the brother of her loved Ellen. There is a stir and a mild thrill through the parsonage: Charlotte has had a proposal. And there is a little laughter, too; Charlotte's big mouth has a twist of rather dry amusement as she pens a reply. Henry Nussey is not an ardent lover, he is on the lookout for a wife and helpmeet and his eyes are fixed upon the foreign mission-field. Later, Charlotte will use him as a lay figure for the portrait of St. John Rivers, but with a difference. Young Mr. Nussey proposes to three young ladies within twelve months and unfortunately keeps a methodical list of his refusals, adding a footnote to the effect that God's will be done. There is in him an element of the *phlegm* which Charlotte so thoroughly despised, making too free and frequent use of the horrid word. But St. John Rivers, in his cold, classical beauty, with his heart set on a girl who will be no helpmeet whatever, in his loveless and ruthless pursuit of Jane, is a figure compelling and memorable.

Jane feels it.

"Oh, St. John!" I said, "have some mercy!"

She is unhappy because she must offend him. She asks his forgiveness, and there was *"no cheering smile or generous word: but still the Christian was patient and placid. . . ."*

Jane, in a burst of healthy exasperation, says, *"I would rather he had knocked me down . . ."* The reader feels more inclined to knock down the Christian.

She goes to the root of the matter in her talk with his

warm-hearted sister (who has no delusions about her saintly brother).

"And then . . . I can imagine the possibility of conceiving an inevitable, strange, torturing kind of love for him: because he is so talented: and there is often a certain heroic grandeur in his look, manner, and conversation. In that case, my lot would become unspeakably wretched. He would not want me to love him. . . ."

The overpowering shadow of St. John rises dimly behind Charlotte as she sits writing her sedate refusal to his pale prototype. She would be a good friend to Ellen's brother, always. She will write him wise and kindly letters through the years to come. But Henry Nussey has dealt her a small wound. The torment of Jane and St. John had its root in her first offer of marriage.

Emily is amused by the whole thing and a little scornful, and laughs her deep, gruff laugh. She does not even see that Charlotte does a courageous thing in refusing this pompous young man. As far as Charlotte's eyes could see, if she did not marry someone her lot was to be a governess till she dropped in the traces and to be an old maid in poverty for whatever remained of her life. Henry was a clergyman; she was a clergyman's daughter, a strict, almost a fanatical churchwoman. Henry was Ellen's brother; and she loved Ellen as a third sister and as her only comfort in all trouble. This marriage might be said to be indicated for Charlotte.

But it is to Ellen that she writes:

"I had not, and could not have, that intense attachment which would make me willing to die for him; and if ever I marry, it must be in that light of adoration that I will regard my husband. . . And if he were a clever man, and loved me, the whole world weighed in the balance against his smallest wish, should be light as air. Ten to one, I shall never have the chance again; but n'importe."

There were steep cliffs and two girls walking over the coarse sea-grass where the shadows of the clouds skimmed under their feet. There was a wind off the sea even on the summer's day, stirring their long, full skirts and whipping their bonnet-strings. Charlotte went quickly as a bird to the edge of the cliff, stood gazing down over the racing tide. When Ellen came running to join her, sprigged skirts billowing and white fringed scarf flying, Charlotte threw out a hand to ward her off; even Ellen. In the shadow of her bonnet her face was streaming with tears.

Her first sight of the sea. And she had longed for it with all her body and spirit. The halcyon plan was proposed by Ellen: a week or more together, by themselves, somewhere by the sea. Not simply a holiday; Ellen's gentle mind knew Charlotte's wild longing for the sea and this was her plan to fulfil it.

It is possible that only persons who share that depth of unreasoning feeling will enter into it. It is something outside and beyond the scope of the seaside holiday, the change of air, etc. There exists in certain people a kinship for the sea, a parched craving for it, a sense of peace, fulfilment, and well-being beside it, to be felt nowhere else. The most beautiful inland country has something lacking, for them. There is, perhaps, something physiological in the craving and the contentment; it is certain that their whole physical being is at its best when they are within sight and sound of the sea—and, nowadays, when they are in it. Their very skin feels dry when they are cut off from it for too long. I have known one such, who, when debarred from the sea through summers, took cold baths so often that the matter became a mild family joke, especially as she invariably took one the last thing at night. I have heard another say in a perfectly matter-of-fact way: "When the time really does come for me to die, I shall have to keep away from the sea. I don't believe I could die if I were near it."

To this company, Charlotte belonged. The sea meant to her what the moors meant to Emily.

"*Your proposal has almost driven me clean daft—if you don't understand that ladylike expression you must ask me what it means when I see you. . . . P.S. Since writing the above I find that Aunt and Papa have determined to go to Liverpool for a fortnight and take us all with them. It is stipulated, however, that I should give up the Cleathorpe scheme. I yield reluctantly.*"

Reluctantly . . . she yielded (perforce) in fierce and thirsting revolt.

A week later the plan draws nearer again. Aunt and Papa

are havering over the Liverpool scheme and it appears to be petering out. (Liverpool in exchange for the sea . . .)

"*The idea of seeing the sea*——" (the word is underlined), "*of being near it—watching its changes by sunrise, sunset, moonlight, and noon-day—in calm, perhaps in a storm—fills and satisfies my mind. I shall be discontented at nothing.*"

But everything worked against her. The only gig for hire in Haworth was out of commission. Papa would not hear of travel by coach. Aunt was most unwilling to hear of their travelling at all, and set out to thwart the whole idea. "*Papa, indeed, would willingly indulge me.*" Papa, indeed, was almost always willing to indulge his girls according to his lights. He was almost as blind mentally as physically, but once some crying need of theirs penetrated his shadowy fastness—"*he did his best, poor old man. . . .*"

Charlotte's letter ends in a very reasonable burst of temper.

But they got to the sea, nearly a month later. And the final obstacle, the last straw was really the most unbearable of all. Something of the tortured exasperation of that tragi-comic episode is alive across more than a hundred years of time. It is Ellen who gives the story with her unvarying simplicity and without anything of Charlotte's pent fury. The two girls, escaping at last for the seaside holiday which was to be for "*a week—at the utmost a fortnight*——" no more, were "*seized upon by over-hospitable friends.*" These un-named worthies were shocked by the idea of two young women roughing it alone at the farm. "*A post-chaise was in readiness, in which they were to be driven off, not to the bourne they were longing for, but two or three miles from it, here they were (though most unwillingly) hospitably entertained and detained (italics by Ellen) for a month. . . .*"

Charlotte only had leave for a week, to be with Ellen. But for these influential friends, time could be no more as far as Papa and Aunt were concerned. She had counted on solitude with Ellen as part of the peace and enjoyment: "*And then I am not to be with a set of people with whom I have nothing in common—who would be nuisances and bores—but with you . . .*" There is a pitiful irony in Charlotte's exultant letter.

Ellen goes on: "*Whenever the sound of the sea reached her ears in the grounds around the house where she was a captive*

guest, her spirit longed to rush away and be close to it."
The promised land, tantalisingly near at hand and just out of reach. Nothing was spared Charlotte, then or at any time, in the matter of thwarting and frustration whenever she planned to snatch a flying joy.

But there, at last, they are. The tiny, sobbing figure above the surge and beat of the waves; and one can experience an actual sense of relief that this ruined holiday has come to its happy ending after all. There is the farm, with "*worthy Mr. H. and his kind help-mate,*" and lamplit windows on the summer night, and "*our merry evenings, our romps with little Hancheon.*" Charlotte and Ellen laughing and gossiping, making fun of Aunt and her obstructions and of their jailers who so nearly killed them with kindness—and who must needs pursue them with hampers of food because one might starve on a farm. It was all funny now that it was over. And now the two girls were free: free to walk by the sea, and to explore the woods, and to talk half the night if they liked, in the big, hard bed under the eaves with the salt tang of the sea creeping through the small, shut window and its sound booming in the darkness. Charlotte even slipped from bed and opened the stiff window and hung out in the dark, breathing, listening, till Ellen, scolding and anxious, made her come back to bed and herself shut the windows. Never again did Charlotte speak of romping with a child. It was the measure of her happiness that she could do so at Easton. . . .

A few weeks later she is asking: "*Have you forgotten the sea by this time, Ellen? Is it grown dim in your mind? Or can you still see it, dark, blue, and green, and foam-white, and hear it roaring roughly when the wind is high, and rushing softly when it is calm?*" When she drew the portrait of Caroline Helstone with a depth of tenderness and over-sentiment and an entire absence of humour, she was making a picture of Ellen fit for a Ladies' Book of Fashions; but she gave to Caroline the words of her own passion for the sea: "*I long to hear the sound of waves—ocean-waves, and to see them as I have imagined them in dreams, like tossing banks of green light, strewed with vanishing and reappearing wreaths of foam, whiter than lilies.*"

Anne's seas are still waters drenched in the setting sun; no titanic storms nor sea-fantasies for Anne. But she enters into

Charlotte's longing. Her way as a governess has taken her to
Scarborough and she loves Scarborough. Emily does not care
for the sea. The moors are hers and that is enough. She shrugs
her shoulders over the pother and distraction which went
before Charlotte's treasured holiday:

"Very tiresome in Aunt. And exactly like her," Emily observes.
And of the overwhelming and hospitable friends: *"Officious,
meddlesome fools! Charlotte is really out of luck."*

Back in the parsonage life suddenly flowers in the sun. It is a
sufficiently short interlude, but for a time the old house and the
surrounding moors are the scene of something light and foolish
and normal, and very endearing. Charlotte's detestation of the
numerous curates who clustered round those remote moorland
livings will be engraved when she comes to write *Shirley.* One
of them, an impulsive Irishman, came to tea, met her for the
first time, and sent a proposal of marriage next day; which was a
good joke for everyone, Charlotte making it that and no more.
Now there came on the scene a curate who was a very different
type of young man. Willy Weightman had the looks of a
handsome schoolboy; he was a devout churchman and
definitely of the church militant; he did not cease from mental
fight even if he limited it to battering Dissent with eloquence,
because it came as naturally to him as it might have come to use
his schoolboy fists. He was extremely warm-hearted,
susceptible, and within the decorous bounds of his cloth,
inflammable. He fell in love, right, left, and centre, usually with
more than one young lady at a time, and confided his affairs of
the heart with disarming candour and ingenuousness. And, like
many artless and natural philanderers, he had a kindness of
heart which made everyone forgive him everything, and a
lightness of heart which made him a godsend. The parsonage
parlour is not merely in a happy flutter, it is full of laughter and
nonsense.

There they go, all walking over the moors together, and the
cottagers hear their gay voices and their peals and giggles
ringing on the empty air. There are giggles at the parsonage
now, like anywhere else. It is a household like any other, now;
full of girls in a state of half-amused excitement, and a young

man who was not only volatile and lovable but who will live in
memory for his kindness. He is a little bit in love with Anne; a
little bit in love with pretty Ellen; and both are a little bit in love
with Willy. Anne, more than a little, as is inevitable for her
gentle and drooping temperament. Anne does not laugh at
Willy Weightman when all the others do.

"*He sits opposite Anne at church, sighing softly, and looking out
of the corners of his eyes to win her attention, and Anne is so quiet,
her look so downcast, they are a picture.*"

Anne with her downcast violet eyes and transparent flushed
cheeks, living her hour of flickering romance among the
encroaching tombstones and menacing memorial tablets. It is
the only sentimental picture in the light-hearted and light-
headed interlude. The rest is laughter. Charlotte sharpens her
dry wit at Mr. Weightman's expense, but indulgently. She was
stirred by Willy. She is writing to Ellen in a quite unwonted
key of excitement, and mocking herself for the excitement, and
breaking into the rather elaborate raillery which is more often
used by thrilled schoolgirls who are not quite clear as to the
source of and reason for the thrill which they feel.

"*It behoves me to write a letter to a young woman of the name of
Ellen . . . if the young woman expects sense in this production, she
will find herself miserably disappointed. I shall dress her a dish of
salmagundi—I shall cook a hash—compound a stew—toss up an
omelette . . . and send it her with my respects.*"

She describes the high wind blowing over the moors in the
same elaborate-comic manner, and then:

"*I see everything couleur de rose, and am strangely inclined to
dance a jig if I knew how. I think I must partake of the nature of a
pig or an ass—both which animals are strongly affected by a high
wind. From what quarter the wind blows I cannot tell, for I never
could in my life; but I should very much like to know how the great
brewing-pot of Bridlington Bay works and what sort of yeasty froth
rises just now on the waves.*"

Who hasn't known that sensation of irrational excitement?
Le vent qui vient de la montague m'a rendu fou.

But at the end of the lengthy letter, Charlotte dropped her
self-conscious humour and was at her tenderest and best.
Willy Weightman had been depressed and out of spirits and

when testily questioned by Papa had said that he didn't know
why, except that, on his round of parochial visits, he had found
one of Charlotte's Sunday scholars dying. And when Charlotte
went to offer some invalid comforts and stimulants she found
that Mr. Weightman was beforehand and with appetising, rather
extravagant delicacies such as perhaps no other curate would
have thought of offering to the Deserving Poor. He was
"always good-natured to poor folks," said the mother of the sick
girl, *"and seems to have a deal of feeling and kind-heartedness
about him."* Charity to the sick was part of a clergyman's
routine. But it would be Willy Weightman to bring a dying
villager precisely the gifts he would have brought to any one of
his numerous young ladies in illness. And to lose his rocketing
spirits and to vex his peevish old vicar because one more
villager was dying in a neighbourhood where they died like
flies and the hammering and chiselling of coffins and grave-
stones was the background music to the empty silence.

"No doubt," Charlotte continued, *"there are defects in his
character, but there are also good qualities. . . . God bless him!
I wonder who, with his advantages, would be without his faults?
. . . Where I am, he shall always find rather a defender than an
accuser."* That was Charlotte honest, generous, and loving.
She adds hastily and firmly: *"You are not to suppose from all this
that Mr. W. and I are on very amiable terms; we are not at all.
We are distant, cold, and reserved. We seldom speak; and when we
do, it is only to exchange the most trivial and commonplace remarks."*

The lady doth protest too much. As though anyone could be
distant, cold, and reserved, with Willy! . . .

(viii)

Now it is bleak northern spring and Valentine's Day in the
offing.

"What's this?" Emily asks, picking up a frivolity of paper-
lace and gilt from the table where Mr. Weightman is scribbling
envelopes for dear life.

"A Valentine, of course!" returns the young man, licking his
fourth or fifth envelope.

Emily laughs and flicks it aside.

"Never saw one before." She picks up another and reads aloud the silly jingle, and snorts disdainfully.

"Heavens! What stuff!"

Willy gazes at her in incredulous dismay. "You never saw one before?"

"Is it likely?" Emily begins scornfully, and Anne says softly from the window-seat "No, never."

"—who would send *us* such things?" Emily concludes, and strides off, calling Keeper for a walk.

Willy is shocked to the marrow of his volatile being. It is unimaginable that no one has ever sent Anne a Valentine. She is made for Valentines. But deeper than this, there is, in his overflowing heart, some perception that these girls, as girls, have been defrauded, in every light and trivial and amiable aspect of living. All the other young ladies of his acquaintance and his ephemeral devotion have pretty gowns and beguiling bonnets with rosebuds and pansies and wide satin bows. They have flirtations, tea-drinkings, croquet-hoops. . . . Here at Haworth there is not only isolation but dreadful, genteel poverty. These alarmingly clever girls have to "go out", like any village girl going out to service. Not only are they destitute of all the pretty things to which girls, in his gentle and susceptible mind, are entitled simply because they are girls, but pretty-Fanny's-way must for ever be a barred road to them.

So, because of these things even more than because of Anne's sweet, downcast face, Willy composes a Valentine for each of them. He has to compose them, because his own stock of paper-lace and rosebuds bought at the Keighley stationer's is bespoken to the last heart and arrow.

And then Willy is to be seen tramping into Bradford, ten miles away, to post his Valentines to Haworth so that they shall come as still more of a surprise. Bradford: he thinks of Branwell as the town comes into sight in the distance. If Branwell were still there in his studio Willy would drop in to see him. But the studio had been no success, and Branwell had been recalled by Papa. In her mad-merry mood, Charlotte wrote to Ellen:

"*A distant relation of mine, one Patrick Branwell, has set off to seek his fortune in the wild, wandering adventurous, romantic knight-errant-like capacity of clerk on the Leeds and Manchester Railroad.*"

Because she was giddy with the excitement of a delayed adolescence over Willy's delightful presence, she tried to speak lightly and foolishly even of Branwell, but the bitterness sounds through the flourish. The lad was general factotum except for one porter at the dismal railway halt of Luddendenfoot, a huddle of huts under a rising cliff where the dank green was blackened by engine-smoke. It was a prison-sentence of loneliness, boredom, and degradation and it marked the fact that the family had renounced all the high hopes which were set upon Branwell. Willy Weightman had shaken his head over the Luddendenfoot plan. He was attached to the boy, who called him "*one of my dearest friends.*" Hard-drinking young Irishmen are easily moved to assert that so-and-so is a dearest friend; but not, perhaps, to include upright young clergymen in the category. Even if it were an exaggeration it indicated that Papa's curate neither judged nor condemned him but cared for him with sorrowful understanding. Willy, at least, had eyes to see that a hutch at Luddendenfoot and the public-house in Luddendenfoot village were as mad and bad a solution as could well be found for a young man with every facile gift of his race, a desperate belief in his own powers and charm, and who was an alcoholic. But Willy's vicar was not going to be taught his paternal duty by his own curate. And he had borne a very great deal, in his heart and his purse, from his unsatisfactory son.

So Willy marched into Bradford and back with only his regretful musings on his friend for company.

Emily did not stand off, nor outside the giddy crew. She could be light-hearted, too, after her own fashion. They go streaming over the moors with Willy and Ellen in the party, and Emily breaks into wild spirits and dances on the rough grass.

And if you think of it for a moment, that must have been a sight to remember! Emily, who had never had a dancing-lesson nor been to a ball in her life: but who had the grace of some

vital young animal and her own wild energy that soared like a
flame and sank like a flame, too, when she was cut off from the
only air, physical and mental, that she could breathe. And she
was the only born musician in that family, the only one with an
inborn sense of rhythm, so that the true lyric note breaks from
certain poems of hers with the piercing sweetness of bird-
song, and is never found in the verse of Charlotte nor of Anne.
It was, conceivably, Augusta Geraldine Almeda, Queen of
Gondal, who danced on the moor . . . while the party merely
saw Emily in a mad-cap mood, and were amused, relieved
(Emily could be a terrible combination of thundercloud and wet
blanket——) and perhaps a little bit admiring. Anne may have
seen deeper. The others flutter and tease and laugh; Anne is
demure and Charlotte flings sallies like pebbles. But Emily's
touch of excitement turns her to a running, dancing hamadryad.

When Willy wishes to take Ellen and her white scarf for an
evening stroll, Emily, inexorably, goes too. He is not to play
his games with Ellen, she says severely. (And still less to give
her little Anne any cause to droop her flower-bell head still
lower.) Because it is all in such a light and painless key, no one
resents this thick-skinned and high-handed behaviour on
Emily's part. It is one more joke in this short season of
laughter. They nickname her The Major, as they have nick-
named Willy Celia-Amelia because of his rosy face and blue
eyes.

And there was the road from Keighley in moonlight, and the
girls and Ellen walking home with Willy Weightman (and a
married clergyman-friend of his as chaperone), at the unheard-
of hour of eleven o'clock; after his lecture at the Mechanics'
Institute. It will be remembered by anyone who reads the other
Charlotte, that in Charlotte Yonge's *Daisy Chain*, Margaret
May cannot go for a walk with half a dozen younger sisters and
brothers and their governess, because a young man visiting the
Mays is of the party. . . . And, incidentally, the unfortunate
girl, going for a drive with Mamma instead, is injured and
maimed for life in the carriage-accident, which seems a shabby
reward for decorum. But when the Haworth party reached
home, Aunt Branwell's only scolding was because she had
prepared coffee and sandwiches for the girls only, and here are

two unexpected guests. And it all ended in laughter because even Aunt B. could not be vexed with Willy for long: no one could.

It was a time of sunlight and moonlight mingling and the choral thunders quiescent and the smouldering clouds rolled back. Willy is always giving or sending presents to the household; his unique gift to the three sisters lay in that he, and no one else, gave them their girlhood.

There is another spring and another Valentine's Day, and Anne is alone at the parsonage with Aunt because Charlotte and Emily are in Brussels. Anne is at home because someone must keep house for Papa and Aunt, and Emily has been besought and beset by Charlotte until she has allowed herself to be dragged to Brussels. As she trips about the house, cooking and cleaning, Anne ponders that it is odd, it is very strange, how ruthless Charlotte can be when she sights something which, in her opinion, must and shall be done. She must know that it may half-kill Emily to be uprooted again. But even so, she has dropped a hint to Anne (not yet to Emily) that the six months in Brussels are only to constitute a stepping-stone; she has every intention of staying for at least three times that period, and she and Emily will have to take situations abroad to make ends meet. If Emily knew that, Anne reflects, she wouldn't even go aboard the packet.

Well—of course—Charlotte is right in one thing; the three of them have not enough of education or accomplishments to enable them to do anything better than this miserable governessing. If Charlotte and Emily learn French and German and Emily works at her music, who knows what may happen? They could aspire to a school of their own.

Somehow, the prospect does not cheer Anne. She sighs a little as she dusts the keys of Emily's piano, and instantly checks the sigh. Tomorrow is hidden in a mist, and a grey mist, at that; but today, here is Anne at home at last, and Mr. Weightman within sight and sound every day. Till now, she has only seen him in her too-short, too-infrequent holidays. And so there has been an added, unadmitted heart-ache in her constant longing for home. He was there. Emily, who didn't care a fig for him or for any man, was there. Charlotte was constantly there, because she would never keep any situation for long; and Charlotte only made fun of him—in a perfectly nice, witty way, for a change. . . . Anne was so seldom there. And it was Anne whose tender, despondent heart quickened at the sound of his bright voice and his schoolboy laugh and the prolonged gaze of his candidly expressive eyes.

Now—how comfortable it could be . . . how very nice . . . and who knew what might happen? If it weren't wrong, you could almost—not quite, but almost—*pray* that Charlotte's ruthless plans might come true. Even if it meant that poor dear Em was *"exiled and harassed"* for a whole year and a half, instead of Anne. A great deal may happen in a year and a half. And meanwhile, there was spring, and there would be summer with the long, light evenings, and presently, winter with the cosy fire and the lamplight in the windows.

But by the end of summer, Willy Weightman is dead. He has died of consumption, at Haworth; and Papa has visited his sickroom twice every day, and Branwell has kept vigil by his bedside and has nursed him.

And what of Anne? Who must slip through the suddenly silent house on her usual duties, and see him there at every turn and find him in everything that she touched as she swept and dusted and polished. And keep a modest silence. Hearing the door open and shut as Papa came in, as Branwell came back; hurrying into the narrow hall, her voice a breathless whisper,

"How is he, Papa?" . . . "Is there—any change, Branwell?" She may ask so much. Has he not been a loved friend and companion to them all? And Aunt weeps a little as she questions her brother-in-law. Anne does not weep. She is always quiet; she is only yet quieter, through those golden September days.

The day comes when Branwell stumbles into the house, and it is he who drops his flaming crested head on his sleeve against the wall, and sobs. Anne does not need to ask any question then. She stands very still, and her hand goes to her side. And she goes slowly upstairs to her room, holding the stair-rail, and bending forward under the driving pain.

Four days later, they bury him in the church, and the place is filled with mourners who loved him. There are sounds of stifled weeping and of clearing of throats, and Papa's fine, clear

voice thickens and breaks as he speaks from the pulpit of the
attainments and zeal of this young man who was a likelier son
to him than his own. Anne is not weeping behind her veil.
Something is dying, numbly and quietly, within her. Anne does
everything quietly. The death of her heart is no more
tempestuous than the death of her body will be, and with as
much pain.

For what remains of her life (and it is not to be much), she
will sit in her father's church on Sunday above the coffin of this
fleetfoot, daydream lover who was no lover, and lift her down-
bent head to his memorial tablet on the wall. His most enduring memorial is in her own artless and poignant verses:

> "Yes, thou art gone! and never more
> Thy sunny smile shall gladden me;
> But I may pass the old church door
> And pace the floor that covers thee:
>
> May stand upon the cold, damp stone
> And think that, frozen, lies below
> The lightest heart that I have known,
> The kindest I shall ever know."

"Someone should write to Charlotte and Emily," Aunt
observes sorrowfully. "Will you do it, my love?" to Branwell.
"Ah dear! the girls will be sorry!"

They are, of course. Emily was "sorry" when her little cat
died. She has a tenderer heart for animals than for human
beings; she affronted her bewildered pupils at Law Hill by
telling them that she preferred the yard-dog to any of them.
She will be sorry, because, in a nebulous way, she has perceived
that Anne's heart was touched by this young man. But it is not
of great importance, after all. In their very limited world,
young women are always imagining themselves in love with
whatever young men came to hand, or vice versa. Ellen, who is
so pretty and so endearing, is in a constant flutter of passing
love-affairs (and will, though no one knows it or could visualise
it, die unmarried at the end of a long life, as lovely an elderly
woman as she was a girl). Her brother has proposed to

Charlotte, and so has another local clergyman. The love-affair and ultimate unsatisfactory marriage of Mary Taylor's brother, Joe, are confided to Charlotte in letters and talks by that young man himself. Emily has seen her share of the tragi-comic problems of the sequestered young women and the work-bound young men of her infinitesimal physical world—and of her period.

It is difficult, today, to visualise the inordinate part played in human lives and emotions by two prosaic facts: Geography and Transport. At Haworth, you are boundaried by a miniature world, in the void immensity of the moors. There is one gig, one, only, in Haworth, to carry you to the outer world; and a gig costs hire-money. You walk the four miles to Keighley, a very small country town, for wooden soldiers, library books, and a train to Leeds or York. There are only so many young men, in the immediate neighbourhood: you either fall in love with one of them and, if you're lucky, marry him; or you go unwed. If, being a Young Lady, circumstances drive you to earning your livelihood, your opportunities are even fewer: because, if you are a governess, gentlemen whom you may encounter do not offer you marriage. Even in the eyes of Emily, who loved Anne better than anyone else did, Anne's *tendre* for Willy Weightman was no more than the faint, dry scent of a pressed flower.

For himself, Emily has all but forgotten Willy, by now. She is concentrated in every nerve on enduring the day as it comes in the Brussels *pensionnat*. She scornfully over-rode the methods of instruction proffered by Monsieur Constantin Héger, which no one had ever called in question before. She was the most incongruous pupil ever to be encountered by that domesticated *savant*. Small wonder that he mopped a mental brow and shook a baffled head as he pronounced *"She should have been a man . . . a great navigator"* . . . Emily would always steer by her own compass and none other.

And Charlotte would have nothing but a swift, passing grief to spare for Willy Weightman, hardly so much as that. Her whole, fiery being, wearing down and shattering her small body, was otherwise occupied. . . .

So, there is one more among the innumerable questions never

to be answered. If Anne had not been so swept into the flame of Emily's imaginings, would she, the least of the three, have managed to find something in life for herself? Emily could tread under her feet those fluttering, localised romances of her time. They showed as the busy crawling of ants, in comparison with the emotions and passions of the world which she had scaled for herself. But if Anne had been left to her own limitations: would she have contrived, as other young women were doing, to bring the shadow-romance with a most lovable young man to a head, and know some simple human happiness before death took him from her?

Death was in it from the beginning. He died of consumption; Anne was to die the same death very soon afterwards. But she might, possibly, have had her own small hour of real joy? . . . And it is not inconceivable that his death hastened her own, loosening her always-fragile hold on life. She was to follow him so soon; she might have been happy for a little while, first. . . .

(ix)

THERE was pain, flickering through the grey rooms and up and down the stone stairs, like a restless ghost. That house held pain and sickness of the body from the hour when the forgotten mother took to her bed to die of cancer; ailments, hypochondria, and mortal malady filled it so constantly through the tale of the years that the walls and stone floors seem to sweat with them. But this was pain of the spirit; and it does not ooze clammily from walls and floor but burns with a scorching, a blistering flame, and flits about the whole place with a fitful energy.

Charlotte darting to the back door to meet the postman. Sorting the few letters feverishly, dropping them on the kitchen table and turning away. Charlotte walking over the moorland roads with Emily in a driving restlessness which could not keep still. She walked so much through those months of harsh spring that she had to make a joke of it: ". . . to the great damage of our shoes, but, I hope, to the benefit of *our health."* These were not constitutionals: Charlotte went walking on the moors, hour after hour, until she was exhausted, as every lover in torment has done, pacing city streets and parks or country roads, goaded by longing and misery.

Emily found it something of a nuisance. There was no evading Charlotte, these days.

"Going out, Eejay? Wait for me—I must just change my shoes."

Emily's eyes studied her with a gleam of exasperation, then a sombre understanding which softened to compassion. *"I have denied myself absolutely the pleasure of speaking about you—even to Emily."* But Emily needed no words. And it was perhaps a merciful state of things that Aunt was dead and Papa, poor man, growing blinder all the time and submerged in his own discomforts; because surely someone would have noticed and questioned Charlotte? A woman distractedly and wretchedly in love is not a spectacle to go unnoticed in the confines of a narrow home.

. . . *"If he were a clever man, and loved me——"* Charlotte had written of her ideal husband. And one of Jane's reasons for feeling that she could come to *"a strange, torturing kind of love"* for St. John is that *"he is so talented."* The words ring very naïvely; but Charlotte was striving to express one of her deepest needs. The power of her own mind, the breadth and height of her own gift, made her hunger for equal, or better still, greater powers in the mind of a man who should be lover and husband. She could not see herself tied for life to any ordinary man.

When, in Brussels, she became the pupil of Constantin Héger she encountered the first good masculine mind which she had met, except her father's. And her father had sunk into mental apathy long before blindness cut him off. Her starved mind and her starved blood fastened upon Constantin Héger, concentrated upon him, and abandoned themselves, immolated, before him. Charlotte in love was wildly battling for her life.

Back to the quill pen and the desk; she is writing letters, demented letters that are cries under torture and frantic appeals for mercy.

"... *while I look upon your letters as one of the greatest felicities known to me, I shall await the receipt of them in patience until it pleases you and suits you to send me any.* ..."

"... *I am firmly convinced that I shall see you again some day—I know not how or when—but it must be, for I wish it so much.* ..."

"... *it hurts to say good-bye even in a letter. Oh, it is certain I shall see you again one day—it must be so—for as soon as I shall have earned enough money to go to Brussels I shall go there—and I shall see you again if only for a moment.* ..."

"... *for six months I have been awaiting a letter from Monsieur —six months' waiting is very long, you know!*"

Mary Taylor's brother returned from Brussels, and presently Mary herself. Joseph Taylor called at Haworth and drank tea.

"I suppose," Charlotte enquired airily while her hands shook so that the cup of tea which she handed to him spilled into the saucer, "you don't happen to have a letter for me, Joe?"

"Letters? No! Was I supposed to collect any letters? Mary said nothing about it——"

"Oh, no matter! I just thought that Polly might be sending me a note by you."

She hummed huskily and tunelessly as she busied herself with the teapot and the kettle and the china clinked and rattled a little.

Mary came home. With this forthright friend Charlotte assumed no brittle armour, Mary's shrewd, direct eyes would penetrate it in any case, and she was past subterfuge by now. She flew at Mary, kissed her, held her by the shoulders.

"Polly—give me my letter?"

Mary looked gravely into her friend's quivering face.

"I have nothing for you from Monsieur Héger, Charlotte. Neither letter nor message."

Charlotte quoted the exact, stolid words in her next frantic letter to him; and went on:

"*Day and night I find neither rest nor peace. If I sleep I am disturbed by tormenting dreams in which I see you, always grave, always incensed against me.* ...

"... *If my master withdraws his friendship from me entirely I shall be altogether without hope; if he gives me a little—just a little—*

I shall be satisfied—happy; I shall have a reason for living on, for working. Monsieur, the poor have not need of much to sustain them. . . . But if they are refused the crumbs they die of hunger. I should not know what to do with a friendship entire and complete— I am not used to it."

And presently, a last cry of despair:

"May I write to you again next May? . . . "

She snatched at less than crumbs. Her horror of strangers amounted to a neurosis but she addressed a French traveller in a Yorkshire railway carriage, simply in order to hear a voice speak the language of Constantin Héger again. *"It sounded like music in my ears—every word was most precious to me because it reminded me of you—I love French for your sake with all my heart and soul."* And ten years after Brussels, she went to hear a French preacher in London (she could allow herself that indulgence since he was a Protestant), and *"it was pleasant— half sweet, half sad—and strangely suggestive to hear the French language once more."*

It is a matter for wonder that anyone who has had access to these letters (and they are to be read in their entirety in the British Museum) could maintain that Charlotte was not in love when she wrote them. But it has been so maintained even after they were accessible. Few writers, if any, have suffered such passionate mauling, such tomb-rifling, as these three sisters, at the hands of those who came under their spell and only desired to serve their memory. Because their written words have endured an unparalleled degree of destruction and obliteration, for many decades there was next to no clue to the enigma which they left. Anyone who chanced to read the fragments torn from context could formulate a theory and voice an opinion, and no one was slow to do either.

Then, at long last, came the laborious and devoted research for which every individual who comes under that intangible, inexplicable spell owes humble thanks. But with it came the swing of the pendulum which swept aside all personal issues as of less than no account and substituted at every step their dream-world. A more dangerous error in its way than even the too-facile labelling which preceded it.

Charlotte was not less desperately in love with her Belgian

tutor because, to the end of her life, she was in love with the colossal heroes of Angria; with Lord Charles Albert Florian Wellesley and the Duke of Zamorna. She was, if anything, more profoundly in love with Constantin Héger because of those giants. She had to love a colossus of some sort; and he, in her dream-blurred eyes, was the only man whom she had yet encountered who approached that height.

She was, of course, a tragic nuisance to M. Héger, as are all women in love and unloved. The irascible pedagogue, the man who was imbued by an actual genius for teaching (even if Emily trod his methods underfoot), the solid, domestic character whose wife ran his home and her *pensionnat de demoiselles* with equal calm and competence. His swarthy eyebrows jumped in horror and dismay as he read Charlotte's rabid intention to return to Brussels whenever she could afford it. He reflected with relief that the salaries of English teachers would take a long, long time to accumulate to that extent. He muttered sharply and vehemently to himself as he read Mary's uncompromising words which Charlotte quoted. So—Mdlle. Taylor knew all about Charlotte's feelings? And so, of course, did Mdlle. Emilie. What unhappy ostriches women were. Had she no idea of how she gave herself away in every line? And the mortal pity of it was that she had so good a mind . . . not a patch on her sister's, which was unique in M. Héger's experience; but a keen pleasure to work with.

He prudently sent no replies at all, after the first one or two. And as these pitiful letters were not important, only embarrassing, and as the good man's conscience was quite unburdened in the matter, he did not even take particular care to destroy them. At last, a letter went to Charlotte which was intended as a *coup de grâce*; it hardly matters whose hand actually dealt it. Constantin Héger, his forehead creased with embarrassment, vexation, and uneasy compassion, writing, while Madame Héger sat beside him. Or Madame, writing while he gesticulated, muttered, and finally waved the whole responsibility away and into her capable hands. ("Say whatever you think best. . . . You will know just what to say . . . ") And it was said with kindliness and with delicacy. Charlotte, whose susceptible nerves were well enough remembered at the *pensionnat,* was deprecatingly advised to consider those nerves and to keep to Shakespeare and the musical glasses.

After that, silence on both sides. Charlotte sent no more letters.

> "I stand beneath the sky's blue cope
> Unburdened even by a hope."

Those two lines, from a negligible and long-forgotten Victorian poet, embody Charlotte. Hastening blindly out to the moors, to drop, breathless, to a hollow in the heather, and to lie there, her face pressed into the bruising tufts till the skin was pitted. Her tiny hands, clenched, beat the ground in a shocking abandonment of frenzy. She wept until she was suffocating, until her small, spent body was shaken by every ignominy of hiccoughs and rumblings. In the hour of death a body may loose hold of the last pitiful controls, may vent or bleed or vomit; something in Charlotte was being done to death now.

Bye-and-bye she dragged herself to a sitting position. Her face was distorted and swollen as though it had been pummelled, pulped, by blows from a fist. She was all but unrecognisable, wrecked under torture. But as she sat, staring before her from eyes half blinded by scalding tears, a thing more terrible than the ravages of her wild grief rose in her face. A poisoned bitterness, and an inflexible resolve. Charlotte, the parsonage daughter, the churchwoman, had only one refuge in her heart-break and humiliation, and it was worlds removed from Christian consolation. Women had looked so, as they turned a wax puppet in their fingers before the embers of a slow fire, and drove pins into the dwindling wax.

In that hour of blistering shame and despair and fury, Charlotte had no clouded crystal to show her a point in time when the whole reading world was to ring with *Villette.* With its compelling figure of Paul Emanuel, part-gnome and part-god, bereft of any trace of male-to-female appeal, but enthralling in vitality and force, idiosyncrasy, idealism, and tenderness beneath hot-headed savagery. And its figure of Madame Beck, unscrupulous, imperturbable, mean in soul, accomplished in strategy, cruel as a Borgia in the person of a stout, Flemish *maîtresse de maison.* Everyone read *Villette.* But reading was not all. With time, and the focus-shifting of the Brontës into fame, numerous persons wrote about *Villette:* and even lectured upon it. So that it was given to a daughter of the Hégers, who had been a small pupil of Charlotte's and who had been fond of her, to sit in a lecture-room and to hear her parents vilified and pilloried by the lecturer.

Madame Héger had retrieved and retained those piteous letters. But she kept them under lock and key, and legacied them to her children with the decree that they should not be made public so long as anyone was alive who could be hurt by the publication; and her children faithfully kept that trust. When Elizabeth Gaskell embarked on her pious and exuberant pilgrimage in order to write Charlotte's Life, she journeyed to Brussels. And with a spurt of exasperated frailty which humanises Madame Héger's impeccable and statuesque figure, she refused to see Mrs. Gaskell. . . . Someone—Constantin Héger or some member of the family—permitted her to see a careful selection of the letters. In Madame's jewel-case they were to be as notable Casket Letters as the pages written by Mary of Scotland had ever been. Mrs. Gaskell, with her unique mixture of decorum, heady indiscretion, and blind-fold loyalty to Charlotte, was so selective that she castrated them. After all, she was Charlotte's biographer at the demand of Charlotte's old father; and Charlotte's widower-husband had given his very reluctant permission for the work. Elizabeth Gaskell detested Papa; and threw Branwell to the wolves with such moral vigour that she brought a libel-case about her charming head. But she loved and honoured her friend, Charlotte; and considering the fact that her friend Charlotte's father and husband were still alive, it is perhaps no matter for surprise that she soft-pedalled the theme of those letters.

So, it was some seventy years after they were written, blotched with tears and scorched with fire, that Charlotte's outpourings were made known to the world. And for sixty-odd years, the Héger family had kept silence while they were slung with arrows, stones, and rotten eggs.

It is difficult to censure Charlotte, the minute, fragile vial charged with such deadly vitriol. She was bricked-up in desolation, and breaking to bits under her own powers. She encountered, at this time, one man whom she could reverence and a dominating personality which enthralled her, which met her masochistic need to be mastered. She said, herself, that it came easily to her to submit. She believed that she had met a man worth her submission. So she spent her heart's blood on Constantin Héger. And it was all delirium and frustration, and back to a living death. Bitterness was her only comfort; and how she used it! . . . She was a more complete pagan than Emily, for all her narrow dogmatism: a littler, punier pagan.

But really, one must salute the *famille Héger*. Charlotte's martyrdom lasted her lifetime and, being what she was, is engraved in words which find an echo in the consciousness of all women in suffering. But the *bonne bourgeoisie*, with the phlegm to which Charlotte harked back as unpleasantly as the dog in the Book of Proverbs, could be martyrs too. In a stoic silence: and with a dignity and a generosity which asked no outlet and disdained outcry.

"What I wish for now is active exertion." Those were Charlotte's words to Ellen at this time. And fate dealt it to her with a generous hand, if not in the form which she visualised or would have chosen. A phrase of a very far later day comes irresistibly into mind, incongruous and grotesque, detonating like stray cartridges into the smothering gloom: One Damn Thing After Another: that, assuredly, summed up the conditions at the parsonage.

The girls were to establish a school of their own, founded on the additional accomplishments acquired in Brussels. It was to lift them one degree above the slavedom of being semi-educated nursery governesses. It was to lift them far and high. Emily had written in one of the secret papers that were between herself and Anne only:

"A scheme is at present in agitation for setting us up in a school of our own; as yet nothing is determined, but I hope and trust it may go on and prosper and answer our highest expectations. . . ."

She goes on to draw a bright picture of all of them established in *"some pleasant and flourishing seminary"*, debts paid off, cash

in hand "*to a considerable amount.*" Emily constituted herself
the business man of the family and landed them in some
difficulties by her inflexible stubbornness and equal ignorance
regarding investments.

This blithe picture is tragic. Not for its total unfulfilment but
for its fact of existence at all. It is Emily in armour before her
own world. Emily, the early Victorian girl, faced with no other
alternative and making the best of it. It is a unique museum-
piece, in that it is the only extant glimpse of Emily attempting
to be the young lady of her time and circumstances.

Now, with Aunt's legacy in hand, Brussels accomplishments
in hand, they set out to form a school. And no school
materialised. Haworth was too remote, too isolated; the house,
even with planned additions, too unsuitable. And above all,
Branwell, at home and on the hands of his family, too insuperable a drawback. They drew up prospectuses, and
pestered their friends and acquaintance with them, but nothing
happened.

"*Depend upon it,*" Charlotte wrote to Ellen, gallant and
grinning, "*if you were to persuade a mamma to bring her child to
Haworth the aspect of the place would frighten her, and she would
probably take the dear girl back instanter.*"

While in her next birthday paper, Emily wrote the truth:

"*I should have mentioned that last summer the school scheme was
revived in full vigour . . . but it was found no go. Now I don't
desire a school at all, and none of us have any great longing for it.*"

So that was that.

Meanwhile, the loads were being built-up around the
inhabitants of the parsonage-house till they threatened to shut
out the sky. Branwell was home, in disgrace, and it was
evident, now, that he would be at home for the rest of his days.
Dismissed from his post of tutor, over a mad, unhappy love-
affair with his employer's wife, he sank without trace into
drink and drugs, wavering about the house in a sodden condition, sneaking down to the "Black Bull", and with spasms of
delirious violence to shatter the apathy. There was a blight on
the house through all the years that he lurked there, disintegrating. And Anne, governess in the same family, must
endure the shame and misery of witnessing the fantastic and

very sordid episode of her brother's love-affair. She gave notice and came home. So valued and so much loved that her pupils made a journey to visit her in her own home which Branwell was turning into an asylum.

Charlotte, who had more to bear than she could well sustain, was rigid and ruthless in disgust. But the old father's instinct was surer and his compassion—or call it indulgence if you choose—unfailing. He saw the broken Icarus in his son; and although he did not dare to admit it to his own soul, in his long, solitary musings old Patrick Brontë had a glimpse, instantly shut out, of something which he shared with the ruined young man. He, too, had wrought wings for his shoulders, long and very long ago, and they had borne him just so far and no farther. From a mud cabin to a wide English parish and the respect due to The Cloth. Charlotte was to stress this element repeatedly when she wrote *Shirley*. The beautiful Mary Cave chose Helstone from among her suitors, *"the clergyman was preferred for his office's sake . . ."* The ranting Irish curate, Malone, was favoured by the rich and fashionable Sykes daughters and their mamma *"because he was a clergyman."* Shirley herself demands of her companion and ex-governess, sedate Mrs. Pryor, *"You do not like Mr. Helstone, ma'am?"* and receives the answer *"My dear, Mr. Helstone's office secures him from criticism."* And Patrick Brontë's wings had also carried him from teaching in the school which he himself collected in an Irish village, to the delight of writing poetry, however bad: the delight was uncritical but how it burned. . . . And then, at some given point, ambition failed and energy died down; and he sank into a recluse and a hypochondriac. They had the same spiritual indolence, the father and son. And the Reverend Patrick Brontë was also fond of his bottle, within limits, but sufficiently fond to make his daughters uneasy and his parishioners critical.

Now that Branwell was helpless and a source of wretchedness to everyone, the old father accepted the burden and dealt with it faithfully and courageously and not without tenderness. The demented young man had a bed in his room and he wrestled with Branwell in body and mind through the terrible nights. It will be remembered—it should be remembered—

that he had constituted himself his wife's best nurse when she
was dying of cancer, and that from devotion not necessity, for
there was a village nurse in attendance on poor Maria Brontë
and there were village servants and nursemaids in the house,
then.

And Emily sat up on guard when Branwell was at the "Black
Bull", and let him in, and put him to bed. Saved him when he
set his bedclothes on fire. And ran down the churchyard to
knock at the taproom window as a warning that her father was
approaching the house. Her wrestling with the fire was the
least of Emily's tasks; she was in her natural element there,
coping with a dangerous emergency. But to run down to the
squalid back window and hear the sudden dribbling out of the
raucous voices at the sound of her knuckles on the pane; the
whispers, a smothered guffaw; that made her feel sick. It was a
contact with sneaking squalor which wounded her fastidious-
ness to the core.

(x)

THE sound of voices in the study across the hall reached Emily
where she sat reading in the parlour window-seat. Charlotte's
voice, a steady murmur as she read aloud to Papa; sudden,
sharp interruptions in Papa's voice raised to a peevish falsetto.
It only came to Emily as the buzzing of midges, troublesome,
and to be brushed aside.

The door opened, letting out a final salvo from Papa, closed,
and Charlotte came into the parlour. The tea-things were on
the table and the kettle just beginning to steam. Mechanically,
automatically, Charlotte put a cup and saucer straight, moved
the sugar-bowl. Then she sat down at the table and dropped her
head in her hands.

"What is it? Has Papa been tiresome again? I thought I
heard him."

"He feels his growing blindness terribly. It is maddening for
him to have to submit to someone reading to him. He is so
used to reading all that he likes, himself. And as for his being
tiresome——" Charlotte's uneasy voice rose, sharpened, the

voice of a person at the end of their tether, "you had better grow used to it. You and Anne may be reading to him before very long. And to me."

"Charlotte, don't talk so. What wicked nonsense——"

"I wish with all my heart it were. I pray it may be. Do you realise, Em—I can't write a page, now, without my eyes inflaming? If I go on writing I shall probably go blind before Papa. . . . And without it—there's nothing. Nothing. Sometimes I feel I'm going mad——"

"You won't go blind," Emily said positively.

"You don't know what it's like. Every day—several times a day—I try to test my sight; sometimes it seems better, and at others, so much worse. If it comes to blindness—enforced idleness—it will be like being chained to a stake . . . I would far rather die. And if we are both blind—Papa and I—what is to become of you all? Aunt's nest-egg won't last for ever. Branwell will never earn a penny again, not as long as he lives. I think God has forsaken us, Emily. I do indeed——"

Emily left her corner, came to Charlotte's side, laid an arm round her convulsed shoulders. A most rare gesture for Emily.

"You are not going blind, my poor dear. Your eyes have always been weak, and you won't wear your glasses, and you've worried yourself to a shadow. You will be stronger, soon. You fret yourself so, Charlotte——"

And, she thought, you have cried so. . . . Night after night, slipping downstairs and sobbing for hours. Crying as you walked in the wind and rain and pretending it was only the wind making your eyes run and the rain on your face. Why—your eyes filled if anyone so much as looked at you.

"Here's Papa coming," she said aloud. "Where is Anne? I'll make the tea, Charlotte."

"*I can hardly tell you how time gets on at Haworth,*" Charlotte wrote to Ellen. "*There is no event whatever to mark its progress. One day resembles another; and all have heavy, lifeless physiognomies. Sunday, baking-day, and Saturday, are the only ones that have any distinctive mark. Meantime, life wears away. . . . Yet it is wrong and foolish to repine. . . . There was a time when Haworth was a very pleasant place to me; it is not so now. I feel as if we were all*"

buried here. I long to travel; to work; to lead a life of action."
It was still alive, the feeling which had taken possession of
her, years before, kindled by a letter from Mary Taylor from
Lille, and which had swept her to Brussels and stung her to life:
"*I hardly know what swelled my throat as I read her letter: such a
vehement impatience of restraint and steady work; such a strong wish
for wings—wings such as wealth can furnish; such an urgent thirst to
see, to know, to learn; something internal seemed to expand bodily for
a minute . . .*"
What remained, from that flight into living?
"*Excuse me, dear, for troubling you with my fruitless wishes . . .
your letters and the French newspapers are the only messengers that
come to me from the outer world beyond our moors . . .*"
The darkness could hardly have been denser. Inside the
strait walls of the house there was blindness, and near-madness,
and a mortal sickness of the heart. And the future so stark and
hopeless that Charlotte at least could only peer at it in a panic of
dread. If Papa went blind (and he was going blind fast and
certainly); if her own eyesight failed; if Branwell were to be on
their hands indefinitely; what was to stand between the Brontë
household and starvation?

And there was most hurtful shame as well. Branwell's
presence in the house cut Charlotte off from her only comfort,
the company of her friend Ellen. Duns arrived on the front
steps. His father must watch the front door of the tavern, to
bring Branwell home, while his sister flew to knock at a back
window in warning. Humiliating rôles for the parsonage
family. Emily's inner world surged and reverberated with evil-
doing and evil-being on a titanic scale; but this was descent to
petty squalor and disgrace. The sordid atmosphere which
Branwell brought into the home lay over it like a film of slime.

And then, light drove through the darkness, pierced it and
scattered it. The shaft came with the apparent suddenness of a
comet but it was no such thing. It was germinating to fulfilment
through the years behind, an intrinsic part of their own beings
for the three young women, so that it did not flame, sink, and
vanish. It brought their lives into the air for which they had
been struggling and groping ever since they were conscious of
themselves at all.

They discovered that they were writers.

Charlotte's muted voice speaks, in her incomparable account of her own and her sisters' work as it came into being. Speaks very simply, in utter sincerity; and spent with long pain:

"*Resident in a remote district, where education had made little progress, and where, consequently, there was no inducement to seek social intercourse beyond our own domestic circle, we were wholly dependent on ourselves and each other, on books and study, for the enjoyments and occupations of life.*"

Ellen's soft shadow wavers in the background, a little hurt, ever so little grieved. At about the same time as Charlotte was writing the threnody which was her preface to the books of her dead sisters, she wrote those words of Ellen to her publisher and good friend, "*A calm, steady girl—not brilliant but good and true. She suits me and has always suited me well.*"

The sisters were with her no longer. And in the shadows of the past lay one short, ecstatic interlude of satisfaction in the classrooms and formal garden of Brussels, followed by starvation. Ellen was never admitted into her mental world of work. She even stayed with Ellen and corrected proof-sheets under her eyes, without vouchsafing a word. And Ellen asked no questions. And here, Charlotte is, in fact, being a trifle high-hat about her dearest and closest friend. . . .

The quiet, sorrowful voice continues:

"*The highest stimulus, as well as the liveliest pleasure we had known from childhood upwards, lay in attempts at literary composition; formerly we used to show each other what we wrote, but of late years this . . . had been discontinued: hence it ensued that we were mutually ignorant of the progress we might respectively have made.*

"*. . . One day . . . I accidentally lighted on an MS volume of verse in my sister Emily's handwriting. Of course, I was not surprised, knowing that she could and did write verse: I looked it over, and something more than surprise seized me—a deep conviction that these were not common effusions, nor at all like the poetry women generally write. . . .*

"*My sister Emily was not a person of demonstrative character, nor one on the recesses of whose mind and feelings even those nearest and dearest to her could, with impunity, intrude unlicensed; it took hours*

*to reconcile her to the discovery I had made, and days to persuade her
that such poems merited publication . . ."*

My sister Emily: Charlotte could not keep away from the
words; she came back to them time after time. If Charlotte had
ever written a life of Emily, that should have been its title.
And with all her prejudices and her misjudgments it would have
been better than anything else which has been written of Emily.

Charlotte's sedate understatement enshrines this epic
occasion almost comically. Her brief, restrained account was an
offering of devotion. She would not, for her life, admit that
my sister Emily flew into one of her terrifying Olympian rages
nor that it took more than hours or days for a shuddering
Charlotte to recover from the scenes. Emily was swept by a
surge of the same brainstorm anger as made her pummel
Keeper half-blind for an act of dog-disobedience. She now
pummelled Charlotte to pulp, not with her clenched fists but
with words. And then swung out on to the moors, and came
back, hours later, to maintain a frozen dumbness more nerve-
racking than her hoarse, deep-throated abuse. Emily suffered
violation of something deeper than flesh when Charlotte pried
into her book of verses.

But the storm wore itself out. And what came after was
newness of life. Charlotte had a mass of poems. Anne *"quietly
produced some of her own compositions, intimating that, since
Emily's had given me pleasure, I might like to look at hers."*

Anne did everything quietly. Nothing could be more
characteristic than her revelation of her verses. And it was
characteristic of something else, too: the tenderness in Emily
which made the youngest sister as naïvely ready as a child to
exhibit her small songs, unabashed, unafraid before the
splendour of the older sister's immeasurably greater gift.

"The book . . . is scarcely known," Charlotte goes on, *"and
all of it that merits to be known are the poems of Ellis Bell."* That
much she recognised even if no one else did until the later time
came when everyone who read the book recognised it:
". . . neither we nor our poems were at all wanted"; (there was a
gleam of Charlotte's acid and valiant humour). *". . . Ill-
success failed to crush us: the mere effort to succeed had given a
wonderful zest to existence; it must be pursued."*

No one has ever put that truth into simpler or more adequate words. The creative worker's necessity to bring his work into the light of day. To make it known. To be acknowledged as a creator. Southey had bidden Charlotte write—now and then—for a pastime and a comfort, but never, never to concern herself with publicity. He might as well have bidden a woman with child to carry it dead in her womb and not give herself the exertion of birth. The least of writers equally with the greatest may share the unrepeatable experience which comes like an accolade, when what has been only a thing of pen and ink and paper suddenly lies before him, a printed book, and for the first time. One has written a book. Its end may be in its beginning; the miracle remains. One wrote a book . . .

In a sense, Emily may be held to blame for an incalculable amount of the theories and arguments which have risen about her, because of what she did with her poems which went into the small green volume. She was impelled to eliminate every trace of Gondal, every clue to her secret world; she lifted fragments, she cut, she isolated, so that they appeared as complete and separate poems. When, in time ahead, the forgotten little book was seized upon, read, discussed, disputed, reprinted, there was no chart to hand, to discover that most of the poems had their place in the Gondal saga and were uttered by or descriptive of Gondal beings. But they are Emily, as they are Gondal. She *was* Gondal. . . .

Emily's poems, as Charlotte said, are the only true poetry in the book. And even so, her work is a matter of fragments of startling beauty embedded in mediocre verse. Nothing of Emily is explicable, first or last; but not the least inexplicable thing about her is that she could write such supreme and such mediocre poetry. . . . Almost everything which she wrote pulses with power. Charlotte was never more apt than when she said that her sister's poetry was totally unlike the poetry which "*women usually write.*" But Sidney Dobell's comment on her work as "the unformed writing of a giant's hand" is more applicable to her poetry than to her one and only book. In *The Philosopher*, there is the perfect phrase "*Space-sweeping soul*", and its final verse is the cry of Emily's own soul, but even that cry falters into inadequate words.

"And even for that spirit, seer,
I've watched and sought my life-time long;
Sought him in heaven, hell, earth, and air—
An endless search, and always wrong!
Had I but seen his glorious eye
Once light the clouds that wilder me,
I ne'er had raised this coward cry
To cease to think and cease to be;
I ne'er had called oblivion blest,
Nor, stretching eager hands to death,
Implored to change for senseless rest
This sentient soul, this living breath——"

Remembrance, the song of Gondal's siren-queen for Julius Brenzaida, is the exquisite threnody which gave rise to the belief that Emily must have known a human lover.

"Cold in the earth—and the deep snow piled above thee,
Far, far removed, cold in the dreary grave!
Have I forgot, my only Love, to love thee,
Severed at last by Time's all-severing wave?

Now, when alone, do my thoughts no longer hover
Over the mountains, on that northern shore,
Resting their wings where heath and fern-leaves cover
Thy noble heart for ever, ever more?

Cold in the earth—and fifteen wild Decembers
From those brown hills have melted into spring;
Faithful, indeed, is the spirit that remembers
After such years of change and suffering!

Sweet Love of youth, forgive if I forget thee,
While the world's tide is bearing me along;
Other desires and other hopes beset me,
Hopes which obscure but cannot do thee wrong!

No later light has lightened up my heaven,
No second morn has ever shone for me;

All my life's bliss from thy dear life was given,
All my life's bliss is in the grave with thee.

But when the days of golden dreams had perished,
And even Despair was powerless to destroy;
Then did I learn how existence could be cherished,
Strengthened, and fed without the aid of joy.

Then did I check the tears of useless passion—
Weaned my young soul from yearning after thine;
Sternly denied its burning wish to hasten
Down to that tomb already more than mine.

And even yet, I dare not let it languish,
Dare not indulge in memory's rapturous pain;
Once drinking deep of that divinest anguish,
How could I seek the empty world again?"

It goes to its own music. So many lines of Emily's sing themselves in the mind. It is too often forgotten or ignored that she alone of the sisters was a musician. Strength and sweetness meet and mingle in her poems.

"The linnet in the rocky dells,
The moor-lark in the air,
The bee among the heather bells,
That hide my lady fair:

The wild deer browse above her breast;
The wild birds raise their brood;
And they, her smiles of love caressed,
Have left her solitude!

I ween that when the grave's dark wall
Did first her form retain,
They thought their hearts could ne'er recall
The light of joy again.

They thought the tide of grief would flow
Unchecked through future years;

But where is all their anguish now,
And where are all their tears?

Well, let them fight for honour's breath,
Or pleasure's shade pursue—
The dweller in the land of death
Is changed and careless too.

And if their eyes should watch and weep
Till sorrow's source were dry,
She would not, in her tranquil sleep,
Return a single sigh!

Blow, west-wind, by the lonely mound,
And murmur, summer streams—
There is no need of other sound
To soothe my lady's dreams."

The middle verses have every flaw, and they sink like the middle of a badly-cooked cake: but the last ten lines break free from Gondal grandiloquence and in their poignant simplicity—their content and their metre—might be Housman. That Emily worked laboriously over her poems, altering, scratching out, is to be seen by anyone who knows the stiff pages of that note-book with its crimson cover which Charlotte found, which anyone may, by simply asking to have it lifted from its glass case in the British Museum. They may see there, and with some-thing of a shock, that in Emily's first version of her splendid line "*Once drinking of that divinest anguish*" she wrote "*delight-ful*", and crossed it out, and substituted "*divinest*". Charlotte says of Emily "*Her will was not very flexible, and it generally opposed her interest . . .*" and that she and Anne ". . . *had no thought of filling their pitchers at the well-spring of other minds . . .*" and there is something at once touching and comic about the careful wording. Charlotte, admitting, deprecating, and glossing over the blunt fact that Emily would brook no word of criticism; and, unlike herself, was no reader. She could not, really, criticise herself to any advantage. So that, throughout her poems, there is the baffling mixture of bathos and sudden inspired beauty. Papa himself in his poetaster days, might have written anything as bad as most of Emily's *Anticipation*, beginning "*How beautiful the earth is still, To thee—how full of happiness!*" but only Emily could have written the lines which break from it in one verse:

> "*Gazed o'er the sands the waves efface,*
> *To the enduring seas—*
> *There cast my anchor of desire*
> *Deep in unknown eternity:*"

One may be thankful that the green published volume includes the immortal "*He comes with western winds,*" encased in ten verses of the very long narrative ballad to which it belongs, because otherwise it might have been lost to the world. It is the ultimate seed from which has grown the obscuring mass of theory about Emily; but she wrote nothing to compare with it and it stands among the great poetry of all time. Her "*To Imagination*" is a turgid poem, stuffed with sufficient allegory to satisfy even Charlotte's weakness for allegory, but the jewels shine from the encrusting pebbles:

> "*Where thou, and I, and Liberty*
> *Have undisputed sovereignty.*
>
> .   .   .   .   .   .
>
> *But thou art ever there, to bring*
> *The hovering vision back and breathe*
> *New glories o'er the blighted spring*"

There has been so much and such dangerous quoting from Emily's poems that it must be reiterated that the beauty goes like a wavering flame through nearly every one of them, but that there is a formidable amount of poor poetry to bank it down. Which only serves to make Emily the poet yet more of the enigma which was Emily in every aspect.

> "*How clear she shines! How quietly*
> *I lie beneath her guardian light;*

While heaven and earth are whispering me
'Tomorrow, wake, but dream tonight.'

The world is going; dark world, adieu!
Grim world, conceal thee till the day;
The heart thou canst not all subdue
Must still resist if thou delay!

.   .   .   .

And this shall be my dream to-night;
I'll think the heaven of glorious spheres
Is rolling on its course of light
In endless bliss, through endless years;
I'll think, there's not one world above,
Far as these straining eyes can see,
Where Wisdom ever laughed at Love,
Or Virtue crouched to Infamy;

Where, writhing 'neath the strokes of Fate,
The mangled wretch was forced to smile;
To match his patience 'gainst her hate,
His heart rebellious all the while.
Where Pleasure still will lead to wrong,
And helpless Reason warn in vain;
And Truth is weak, and Treachery strong;
And Joy the surest path to Pain;
And Peace, the lethargy of Grief;
And Hope, a phantom of the soul;
And Life, a labour void and brief;
And Death, the despot of the whole!"

All her rolling allegories cannot mar the splendour of the last
four lines—(nor can her exasperating use of the everlasting
semi-colon and exclamation-mark . . .)

The lyric, unfortunately entitled "*Sympathy*", is music again:

"There should be no despair for you
While nightly stars are burning;

> *While evening pours its silent dew*
> *And sunshine gilds the morning.*
> *There should be no despair—though tears*
> *May flow down like a river:*
> *Are not the best beloved of years*
> *Around your heart for ever?"*

In *"Plead For Me"*, Emily's apologies for her whole way of life, there are verses which sound like a shoddy hymn for an evangelistic revival, and then:

> *"And gave my spirit to adore*
> *Thee, ever-present phantom thing;*
> *My slave, my comrade, and my king.*
>
> *A slave, because I rule thee still;*
> *Incline thee to my changeful will,*
> *And make thy influence good or ill*
> *A comrade, for by day and night*
> *Thou art my intimate delight—*
>
> *My darling pain that wounds and sears*
> *And brings a blessing out from tears*
> *By deadening me to earthly cares;*
>
> . . . .
>
> *Speak, God of visions, plead for me.*
> *And tell why I have chosen thee!"*

This is Emily maintaining her right to her life of the imagination; no more. But it is indissolubly linked to the superb poem which had no place in the collection and which Charlotte believed to be her sister's last written word. This rather dramatic footnote of Charlotte's is open to question, and is unimportant anyway. The poem needs no such dramatic enhancement. It is the heart and core of Emily throughout her life:

> *"No coward soul is mine,*
> *No trembler in the world's storm-troubled sphere:*

I see Heaven's glories shine
And faith shines equal, arming me from fear.

O God within my breast,
Almighty, ever-present Deity!
Life—that in me has rest,
As I —undying Life—have power in Thee!

Vain are the thousand creeds
That move men's hearts; unutterably vain;
Worthless as withered weeds,
Or idlest froth amid the boundless main,

To waken doubt in one
Holding so fast by Thine infinity;
So surely anchored on
The steadfast rock of immortality.

With wide-embracing love
Thy spirit animates eternal years,
Pervades and broods above,
Changes, sustains, dissolves, creates, and rears.

Though earth and man were gone,
And suns and universes cease to be,
And Thou were left alone,
Every existence would exist in Thee.

There is no room for Death,
Nor atom that his might could render void;
Thou—THOU art Being and Breath,
And what THOU art may never be destroyed."

This is the Hound of Heaven. The "tremendous Lover" of Francis Meynell's kindred poem. "Lo! naught contents thee, who content'st not Me". It is supreme recognition that the soul's quest is mutual, not one-sided. "My slave, my comrade, and my king", was as far as Emily dared to go when she spoke of the power of her secret imaginings, the "God of visions". Now, in the later poem (and who is to say how little later?) she is voicing a recognition so stupendous that any comment is hazardous. The union of the human soul with the more-than-human. The soul vitalised in God: but, also, God completed by His creature. . . .

Other lines from "The Hound of Heaven" steal on the ear to link with this poem:

> ". . . faileth the dream
>   The dreamer, and the lute the lutanist."

The dream was not so much failing as merged, lost in the blinding light of unspeakably deeper experience. Gondal had stretched to the feet of God.

Charlotte's poetry is a curio and a museum-piece, at kindliest computation. It is about as bad as it could well be . . . She indulged in the narrative poem of her period and no form of verse is more disastrous when used with rhyme. It lies wide open to every grotesque banality. Her results are on a level with the pious and forgotten effusions of Frances Ridley Havergal. But there is, inevitably, some reality in the poems, which, if anything, makes the whole thing worse. *Mementos*: a woman devoured by secret and unhappy love.

> *"She bore in silence—but when passion*
> *Surged in her soul with ceaseless foam,*
> *The storm at last brought desolation*
> *And drove her exiled from her home.*
>
> *And silent still, she straight assembled*
> *The wrecks of strength her soul retained;*
> *For though the wasted body trembled,*
> *The unconquered mind, to quail, disdained."*

This is Charlotte; though she did not keep silent, and though the woman of her poem is driven to restless travel by her pain, when Charlotte was compelled to endure hers, bound and confined in her home. Her own straining desire to get away from the familiar scene, is speaking.

"I am resolved our souls shall burn
With equal, steady, mingling shine."

A refugee in flight in time of war is speaking, but she voices
Charlotte's paramount demand of the heart and brain which
caused her to refuse marriage with several suitors who could not
satisfy it.

Frances, a lengthy ballad of yet another woman whose lover
has grown cold to her, besides containing a gruesome line in the
familiar churchyard key *"Released from shroud and wormy clod"*,
has a description of a love fading gradually under the baffled
eyes of the still-faithful woman, which is Charlotte, again,
baring her heart, even though it is bared in atrocious verse.

"It fell not with a sudden crashing,
It poured not out like open sluice;
No, sparkling still and redly flashing,
Drained, drop by drop, the generous juice.

I saw it sink, and strove to taste it,
My eager lips approached the brim;
The movement only seemed to waste it,
It sank to dregs, all harsh and dim . . .

Yet whence that wondrous change of feeling,
I never knew, and cannot learn,
Nor why my lover's eye, congealing,
Grew cold and clouded, proud, and stern.

Nor wherefore, friendship's forms forgetting,
He careless left, and cool withdrew;
Nor spoke of grief, nor fond regretting,
Nor even one glance of comfort threw.

And neither word nor token sending,
Of kindness, since the parting day,
His course for distant regions bending,
Went, self-contained and calm, away.

. . . .

Rebellious now to blank inertion,
My unused strength demands a task . . ."

And Charlotte was writing to Ellen, in the blank and bitter time after her return from Brussels: *"What I crave now is exertion."*

In a word: the only value to be found in Charlotte's verse is the occasional trace of Charlotte herself. She was no poet. But everything of Charlotte is there. Her stumblings into bathos, which were to occur through her real achievement, her three great novels; exemplified by such lines:

"Some soft piano-notes above
Were sweet as faintly given,
Where ladies, doubtless, cheered the hearth
With song that winter-even."

In *The Teacher's Monologue,* four and a half lovely lines occur in a dreary piece of doggerel:

"The room is quiet, thoughts alone
People its mute tranquility;
The yoke put off, the long task done,
I am, as it is bliss to be,
Still and untroubled . . ."

Passion: *"Some have won a wild delight*
By daring wilder sorrow;
Could I gain thy love tonight
I'd hazard death tomorrow."

Evening Solace: (Charlotte was more fortunate in her titles than in what followed them.)

"The human heart has hidden treasures,
The secret kept, in silence sealed;—
The thoughts, the hopes, the dreams, the pleasures,
Whose charms were broken if revealed.

. . . .

But there are hours of lonely musing,
Such as in evening silence come,
When, soft as birds their pinions closing,
The hearts's best feelings gather home."

This is one of her very few poems to show a lyric touch. It is akin to Alice Meynell's "The dovecote doors of sleep . . ." But Charlotte has to spoil it by a pathetically gaudy picture of the full-blooded life which so intrigued and appalled her— Angria, in fact, breaks in:

> *"And days may pass in gay confusion,*
> *And nights in rosy riot fly,*
> *While, lost in Fame's or Wealth's illusion,*
> *The memory of the Past may die."*

A long and ponderous poem in rhyming couplets is entitled *The Missionary* and is ludicrously suggestive of "Where the remote Bermudas ride". It contains the germ of the St. John Rivers part of *Jane Eyre*, even to the renounced love of Rosamund. Its sole value is its proof (if any proof be required) that *Jane Eyre* was taking form and life in Charlotte's brain long before *The Professor* which preceded it. Which has no real importance, since any writer knows to what an extent ideas are formed, lie dormant, take life later on, and that one book may be in-the-writing while another, or even more than one other, is in-the-conceiving.

When Charlotte had found herself, come into her own, as a novelist, she could say of her own poetry, as she gave a copy of the book to Elizabeth Gaskell: *"to prevent you from throwing away four shillings in an injudicious purchase. I do not like my own share of the work nor care that it should be read: . . . Mine are chiefly juvenile productions; the restless effervescence of a mind that would not be still."* Which is a fairly universal experience for poets, lesser or greater.

"I could not but be a partial judge, yet I thought that these verses, too, had a sweet, sincere pathos of their own." It is Charlotte speaking, and of Anne's poems. And the truth is that it is

hard to criticise Anne: for the frail, courageous figure, with its quiet dignity and artless grace, rather silences criticism. It is even pleasant to know that her plaintive tinklings had a certain success of their own. Anne was found by Ellen smiling happily over a number of *Chambers' Journal* and when asked, more or less, what was funny in that sober periodical, replied that it wasn't a question of being funny, "*I see they have inserted one of my poems.*" One or two of them are also to be found in hymn-books, which is exactly where Anne would have wished them to be. And there the matter rests. They are sad little poems, full of a sense of sin and of the righteous indignation of her God. Full of a piteous homesickness, and a love for leaves and grass and small, shy flowers. One lilting little song is Anne in a rare buoyant mood: *Lines Composed in a Wood on a Windy Day:*

"*My soul is awakened, my spirit is soaring
And carried aloft on the wings of the breeze;
For above and around me the wild wind is roaring,
Arousing to rapture the earth and the seas.*

*The long withered grass in the sunshine is glancing,
The bare trees are tossing their branches on high;
The dead leaves beneath them are merrily dancing,
The white clouds are scudding across the blue sky.*

*I wish I could see how the ocean is lashing
The foam of its billows to whirlwinds of spray;
I wish I could see how its proud waves are dashing,
And hear the wild roar of their thunder today.*"

Like Charlotte, Anne was drawn to the sea. When she was dying her one plea was, "*Oh, if I could but get to the sea!*" and she died beside it.

The Student's Serenade is a naïve Gondal poem, with the lover waking the lady to come out and see moonlight on the snow. ("*Then awake! Maria, wake!*") And naïve, also, is the narrative-poem, *Self-Congratulation*, which reads almost like something from the cautionary tales in verse written for children by Anne and Jane Taylor—except that the Ellen of

this poem confesses to a hidden love and congratulates herself
that no one would guess it. There is the *"sweet, sincere pathos"*
in this poem for all its primness.

"Last night as we sat round the fire
Conversing merrily,
We heard, without, approaching steps
Of one well-known to me!

There was no trembling in my voice,
No blush upon my cheek,
No lustrous sparkle in my eyes
Of hope, or joy, to speak;
But oh! my spirit burned within,
My heart beat full and fast!
He came not nigh—he went away—
And then my joy was past.

. . . .

They little know my hidden thoughts;
And they will never know
The aching anguish of my heart,
The bitter burning woe!"

You can hear the study door open, Willy Weightman's voice
speaking to Papa, his step going past the parlour door and out
into the dark. Perhaps he is undergoing a spasm of prudence?
He is getting, maybe, a little too fond of Anne? . . . he does
not want to grow *too* fond of anyone, just yet . . . and there
must be no awkward situation at the Parsonage. Or perhaps—
and this is more like that "kindest heart"—he realises that
Anne is more deeply touched at her gentle heart than will make
for her peace of mind. Whatever the reason, his boots creak
past the parlour door and the front door shuts.

"These are very pretty. Very pretty indeed," says Emily,
turning the manuscript pages of the selected poems by Anne.
"But you have others, Anne—some of them better than these.
Different from these. What about 'Come to the banquet'—or
'The Dungeon'?"

"No, no," Charlotte interposes with some vehemence. "We must on *no* account let . . . people would not understand. . . . We must be exceedingly careful not to seem . . . queer in any way——"

"We are going to use pen-names," Emily says stubbornly. "Men's names, even."

"Charlotte is right, dear," says Anne's subdued voice. And Emily shrugs, as usual.

(xi)

THERE is a sense of something, irresistible in force but very gradual. Certain pen-pictures of the sisters would suggest that, in spite of their lifetime of writings known only to one another and Branwell, they fell to the writing of their actual novels solely on the impetus of a book of poems which dropped dead from the press. It was not so. It could never have been so, in the nature of things. All of Emily's conscious existence went to the making of *Wuthering Heights*. She is living it, writing it, destroying and writing afresh, for no one may know how long before ever the girls broke into print with their poems. Charlotte's *Professor* is working in her mind through the two years of heart-ache after Brussels. She dared not let herself go, in this book. She kept it flat and tame and passionless, and made of it as dull a book as she was capable of writing. The tragedy of the Pension Héger was still too close at hand. Anne's prolonged, uncomplaining penance as a governess is being wrought into the tepid little volume of *Agnes Grey* before ever she returns to her home.

The germs of every being and of most events in their books can be traced to their copious writings of the dream-worlds. But there is no disentangling the consuming power of the dream from the material they also used which was the stuff of everyday life as it lay before their eyes. Charlotte's tragedy of the heart was not less real because Paul Emanuel had his prototype in an Angrian figure as well as in the solid flesh of Constantin Héger. Emily, more than any of the three, lived in the essence of the characters whom she created in Gondal.

But who shall venture to dissect Emily-the-medium in Emily-the-girl? To assess her own personal experience, mental and spiritual, as apart from the experience of her dream-creatures? It matters not at all that her most timeless and immortal words are uttered in the voices to which she gave other (and such copious!) names. It is still Emily speaking.

The fact of having published a book—even if no one read it— did give a final touch or spur. It is possible, it is just conceivable, that but for that slim, inconspicuous book the stories which were presently given to the world might have been lost among their other lost writings, or mutilated, or destroyed. It does not bear thinking of. . . . They finished *The Professor*, *Wuthering Heights* and *Agnes Grey*.

"*These MSS*" (Charlotte again), "*were perseveringly obtruded upon various publishers for the space of a year and a half; usually their fate was an ignominous and abrupt dismissal.*

"*At last* Wuthering Heights *and* Agnes Grey *were accepted on terms somewhat impoverishing to the two authors. Currer Bell's book found acceptance nowhere, so that something like the chill of despair began to invade his heart.*"

Anne shed a few tears.

"Charlotte—it is too hard! It's all wrong—I wish they had taken *The Professor*—I wish they had taken it instead of *me*. . . ."

"Stuff and nonsense!" Charlotte retorted hotly. "It will find its way, sometime!"

Emily held her peace. How much—or how little—did it mean to her, when her book was taken? Did she feel an exultant triumph and go striding out to the moors with it? Or did it really not signify very greatly? because, taken or rejected, Emily was utterly sure of herself and as unassailable by criticism as by advice.

At least she said nothing to Charlotte about Charlotte's failure. She knew, better than Charlotte knew, what had wrecked *The Professor*. You cannot write a book merely as an emotional discipline, binding and gagging your people until they are numbed almost to death, and expect it to be readable. But Emily would not lay a probing finger on Charlotte's too-visible scars.

Then, back to nothingness. The life at Haworth closed over

their heads again, quite unchanged in its dreariness except to
grow worse with the weeks and months.

"*You say I am to tell you plenty? What would you have me say?
Nothing happens at Haworth; nothing, at least, of a pleasant
kind . . . the arrival of a Sheriff's officer on a visit to Branwell,
inviting him either to pay his debts or take a trip to York. Of course
his debts had to be paid*" . . .

　. . . "*I feel as if it was almost a farce to sit down and write to
you now, with nothing to say worth listening to . . . (but) I have a
haunting terror lest you should imagine I forget you—that my
regard cools with absence. It is not in my nature to forget your
nature. . . .*"

She was only separated from Ellen by a few miles. But the
state of things at home was an unsurmountable barrier.

Even the triumph of Emily and Anne was proving a mirage:
the cheating publisher into whose hands they had fallen was
doing nothing about their books.

But one thing remained unquenchable and indestructible.
Charlotte was writing *Jane Eyre*; Anne was writing *The Tenant
of Wildfell Hall*. Emily? It will never be known whether Emily
was writing another book. Charlotte stated that she, with
Anne, was "*prepared to try again. Energy nerved the one, and
endurance upheld the other.*" She would never allow herself to
see Anne's second book as anything but a self-imposed penance,
but she could not fail to recognise the dæmonic vitality of
Emily's mind even if she had to water it down to "*energy*". It is
reasonable to feel that the mind which had just given such
titanic birth would, in the nature of itself, subside into rest and
fallowness for a time. It is really not imaginable that the girl
who could write *Wuthering Heights* would write at the speed
and ease of an Edgar Wallace.

But the other two were writing. And each, so different in
temperament from the other, was writing from the same
impulse. Charlotte was tearing off the shackles and bandages
which kept her as maimed and rigid as her William Crimsworth and Frances Henri, in *The Professor*. And Anne was
letting loose the small wellspring of melodrama, the hidden
store of strength, the innocent taste for the swashbuckling
and the daredevilling, which was deep down within her.

"*I will show you a heroine as plain and as small as myself, who shall be as interesting as any of yours,*" Charlotte flashed at her sisters. And added, later, very carefully, of Jane, "*but she is not myself any further than that . . . .*" Which, of course, was untrue. Jane was Charlotte's unforgotten and unpardoned wrongs at Cowan Bridge; her romantic passion; her desire to be mastered in love; her lifelong sense of her own physical deficiencies. The first plain and insignificant heroine in English fiction; the first firebrand in the shape and dress of a demure underling. Jane was not a thesis, she was flesh and blood, quivering and courageous flesh, and very hot blood indeed. Charlotte said that "*when she came to Thornfield, she could not stop.*" She wrote at white heat till her eyes gave out.

And Papa went totally blind. There was a journey to Manchester, an operation (mercifully successful), with Charlotte "*in the room all the time, as it was his wish that I should be there.*"

And Charlotte was in the sitting-room of the Manchester lodgings, sick and shaken from the ordeal, and worried about the nurse because that hearty Gamp must of course live better and feed higher than either the convalescent or herself. "*I am afraid of not having things good enough for her.*" The street lay grey outside the windows, Manchester on an August day, and the comfortable sitting-room felt airless. And the post brought a parcel. *The Professor* returned again. That was a dark hour.

When she brought Papa home, she needed Ellen so desperately that she set about arrangements for getting her to Haworth. Warning her to expect a great change in Branwell's looks and that he was broken in mind as well as in health. The arrangements fell through, of course; they nearly always did, when Charlotte clutched at a solace. She sent Ellen a fierce little note, wrung from exacerbated nerves and heart: "*This is bitter, but I feel bitter.*"

But Ellen's love and understanding could put that aside and make her resolute to go to Haworth as soon as she could. She came in a golden season of harvest, and the girls could escape into the open air and on to the miles of purple heather. Charlotte looked down at the white-gold fields in the valley, and said:

"I hope—I so much hope—that there will be Harvest Thanksgiving in every single church hereabouts. I must speak to Papa——"

There was harvest-time in her heart, and the great hour was very close at hand. A courteous publisher who had refused *The Professor* had asked to see a longer book. She had all but finished *Jane Eyre*: it would go to him before the fields were reaped.

And so to the day which no other day in Charlotte's life would ever quite equal nor reach for zenith. *Jane Eyre* was taken; was brought out in a matter of weeks; and took the public by storm. The reviewers might be cautious, might be variable, but everyone was reading it. Even the shady publisher who had netted *Wuthering Heights* and *Agnes Grey* rushed them belatedly to press on the strength of it.

"I believed that what had impressed me so forcibly when I wrote it, must make a strong impression on anyone who read it . . . but I hardly expected that a book by an unknown author could find readers."

That conviction was Charlotte's mainspring. What she wrote might or might not find anyone to read it: but what she wrote, in itself, had the spark of live fire which nothing could quench. She believed in herself and her gift. That belief carried her through the grey years, and the uttermost darkness, and the deathly twilight.

And now life moved into a wholly new dimension. There were all the exhilarating and the exasperating incidents which are the lot of the successful writer, crowding upon the parsonage by every incoming post. There was the sudden rush to London to counteract the double-dealing of Emily's and Anne's publisher, Newby, a spiv-before-his-time, and to convince their own Smith & Elder of their identity, and—more important still—of their integrity.

Emily took no part in it all. Newby had requested another book from either sister but it was only Anne who offered *Wildfell Hall*. Emily was not hurrying to write another book. It was so fully accepted that Emily stood above and apart from all the besetting public life which had borne down on the grey roof like a tornado, that when Charlotte faltered to the baffled George Smith "*We are three sisters,*" she was instantly seized by compunction and panic. Emily would be furious . . . oh, kind heaven! remember the day of the pillaged notebook? . . .

"Ellis Bell will not endure to be alluded to under any appellation than the nom-de-plume. I committed a grand error in betraying his identity. . . . It was inadvertent—the words 'We are three sisters' escaped me before I was aware. I regretted the avowal the moment I had made it. I regret it bitterly now."

But Charlotte and Anne made that characteristic journey on the spur of the moment. Sent a small box to Keighley station by cart and walked the four miles through a summer thunderstorm; which must have been no good for delicate Anne, and which threw Charlotte into a torment of anxiety for her. They almost missed their train; they travelled all night from Leeds to London in their damp clothes.

Once they walked, shrinking and resolute, into George Smith's room in Cornhill, they walked into the new life which was to bring to Charlotte, at least, all the stimulus, the contacts, the correspondence, the books, the periodicals, for which she had ever hungered or could ever want. And most of all, it brought her from totally unknown seclusion into the vital mental company of men and women whose brains were at any rate commensurable with her own. Charlotte walked out of that room his star author.

That was not, however, what occupied Charlotte and Anne just then. The two small figures discreetly dressed in black, though this was one of the times when the Brontës were *not* in mourning, were caught up and whirled like two frail leaves in the blast of London noise and movement, crowds and traffic. They were nothing so much as terrified, Charlotte shaking with agitation, Anne "*calm and gentle, which she always is.*" Look at them; ensconced in the Chapter Coffee House in Paternoster Row, of all odd places, because they knew no London hotels and Papa had stayed there many years ago.

"Branwell could tell us——" Anne hazarded as they made their rapid plans and arrangements at home. "Remember, Charlotte, how he was always poring over maps of London?"

Charlotte stiffened over her packing.

"I should doubt whether any place that he recommended would be to our taste," she returned coldly.

It may be doubted whether the City coffee-houses were much to their taste, either, but there they were.

The offices of Smith, Elder & Co. were in Cornhill. About half a mile off. "We will take a cab," Charlotte decreed, when they were discussing their plan of action in the train; but by this time they were so dazed and wrought-up that they forgot the existence of cabs. They went down and into the surging City streets. It was like plunging into high seas.

They took an hour to make their way from Paternoster Row to Cornhill, bewildered by traffic, and Charlotte shrinking in terror from the clopping hooves and mammoth, looming noses of the dray-horses. Unlike Emily and Anne, she was no lover of animals and almost any animal appeared larger than she was. . . .

They returned from Cornhill to their coffee-house even more dazed than they set out. Charlotte was violently sick, and her temples hammered with migraine. She dosed herself with sal volatile because Mr. George Smith, that dumbfounded young man, had talked eagerly of entertaining them, had named half a dozen plans for their amusements and interest, and had mentioned the ladies of his own family. Charlotte, knowing only too well what would happen to her head and her stomach, had sufficient strength to decline everything, to murmur that she and her sister had not come to town equipped for anything but the shortest stay etc. But even in her wretched discomfort Charlotte was aware of what was due to her; she was always acutely aware of that; and she knew that the Smith ladies would call sometime during the day. And call they did, in evening dress, to take George's odd little golden geese to the Opera. . . .

Perhaps Charlotte's minute dignity never rose to better heights than in that dismaying moment. She was, though she might not know the terms, a victim of acute nervous debility and her nerves played havoc with her little body. Anne's unrufflable calm was her perpetual admiration, and no one need belittle that trait in the gentle, accommodating girl. But Anne's calm was due in part to the fact that there was not enough life left in her to agitate. Always delicate, usually a little ailing, she was drained of vitality. Charlotte vibrated to every pressure on the nerves with devastating response. Now, she accepted the Opera. Dizzy with sal volatile and with nothing but *"plain, high-made country garments"* for evening gowns, they stepped into the Smiths' carriage. In a gallant witty letter to Ellen, Charlotte described her state of *"headache, sickness, and conscious clownishness,"* and said that she felt *"pleasurably excited"*, nevertheless.

Next day they asked to be taken to church. The day after, to the National Gallery. They walked through Kensington Gardens on the Sunday and Charlotte said that she was *"struck with the beauty of the scene, the fresh verdure of the turf, and the soft rich masses of foliage."*

> "You need not be a chamber to be haunted—
> You need not be a house."

You could be the green reaches and mirror-smooth water of Kensington Gardens in the first flicker of wind of a summer daybreak; and the skimming, shadowy figures of the thousands and tens of thousands of persons who have walked those paths and lawns: the lovers and the losers; the exultant and the defeated; the ones who sauntered in content and the ones who hurried to outstrip the corroding trouble at their heels. And among them, two slight figures in black gowns and scarves and white bonnets, moving very lightly over the grass, between church and a tea-drinking at the house of kindly Mr. Williams with his eight children. They go out through the gate into the wide Bayswater road; and one of them is walking through the gate into enduring fame.

They went back to Haworth with their modest dress-box weighted with books from George Smith. Charlotte had lost pounds in weight, of which she had none to spare, and when she looked into the glass she saw herself looking positively old, greyish of skin and with the lines from nostrils to lips *"ploughed in"*. And her eyes strained and protruding from three days' constant staring.

"I was weak and excited yet restless."

Charlotte's meticulous use of the *mot juste* is even more

frequent and striking in her intimate letters than in her books: this brief sentence condenses a tragedy. "Life defeated of its dues" was coming into its own, for her, but too late for nerves and flesh to bear. She had starved for the companionship of her peers in mind and brain; now it was to be offered her, poured out to her, thrust upon her, through the years to come: and she was such a nervous and physical wreck that the strain prostrated her. She had longed for more books than came within her reach, for more news of the outside world; now her publishers, who were to become her friends, kept her abundantly supplied by post after post; and her eyes had become so weak that when it came to the evening, and comparative leisure and the time when she might expect to relax, she was reduced to knitting, not reading, because one can knit without counting stitches. There was to be keen, acute enjoyment for Charlotte, but at such a price that it could be said to have come too late.

(xii)

". . . *faith and resignation are difficult to practise under some circumstances.*"

Charlotte's precise, almost priggish words are a cry under excruciating pain. And reading them, oneself feels exasperated revolt and useless protest at the turn of events which followed instantly upon that triumphant sortie which was to make all things new for the Brontës.

It was a fearful drop from Parnassus to come home to find Branwell almost insane, Papa tremulous and yearning over his lost child with more pitiful affection than ever before, and the whole house steeped in the black shadow. It stirred Charlotte to bitterness. Anne was sunk in dread for the derelict's soul; Emily, always apart and aloof from the welter of publishers and reviewers and acclaim, hardly seemed to realise what a triumph Charlotte had just experienced. She was mutely and profoundly concerned with her brother. She was equally removed from Anne's trembling fears for him and from Charlotte's rectitude and disgust, since no such elements were in her. And really, Charlotte felt with fierce resentment, she seemed to care nothing for what was happening to *Wuthering Heights* or *Jane Eyre*.

A very little later, when Emily was so ill that she could hardly breathe, Charlotte read aloud an American article which drew a grim, censorious picture of the three immoral and dangerous writers, Currer, Ellis, and Acton Bell. Emily *"smiled half-amused and half in scorn,"* Charlotte told Mr. Williams. Even before that day, Emily was beyond caring what anyone said or thought. She was always beyond it.

So, the house was no place for a victorious author's return. And Charlotte was sick from excitement, strain, and the journey, and would have appreciated a little cosseting for a change. But no one had thoughts to spare for her. . . .

Then, everything of disappointment and resentment was forgotten. One day Branwell went wavering down the village street as usual: two days later, he died.

"All his vices were and are nothing now. We only remember his woes," Charlotte wrote. She was overcome by contrition and compassion. She broke down and was in bed on the day of Branwell's funeral.

But Emily followed her brother's coffin. She was ill already, and coughing, and the tale is told that she caught an added chill, while the villagers said, affectionately and loyally, that she had grieved herself sick for her brother. But no chill nor wind was needed, and though Emily had stood staunchly by her brother, no human love weighed heavily enough to destroy her. They were riddled with tuberculosis, and slow-poisoning from a home where the churchyard drained into the kitchen. In *Shirley*, Charlotte makes Caroline speak uneasily of the grave-stones under the kitchen floor; and Shirley briskly urges her not to think about them. . . . It seems to have entered no one's head, least of all Charlotte's, that it might be better to think of them to some very practical purpose.

So now began Emily's terrible dying. It was an eight weeks' agony; and Emily herself made it an agony for her sisters even worse than her own. Charlotte's letters, of recent years and to the end of her life, were at all times distressingly full of details of ill-health, her own and her family's, which is not unnatural since her life was corroded by illness and the code of her day decreed no reticence about it. She dwelt on symptoms with such morbid and piteous insistence, and always with her own power of words, that Emily's suffering is almost unbearably forced home. She was suffocating, she was stabbed by pain, she was wasting from continuous diarrhœa. Her pulse, *"the only time she allowed it to be felt,"* was found to be 115. And she *"declares no 'poisoning doctor' shall come near her";* she refused any medicine, she would answer no enquiries, and she resented every attempt to help her. *"Our position is and has been for some weeks, exquisitely painful . . . I think Emily seems the nearest thing to my heart in the world."* Charlotte's words are a cry wrenched from her.

Emily, who had already withdrawn so far to the brink of the *"final bound"* that she could not reach back in compassion to spare Charlotte, frantic and helpless in devotion, nor Anne, her own dearly-loved, could remind her sister to thank Ellen for a crab-apple cheese that she could not touch, and would so linger in the memory of the servants for her kindness of heart that they murmured that she neglected herself because she did not want to give trouble. . . . An incongruous and grotesque piece of loyalty; she gave more than trouble, in her fanatic self-immolation.

No words dare take the place of Charlotte's own words.

"Never in all her life had she lingered over any task that lay before her, and she did not linger now. She sank rapidly. She made haste to leave us. Yet, while physically she perished, mentally she grew stronger than we had yet known her. . . . I have seen nothing like it; but, indeed, I have never seen her parallel in anything. Stronger than a man, simpler than a child, her nature stood alone. The awful point was that, while full of ruth for others, on herself she had no pity; the spirit was inexorable to the flesh. . . . To stand by and witness this, and not dare to remonstrate, was a pain no words can render . . . the day came at last when the terrors and pains of death were to be undergone by this treasure, which had grown dearer and dearer to our hearts as it wasted before our eyes."

Charlotte writes the biographical notice of her sisters two years afterwards. And in her hell of desolation, and with the ink blurred and running with her rain of tears, the barriers of her reticence, her undemonstrativeness, splinter and go down. She so loved Emily; who had no special affection for her, only for Anne. She so worshipped Emily's brain; which Emily always knew was immeasurably greater than her own. . . .

The day came at last. It came in Christmas week. Emily got up, dressed herself, could not even pick up her comb when it fell from her fingers on to the hearth and was charred. She got herself downstairs, fed the dogs, took up her sewing. Surely it is one of the strangest days in all the story of human suffering? She sat on the parlour sofa waiting for death. And the whole household waited with her. . . .

When she could scarcely speak she gasped to Charlotte *"If you will send for a doctor, I will see him now."* She could afford to do that, now. Knowing, triumphant, that no doctor could hinder her from dying in this last hour. But—with a last spurting flicker of compassion—it might comfort Charlotte. It might, even, silence village tongues, which would, more than likely, mutter about why-no-doctor. . . . Emily knew how tongues wag in a village.

She only had to bear another two hours. About two of the clock, Emily died.

"Emily suffers no more from pain or weakness now. She never will suffer more in this world. . . . Yes, there is no Emily in time or on earth now. Yesterday we put her poor, wasted mortal frame under the church pavement. We are very calm at present. Why should we be otherwise? The anguish of seeing her suffer is over; the spectacle of the pains of death is gone by. . . . No need now to tremble for the hard frost and the keen wind. Emily does not feel them. . . . She died in a time of promise. We saw her taken from life in its prime. But it is God's will. . . ."

That is open to question. But one thing at least is certain; it was Emily's. She died, exactly as she made Heathcliff die, straining toward the hour of tryst and ultimate fulfilment. *There was no room for Death*, as a thing to dread, to shrink from, to put off as long as it could be done. Emily brushed death aside, put it out of her way, brusquely, relentlessly, and strode past it into life. The voices besetting and beseeching her, the sound of tears, were scarcely audible to her. She only saw the faces about her as an intrusive interruption and the fond, troublesome hands were only holding her back.

"*We feel she is at peace,*" Charlotte writes to Ellen. And that is partly the desperate relief after the long, futile helpless watching of pain; and a little, maybe, the parsonage Charlotte speaking. *Someone,* after all, should say that Emily is at peace. But what a word for her. See, rather, her freed spirit go winging its way out over her moors in the December wind, and in the wind a voice laughing, breathing clear and deep in painless freedom, and a voice, like Cathy's, *sobbing for joy.*

Charlotte's letter ends with a plea to Ellen, whose prosaic, small details make it the more poignant:

"*Could you now come to us for a few days? I would not ask you to stay long. Write and tell me if you could come next week and by what train. I would try to send a gig for you to Keighley. You will, I trust, find us tranquil. Try to come, I never so much needed the consolation of a friend's presence.*"

A magazine has just come for Charlotte by the post.

"The *Quarterly?*" says Anne listlessly and without any particular curiosity. "Is there anything about———"

"No. No. It is only *Jane Eyre.* And Mr. Thackeray's new book."

Charlotte speaks hastily, her eyes running down the page; her lips are compressed in a tight line and she is frowning.

"I *told* them to be certain to send me any bad notices. I am far more anxious *not* to miss them than the good ones. They should have sent it before. It came out last month."

"Last month———" Anne whispers thickly. This is only January. Last month—is it any wonder that the kind and sympathetic Mr. Williams should have spared Charlotte in that wild December? thinks Anne wearily.

But life does not spare Charlotte. Not at any time. The notice which reaches her at her special request three weeks after Emily has died belongs less to book-reviews than to the gossip-paragraphers of a later day. It is curious about Currer Bell. And announces that, if C.B. is actually a woman, "*She must be one who for some sufficient reason has long forfeited the society of her own sex. . . .*"

The day that Charlotte sat beside her father as the surgeon cut the cataract from his eyes, *The Professor* was returned to her. On a morning not a month later than the shattering ordeal of Emily's dying, she is grossly insulted in the press.

"Is it a very bad notice?"

"It does not signify at all," Charlotte answered harshly and tightly.

It signified very much indeed. It could wound her far more deeply than any criticism of her work, in itself. It slashed, not at her gift, of which she was sure, even cocksure, but at the innermost Charlotte, the respectable churchwoman who was her own worst enemy and to whom she clung as her own best refuge.

When Elizabeth Gaskell came to learn of this trivial hurtful incident, she was so angered that she was moved to one phrase of unaccustomed and sonorous greatness. She spoke of the ignorant stone-slinging at one who had borne *"trials, close following in dread march through (her) household, sweeping the hearthstone bare of life and love."*

Anne said:

"It was kind in them not to send the *Quarterly*, Charlotte. It was kindly meant. Just now——"

"Kindly meant, yes," Charlotte retorted, rising from the table. "But I do not want indulgence—because Emily is dead."

And as Anne gave a faint, choking cry, Charlotte turned at the door to add through her shut, discoloured teeth:

"Wouldn't she have laughed at the notion?"

"We thought this was enough," Charlotte wrote, of Emily's death, *"but we were utterly and presumptuously wrong."* Her voice rises in the words, harshens to the strident note of a cry torn from the throat.* *"She had not been committed to the grave a fortnight, before we received distinct intimation that it was necessary to prepare our minds to see the younger sister go after the elder."*

It was as quick as that. Charlotte's letters can scarcely keep pace with the rapidity of Anne's decline. She was far gone in tuberculosis when the doctor first saw her.

* *"She was not buried ere Anne fell ill."*

Now sickness has infested the very walls of the grey house like a plague, and has taken possession of Charlotte's mind and thoughts, quite inevitably, and to the exclusion of all else. Her letters to Ellen—always her one safety-valve—are almost a day-to-day chart of Anne's symptoms and treatment, with an occasional cry of Charlotte's own anguish and a reiteration of her intense efforts at control. The reek of the nauseous cod-liver-oil soaks the pages (*"it smells and tastes like train-oil . . ."*) and then Charlotte's despair tears them.

"I avoid looking forward or backward, and try to keep looking upward. This is not the time to regret, dread, or weep. . . . The days pass in a slow, dark march; the nights are the test; the sudden wakings from restless sleep, the revived knowledge that one lies in her grave, and another not at my side, but in a separate and sick bed."

". . . We received the box and its contents quite safely today. The penwipers are very pretty, and we are very much obliged to you for them. I hope the respirator will be useful to Anne in case she should ever be well enough to go out again . . . I fear it would be only self-delusion to fancy her better."

". . . You are right in conjecturing that I am somewhat depressed; at times I certainly am." (Is there a note of tense sarcasm in the voice now?) *"It was almost easier to bear up when the trial was at its crisis than now. The feeling of Emily's loss does not diminish as time wears on. . . . It brings too an inexpressible sorrow with it. . . . Yet I am well aware, it will not do either to complain or sink, and I strive to do neither. . . I do not wish for any friends to stay with me; I could not do with anyone—not even you—to share the sadness of the house; it would rack me intolerably. . . . It is my nature, when left alone, to struggle on with a certain perseverance, and I believe God will help me."*

She is enduring delayed shock without knowing the meaning of such a thing. *". . . I must confess that, in the time which has elapsed since Emily's death, there have been moments of solitary, deep, inert affliction, far harder to bear than those which immediately followed our loss . . . the desolate after-feeling sometimes paralyses."*

She is nursing Anne, ministering to Anne, thinking of and planning for her, even though without hope or delusion: but it is Emily for whom Charlotte's heart is breaking.

And although nothing could have saved Anne, Emily's dying
has weakened her slight hold on life. Emily needed no one;
though she loved her younger sister as much as she could love
any human being. But the loss of her is something from which
Charlotte is never to recover, and Anne's shadowy life goes
wavering after her and flickers out.

As spring drew on, Anne's one longing was to get to the sea.
Hers are still waters drenched in the setting sun, no storms or
sea-fantasies for little Anne. Charlotte, torn in two between the
wish to humour Anne and her fear of sea-winds, put it off until
spring was into earliest summer. Ellen was to go with them.
And there remains Anne's letter to her, than which there is no
greater example of very quiet courage and utter simplicity in the
letters of humankind.

". . . I hope I should not be very troublesome. . . . I should be
reluctant to wait till then (the end of May) if the weather would at
all permit an earlier departure . . . we are almost certain of some
fine, warm days in the latter half, when the laburnums and lilacs are
in bloom . . ." She goes on to explain that doctors "say that
change of air or removal to a better climate would hardly ever fail of
success in consumptive cases if the remedy were taken in time. . . .

". . . Under these circumstances, I think there is no time to be
lost," says Anne simply. And continues

"I have no horror of death: if I thought it inevitable, I think I
could quietly resign myself to the prospect, in the hope that you, dear
Miss Nussey, would give as much of your company as you possibly
could to Charlotte, and be a sister to her in my stead. But I wish it
would please God to spare me. . . . I long to do some good in the
world before I leave it. I have many schemes in my head for future
practice—humble and limited indeed—but still I should not like
them all to come to nothing, and myself to have lived to so little
purpose. . . ."

The only complaint which Anne is known ever to have
expressed is in her secret birthday paper when she was twenty-
four: "I for my part cannot well be flatter or older in mind than I
am now——" and the word "flatter" is underlined. Flatter:
so little purpose. Her gentle spirit felt useless. In the face of
death, she only asked for a little more time, to be of some
use.

The plans advanced slowly, for Scarborough. And in the midst of practical details of board and lodging ("*I should wish to be boarded. Providing oneself is, I think, an insupportable nuisance . . .*") Charlotte's mounting, overwhelming grief for the other sister breaks out once more:

"*. . . I cannot forget Emily's deathday; it becomes a more fixed, a darker, a more frequently recurring idea in my mind than ever. It was very terrible. She was torn, conscious, panting, reluctant, though resolute, out of a happy life. But it will not do* (underlined by Charlotte) *to dwell on these things.*"

She could not be further wrong, of course. And one feels that she knew it; but she dared not face the truth: that Emily was not torn, reluctant, from life. The rending and the conflict were because she could not slough it fast enough.

Of Anne, she says:

"*There is some feeble consolation in thinking we are doing the very best that can be done. The agony of forced, total neglect, is not now felt, as in Emily's illness. Never may we be doomed to feel such agony again. It was terrible.*"

It is perhaps worth remembering—even fitting to remember —that Papa rose to this occasion, crippled with loss and grief as he was already.

"*You ask how I have arranged about leaving Papa. I could make no special arrangement. He wishes me to go with Anne, and would not hear of Mr. Nicholls' coming, or anything of the kind. . . .*"

They set out, breaking the journey at York, where Anne even wished the other two to do some shopping.

"*I wish it seemed less like a dreary mockery in us to talk of buying bonnets etc.,*" says Charlotte piteously.

Did Anne, at that halt, remember the last time that she was in York? With Emily; and when they were Ronald Macalgin, and Henry Angora, and Cordelia Fitzaphnold, and the rest.

And so they reached Scarborough. And on the last evening of her life Anne sat beside the sea. "*She loved the place,*" Ellen says, "*and wished us to share her preference. . . . The evening closed in with the most glorious sunset . . . the distant ships glittered like burnished gold; the little boats near the beach heaved on the ebbing tide.*"

Anne drove on the sands in a donkey-chaise, and took the

reins herself because the donkey-boy was not being considerate to the poor animal, and was heard by Ellen and Charlotte making him promise to treat it better.

Next morning, she felt a change. A doctor came at once, and, Ellen says, *"with perfect composure"* Anne begged him to tell her the truth. Unwillingly, the kind stranger admitted to this frail and fearless lady that she would probably die at any minute now. . . . *"She thanked him for his truthfulness."*

There are times when Ellen's unstudied simplicity all but transcends Charlotte's mastery of words: as now, when she gives the last picture of Anne: *"She still occupied her easy chair, looking so serene, so reliant."* There Anne sits, her full black skirts falling wide and limp about her emaciated frame, her hands clasped in her lap, waiting to die. She said a prayer for Charlotte and one for Ellen; and Ellen does not speak of any prayer for herself. She repeated to Ellen *"Be a sister in my stead. Give Charlotte as much of your company as you can."* And to Charlotte, who was in tears, *"Take courage, Charlotte; take courage."* There is an echo in the words: eight years before, Emily ended her birthday paper with *". . . courage, boys! courage, to exiled and harassed Anne, wishing she was here."* Anne was nearly there, now; and even Emily could teach her nothing about courage. . . .

They lifted her on to the sofa, presently. And there she died, as Emily had died on the parlour sofa at home only five months ago. But Anne died, as she lived, so quietly, so wholly without disturbing anyone, that the landlady put her head in at the door and announced dinner, and clapped a hand to her lips as she saw that Charlotte was closing her sister's eyes.

(xiii)

THE curate, Mr. Nicholls, whose company in the house Papa had refused, was rising to take leave after an evening call on his vicar. The most difficult visit which he had ever had to pay in the way of Arthur Nicholls' conscientious duties, since he was filled with compassion for a man whom he could neither like nor respect and from whom he differed on every point of behaviour if not of doctrine. He was calling on his vicar, an irascible, self-absorbed, and moody old man: but he was visiting an old man dazed, dumbfounded, by grief, who had lost three of his children between summer and spring and who had been male nurse and keeper to his son for years before he died. Mr. Brontë was very quiet tonight. Sunk in his chair, his chin plunged in the stiff folds of his high stock, looking like some grotesque white-headed puppet with a limp neck.

"Well, sir, I will be going," said Arthur Nicholls into the heavy silence. And the old man made a vague motion of his sunken head but said nothing.

"You will have Miss Brontë home tomorrow. Or one day this week," Arthur Nicholls reminded him, as the one thing which he could think of which might bring a crumb of comfort to the broken old figure in the leather chair. Speaking, too, his own hope. Sick, distracted, absorbed, and oblivious of his own existence as she might be, the fact that she was somewhere in the desolate grey house was like a lamp in one of its windows to Mr. Nicholls in his rooms across the street at the house of John Brown, the sexton.

Mr. Brontë slowly raised his jaw from the stock and shook his white head.

"Not . . . ?" Arthur Nicholls queried in surprise.

"Not yet," said old Brontë in a thin whisper. "I have written. She must stay from home for a while. She must . . . take a change . . . recover some of her strength. . . . The sea. Charlotte has a liking for the sea."

Arthur Nicholls was never more surprised. The selfish old man; who depended so pitifully on her that his cry throughout the dreadful winter of Miss Emily's illness had been "*Charlotte, you must bear up. I shall sink if you fail me*"; had told her to stay from home. Had made the decision without hint or advice (which he would have refused anyway). In his bereavement and loneliness, in his sorrowful musings, he had found room to think of her and her needs—he had even entered into those needs. He had set her free to stay by the sea which she loved and with the friend whom she loved. Arthur did not care for Miss Nussey. Amiable girl, beyond doubt, and an exemplary churchwoman, and of pleasing appearance, undeniably; but he did not like these close young-lady friendships. Still—if anything or anyone could be of comfort to Miss Brontë in this hour of bereavement and loneliness—who was he to be behind-hand in self-sacrifice with his vicar, who was, after all, her father and at no time remarkable for that virtue?

"I am glad," said poor Arthur Nicholls, soberly. "Very glad. You are in the right. I will bid you good evening."

His vicar merely grunted. And Mr. Nicholls went out into the June evening with an ache beneath his tight-buttoned black coat. He was jealous of Ellen; though he could not admit it because he did not know it. . . .

They went back to Easton, to the farm where they had had that short, carefree holiday and where they had romped with little Hancheon in the parlour. And there is silence. A month of summer hangs in that year of darkness like an empty crystal. There is not a word either from Ellen or Charlotte to tell of it. Two young women in deep mourning walked on the cliffs and sat listening to the sea and perhaps walked in the woods as they used to do; but Charlotte was worn out, tired to death, she was not equal to the long, energetic walks which she had always taken. Presently Ellen must go home. And Charlotte stayed on, alone, for a little while longer.

Not quite alone, it may be. Anne's gentle spirit could be left to rest; Anne would be as unobtrusive, as untroubling, in death as in life. But I think that the hankering sense of Emily's overmastering self, and the longing for her, and the ineffaceable memory of how she died, kept step with Charlotte on the cliffs and at the edge of the sea. She was never to get away from Emily. No one does, who has ever felt the power of that personality, and even without other sight of her beautiful face than Branwell's cracked and peeling daubs.

And bye-and-bye, Charlotte went home. To a haunted solitude and a loneliness—(which are two states, not one and the same)—that are not to be conveyed, going beyond words. Charlotte's words, however, give unforgettable pictures of it, made the more so because she held fast and indomitably to something which is perhaps best described as her sheer common-sense. She was pre-eminently sensible and practical, this minute woman; she was drowning, suffocating in loneliness, but drown to death she would not.

She reached home in the deep gold of a July evening, "*a little before eight o'clock,*" and even that scrupulously clean and neat house had been given an extra turn-out in her absence and "*all was clean and bright waiting for me.*" Papa and the servants gave her such a welcome that she felt conscience-stricken because it wrung her heart rather than comforted. "*The dogs seemed in strange ecstasy.*" Charlotte did not love animals, but she knew what was in the minds of Keeper and of Flossie. Everyone who has ever known a dog well will recognise that turn of the screw for Charlotte, as they jumped upon her and gave tongue rapturously and then rushed past her to greet the others who did not come. It would be all too easy to build a legend round Keeper; but no legend could be truer to nature than the plain, simple incidents, authentic and attested, which concern that huge, ungainly, and lovable mongrel. When the old vicar walked stiffly and painfully down the churchyard path after his daughter's coffin, Keeper suddenly emerged from the garden bushes and fell into place beside him; and no one thought of driving him away or forbidding him to come into the church. When they returned, leaving Emily under the stone flags of the church floor, Keeper went upstairs and established himself across the door of the bedroom where Emily had beaten him for sleeping on the white counterpane. And because this is the truth and not legend, Keeper did not give up the ghost across Emily's threshold; he lived to a great old age and a very ferocious one, and a diffident young pilgrim who visited Charlotte was dismayed by the noisy onslaught of an old, stiff dog and slightly affronted by the old, stiff vicar's smiling indulgence to the objectionable animal. . . .

Charlotte might never come to love a dog; but Emily's dog was precious and to be cherished to the end of his days. And how right that is.

Charlotte bore the welcome, and tried to respond to it, and presently went into the parlour and shut the door. "*I tried to be glad that I was come home.*" Her hypersensitive conscience and her steel self-discipline must goad her, even in that terrible hour. She had always been glad to come home, she reminded herself—

except once—when she came home from Brussels; "*even then I was cheered.*" But now "*I felt that the house was all silent—the rooms were all empty. I remembered where the three were laid—in what narrow dwellings—never more to reappear on earth. So the sense of desolation and bitterness took possession of me. The agony that was to be undergone, and was not to be avoided, came on. I underwent it . . .*"

"*. . . The great trial is when evening closes and night approaches. At that hour we used to assemble in the dining-room—we used to talk. Now I sit by myself—necessarily I am silent. I cannot help thinking of their last days, remembering their sufferings, and what they said and did, and how they looked in mortal affliction.*" And then, bracing herself staunchly, "*Perhaps all this will become less poignant in time.*"

· · · · · ·

"*. . . I do not much like giving an account of myself. I like better to go out of myself, and talk of something more cheerful. . . . Say nothing about (my cold), for I confess I am too much disposed to be nervous. This nervousness is a horrid phantom. I dare communicate no ailment to Papa; his anxiety harasses me inexpressibly.*

"*My life is what I expected it to be. Sometimes when I wake in the morning and know that Solitude, Remembrance, and Longing are to be almost my sole companions all day through—that at night I shall go to bed with them . . . that next morning I shall wake to them again—sometimes, Nell, I have a heavy heart of it.*"

There is a swift check, a determined pulling-up. She will not allow herself to dwell on it. "*I have a heavy heart:*" that is all.

"*. . . I have some strength to fight the battle of life. . . . Still I can get on.*" Then the agony breaks through: "*But I do hope and pray, that never may you, or anyone I love, be placed as I am. To sit in a lonely room—the clock ticking loud through a still house. . . .*"

That clock ticks through the tomb-like silence of the next five years. Elizabeth Gaskell, staying with Charlotte at Haworth, tried hard to find something cheerful to say about the place: "*I don't know that I ever saw a spot more exquisitely clean; the most dainty place for that I ever saw.*" Then, she herself, the mother of a large household, gives way to truth, and you can almost see her shiver: *"To be sure, the life is like clock-work. No one comes to the house; nothing disturbs the deep repose; hardly a voice is heard; you catch the ticking of the clock in the kitchen, or the buzzing of a fly in the parlour, all over the house. . . ."*

Now began the existence which was the strangest that a woman could well be called upon to lead and to endure. Charlotte took up the writing of *Shirley* again, and worked hard at it. She took it up at the chapter headed *"The Valley of the Shadow of Death"*, and the opening paragraphs have a terrible sincerity. The fact that she was drawing a fanciful portrait of Emily in the figure of Shirley kept her absorbed in the book as perhaps no other work could have done just at that time. She finished it ten weeks later.

She worked, enclosed in the intolerable loneliness of the parsonage, thronged with memories and shadows; but now she was famous. And at intervals, she slipped from the shadows into the great world. To London, to Scotland, to the Lakes, to Manchester, to the company of the Smiths, her publishers, and their wide London circle, to Harriet Martineau, to Elizabeth Gaskell. She was fêted to the limits of her endurance and beyond it. She met Thackeray, whom she considered the greatest writer of the time: *"Some people have been in the habit of terming him the second writer of the day . . . He need not be the second. God made him second to no man."* George Smith, eight years younger than Charlotte and a debonair, handsome man, was sufficiently attracted to his strange, incurably shy author to give his mamma cause for anxiety. . . . She drew him as John Graham Bretton in *Villette*, with an enduring tenderness and charm of touch. And a letter to Ellen concerning the matter is among the most dignified of Charlotte's letters:

". . . Were there no vast barrier of fortune etc., there is perhaps enough of personal regard to make things possible which are now impossible . . . but other reasons regulate matrimony, reasons of convenience, of connection, or money. Meanwhile I am content to have him a friend and pray God to continue to me the common sense to look on one so young, so rising, so hopeful, in no other light."

It seems unnecessary to dwell in detail on Charlotte's excursions into public life, for they belong to literary and social history. So many of the persons who took part in them have left the scenes and incidents on record. She was part of the phenomena of her day, now. Everyone was reading Charlotte Brontë, everyone wanted to meet Charlotte Brontë; and the stories multiply and overlap of the paralysing shyness and sickness of nerves which too often made such meetings a disaster that would be comic if such depths of tragedy did not lie beneath it. The famous party at Thackeray's house in Kensington where Charlotte *"enters in mittens, in silence, in seriousness,"* said his lively daughter, and *"the little lady looked tired with her own brains,"* said Millais. Where she was so mute a failure that Thackeray himself was found, later in a very heavy evening, slipping out to his Club in desperation. . . .

There is a kaleidoscope quality about Charlotte's public life. It never seems quite real . . . this whirling scene of notable figures and historic sights. And the tiny figure of Charlotte somehow moves like a dainty puppet, in the sedate, carefully-chosen clothes which cost her so much anxious thought and scrupulous expenditure. The white lace cloak . . . the black satin gown which was an economy and which she regretted because *"Papa said if he had known he would have lent me a pound."* The muff and cuffs of sable, and another of dark grey squirrel, because she admitted that she liked dark fur better than brown or yellow. (Can you see her in yellow fur?) Incidentally, Charlotte sent Ellen a five-pound note to buy her the furs and a shower-bath; and there was enough change left for her to press it upon her friend to use toward Ellen's bridesmaid outfit for a brother's wedding; which gives to think, on the matter of changing values!

But it was all too late, the good company, the good talk, the Cinderella-dreams, the tumult and the shouting. Something was broken in Charlotte, and past healing. She was ill with her old malady: violent headaches, sickness, faintness, after all encounters. *"As to being happy, I am under scenes and circumstances of excitement; but I suffer acute pain sometimes—mental pain, I mean . . ."* *"I should highly praise the advantages to be gained in an extended range of observation; but I tremble at the thought of the price I must necessarily pay in mental distress and physical wear and tear."*

"... *I used to bear up as long as I possibly could, for, when I flagged, I could see Mr. Smith became disturbed* ..."

Poor Mr. Smith; well he might. The featherweight, trembling burden on his arm was a baffling and heavy burden on his mind, as publisher and producer.

Perhaps it would always have been too late. Perhaps the great world was too close to the borders of forgotten Angria, and Charlotte of Haworth parsonage would always peer through the gates and shrink back and flee home from the serpent and the apple among the glittering leaves. She was trapped in her own quivering spirit and shattered body. Wasting in the fearful loneliness, hag-ridden by memories, still and for ever hungering for companionship: and unequal to it when she encountered it.

"*Sometimes I have been tempted to murmur at Fate, which compels me to comparative silence and solitude for eleven months in the year, and in the twelfth, while offering social enjoyment, takes away the vigour and cheerfulness which should turn it to account. But circumstances are ordered for us and we must submit.*"

Letters were a safer solace. Through these desolate years Charlotte maintained an enormous correspondence. That good friend, Mr. Williams, kept her supplied with never-ending books and papers and extended his supplies to Papa. It is not always known or remembered that Charlotte developed, in these years, a keen, high-mettled sense of literary criticism alongside with her gift as a novelist. Her letters to Mr. Williams, to George Lewes, to Sidney Dobell, and others are memorable reviews.

But it is still the letters to Ellen which reveal the real life, the death-in-life, that she is living. There is a new gentleness in Charlotte's manner now, a softening from such utter exhaustion of spirit that one regrets the spurts of impatience of former times. It is even possible to be glad for the burst of temper with which she blasted George Lewes for a review which nettled her:

"*To G. H. Lewes Esq. I can be on guard against my enemies, but God deliver me from my friends! Currer Bell.*"

There are moments of lightness which lift the dark, now and again. The letter from a stranger, "*not quite an old maid, but nearly one, she says . . ."* who averred that she was in love with Mr. Rochester and Robert (or Louis?) Moore, and that if Currer Bell were *"a gentleman and like his heroes,"* she would fall in love with *him*. . . . *"She had better not . . ."* Charlotte comments, adding shrewdly *"You (Mr. Williams) and Mr. Smith would not let me announce myself as a single gentleman . . . but if you had permitted it, a great many elderly spinsters would have been pleased."*

Martha, the young servant who helps old Tabby, comes flying in, *"puffing and blowing and much excited,"* to announce that all the local world knows about *Jane Eyre* and *Shirley, "the grandest books that ever was seen"*—and they are being ordered for the Mechanics' Institute. *"I fell into a cold sweat.* Jane Eyre *will be read by* (here follows a list of initials). *Heaven help, keep, and deliver me!"*

And there is the moving incident of the scrap of paper on which a sick labourer in the village had written his appreciation of *Jane Eyre,* which Charlotte *"considers one of the highest, because one of the most truthful and artless tributes her work has yet received. I do you* (to Ellen) *great honour in showing it to you."*

Through her publishers Charlotte acquired not only certain lifelong friends and a wealth of reading and enlivening correspondence; but another suitor. It is, naturally, to Ellen that she confides the story. Mr. Taylor, who was a reader for Smith, Elder & Co., apparently fell in love with her over the negotiations concerning *Shirley,* and for a year and a half, having been refused by Charlotte, continued a stiff, persevering courtship by sending her a weekly newspaper and an occasional lengthy letter. He appears to have been an unfortunate figure of a man, markedly repellent in appearance and manner, with a nose which, Charlotte said, *"when poked into my countenance cuts into my soul like iron . . ."* Between herself and Ellen he was the *"little man with his little newspaper."* But Charlotte was incapable of making fun of anyone who deserved nothing but compassion. She gibed at her Mr. Taylor because she came perilously near to accepting him. . . . He had a stern strength of character, he was acutely intelligent, he was stubbornly devoted. He mesmerised and repelled her at one and the same time. *". . . His absence and the exclusion of his idea from my mind leave me certainly with less support and in deeper solitude than before . . ."* Finally, Charlotte admitted the insuperable barrier: *". . . though clever, he is second-rate—thoroughly second-rate . . . I could not, could not look up to him . . ."*

He departed to India to the firm's branch in Bombay. And in spite of his raking nose, his common manner, and his second-rate mind, *". . . I shall not soon forget last Friday, and never, I think, the evening and night succeeding . . ."*

The darkness and the silence closed in again.

(xiv)

BESIDES her own work on *Villette,* Charlotte has accepted another task. She is editing Emily's *Wuthering Heights* and Anne's slight *Agnes Grey* for a new edition. The work has taken her back into their company with such an intensity that it has prostrated her with sorrow and longing and the over-whelming sense of her own utter desolation.

". . . The reading over of papers, the renewal of remembrances brought back the pang of bereavement, and occasioned a depression of spirits well nigh intolerable. For one or two nights I scarce knew how to get on till morning; and when morning came, I was still haunted with a sense of sickening distress. I tell you these things because it is absolutely necessary to me to have some relief. You will forgive me . . ."

There is a desperate tension in the words. The letter is in answer to an anxious enquiry from Ellen, who had not heard from her for longer than usual: Charlotte has been maintaining a silence until she can bear it no longer and the answer that she sends is a bursting cry. Her fingers are tightened on the pen.

Even her own writing has failed her at this time. She cannot drive her tired brain and her sick body to any creation. *". . . The deficiency of every stimulus is so complete. You will recommend me, I dare say, to go from home; but that does no good, even could I again leave Papa with an easy mind. . . . I cannot describe what a time I had of it after my return from London, Scotland, etc. There was a reaction that sunk me to the earth; the deadly silence, solitude, desolation, were awful; the craving for companionship, the hopelessness of relief, were what I should dread to feel again. . . . Dear Ellen, mentally, I fear you also are too lonely and too little occupied. It seems our doom, for the present at least. May God in His mercy help us to bear it!"*

Chance visitors who journeyed to Haworth have left descriptions of their shivering dismay at the way of life of which they had a glimpse. The *"dreary, dreary place, literally paved with blackened tombstones . . . an old man in the church-yard brooding like a ghoul over the graves with a sort of grim hilarity in his face . . . a superannuated mastiff . . . (poor old Keeper) . . . the sight of that little creature entombed in such a place, and moving about, herself like a spirit, especially when you think that the slight still frame enclosed a force of strong fiery life which nothing has been able to freeze or extinguish. . . . We hurried off . . ."*

You can hear the relief in the very rustle of skirts as they climbed into the gig and went down that precipitous street, back to life.

A force of strong fiery life. Yes, if you like. It is a facile comment, and a little too ready-to-hand. It makes an obvious picture, the little creature, a tiny lamp for an inextinguishable point of flame. *Burn then, little lamp.* It was not unreasonable that the shuddering visitors, scurrying away, should miss something which was, in a way, the foundation of Charlotte's life in her living tomb: the solid bedrock of her valiant common-sense.

These years are a fantastic turning of a wheel on which she is being broken: but the most fantastic element in them is the recurrent contrast between her slow torture and the way in which she insisted on surviving. . . . She is ill, she is almost demented with depression; and the next thing is Charlotte penning the energetic, brilliant letters to her publishers, to her reviewers, to Elizabeth Gaskell, to all and sundry who belonged to her outer world of priceless mental contacts. And then another wrenching of herself from the bonds and the wheel, another essaying of the social world, of company; and another return, shaken and thankful, to the bonds and the wheel. She fled back to them with the same shivering relief as strangers fled from the Haworth scene. There has never been anything quite like that see-saw existence.

Directly the task of love and anguish concerning the books of Emily and Anne was completed, Charlotte went, firmly and deliberately, on a visit.

"I can write to you now, dear Ellen, for I am away from home, and relieved, temporarily, at least, from the heavy burden which, I confess, has for nearly three months been sinking me to the earth. I shall never forget last autumn! Some days and nights have been cruel; but now, having told you this, I need say no more on the subject. My loathing of solitude grew extreme; my recollection of my sisters intolerably poignant. I am better now. . . ."

And so it went on.

She is working at *Villette*. It is going slowly, because Charlotte is so bone-tired and spent, and Smith, Elder etc. are harrying her, a little bit, in a most kind and flattering way; and Papa is chivvying her, too. The *"poor old man"* is consistent and true-to-himself, all through. When his flock of children were small, he was proud of their infant precocities and encouraged and supplied their little minds. Now there is left to him only one of that teeming brood; and all his pride and ambition is rather fearsomely concentrated upon her. This is still an age when young women who indulged in writing were looked upon askance; something rather more dubious than Blue-stockings. At the end of the preceding century, Miss Fanny Burney hid under the breakfast-table in abashment and fear, when her first book came to the notice of her very indulgent and amiable father. And at about the same period, actors and actresses in France were denied church burial. . . . The Reverend Patrick Brontë had been a young man in those times: in old age, it is something to be said for him that he honoured his daughter's gift while pestering her to frenzy with anxiety for her health and harried her to finish her book even while he interfered with its ending. His mentality, in old age, was that of the magazine-reader: he demanded a Happy Ending.

But Charlotte, faithful to the mastery of her gift, would not be hurried. *". . . I shall get on with it as fast as is consistent with its being done, if not well, yet as well as I can do it. Not one whit faster."*

She was sunk in illness, that winter, living for a while on a half-cupful of beef-tea a day, but keeping up and about—heaven knows how—because, if she took to her bed, Papa would worry her, as well as himself, nearly mad.

There are always last straws for Charlotte: and so, this winter, old Keeper had to die.

"*He went gently to sleep; we laid his old faithful head in the garden. . . . I am glad he met a natural fate. People kept hinting he ought to be put away, which neither Papa nor I liked to think of.*"

So there went the last live link with Emily.

She rallied herself from illness and semi-starvation, into a miserable void and blankness, because *Villette* was at a standstill. She could not bring it to life. Perhaps only a fellow-writer can realise just what despair this means. And even so, it would have to be a fellow-writer placed as Charlotte was placed: with nothing else left to make life continuable and endurable at all.

"*You say, dear Ellen, that you often wish I would chat on paper, as you do. How can I? Where are my materials? Is my life fertile in subjects of chat? . . . No, you must chat, and I must listen, and say 'Yes', and 'No', and 'Thank you!' for five minutes' recreation.*"

She wrote to Mary Taylor in far-off New Zealand:

"*It cannot be denied that the solitude of my position fearfully aggravated its other evils. . . . Sleepless, I stay awake night after night, weak and unable to occupy myself. I sat in my chair day after day, the saddest memories my only company. It was a time I shall never forget; but God sent it, and it must have been for the best.*"

It is exasperating, that deadly acquiescence amounting to fatalism which weaves through Charlotte's consciousness from childhood onwards. It exasperated Elizabeth Gaskell. Fate, and the dread Will of God, seen as one: and no recognition, none whatever, of such contributing elements as a home established on a graveyard, and a family riddled with phthisis cooped on top of one another day and night. But there is matter for consolation in that suicidal ignorance. Charlotte, who was a blinkered, reined and bitted churchwoman, first and last; who never knew an hour's vision of true Christianity; could hug to her lacerated soul the Will of God. There is no knowing whether, in any hour of bedrock desperation, she cried out upon it in revolt. She never uttered any such cry audibly. And since, if she had, it would have been useless, there is place for hope that it was never uttered. She could not have drained and rebuilt the parsonage; nor isolated two sisters far gone in tuberculosis before it was admitted. She could only have cursed God and died. . . .

Instead, she dragged herself up and set herself going again. And when Charlotte set herself going, the pace was reassuring. It is a pleasant surprise to hear her, thus:

"*I am amused at the interest you take in politics. Don't expect to rouse me; to me, all ministries and all oppositions seem to be pretty much alike. D'Israeli was factious as leader of the Opposition; Lord John Russell is going to be factious now that he has stepped into D'Israeli's shoes. Lord Derby's 'Christian love and spirit' is worth three half-pence farthing.*"

Well, Charlotte should know. Her own was not worth much more. . . . But this voice speaks all but a hundred years ago; and the echo chimes on the ear with a peculiar insistence; the voices about one's head in the street, the queue, the bus, are saying exactly those words with a negligible change of names: that is the only difference. . . . In Charlotte's tones, it is a weary yawn of disillusionment. It is not so long since Charlotte, the child and schoolgirl, was a rabid politician. She was not quite fourteen when she could write of the parsonage household:

"*Nobody could write, think, or speak on any subject but the Catholic question, and the Duke of Wellington, and Mr. Peel. I remember the day when the 'Intelligence Extraordinary' came with Mr. Peel's speech in it. . . . With what eagerness Papa tore off the cover, and how we all gathered round him, and with what breathless anxiety we listened. . . .*"

It is a month of June; and Charlotte has gone to the sea, "*utterly alone. Do not be angry, the step is right. I considered it and resolved on it with due deliberation.*" She has been to Scarborough, and she has looked to the care and alterations of Anne's tombstone.

"*That duty, then, is done; long has it lain heavy on my mind; and that was a pilgrimage I felt I could only make alone.*"

Now she lingers by the sea. It has *"all its old grandeur. I walk on the sands a good deal, and try not to feel desolate and melancholy. How sorely my heart longs for you, I need not say. I have bathed once; it seemed to do me good."*

If an intensity of living leaves its imprint on an environment after the human soul and body, with its localised conflict, has vanished; or if the human soul can be drawn back by love and longing to an earthly scene; then, surely, there should be tracts of north-country headlands and sand where a small, sedate figure, always dressed in voluminous black and a coal-scuttle bonnet concealing big eyes and sleek bandeaux of hair, skims the salted turf and the damp flats of sand with the swift, light-foot walk which has gone out with her period?

Difficult to picture Charlotte bathing. . . . There was a white hooded bathing-machine drawn by a patient and boney horse. And an ample serge garment, and a rope to cling to, and probably a fearsome figure of an old bathing-woman to bark encouragement and offer to duck the shrinking, childish bather. Through the smothering folds of the decorous costume and in spite of the hoarse admonitions of the bathing-crone, the healing spell of the sea-water would reach and lave her body and spirit. It is a spell as incommunicable as any rite or mystery. You either belong to that ritual or stand outside it. Charlotte, and numberless and nameless other women of her day, belonged to it. And all the cumbering folds and hoods and intrusive bathing-harpies could not nullify it. *"The sea has all its old grandeur."*

Now she is labouring to finish *Villette*.

". . . I really must not trust myself to say how much I wish the time were come when, without let or hindrance, I could once more welcome you to Haworth. But oh! I don't get on; I feel fretted—incapable—sometimes very low. . . . Less than ever can I taste or know pleasure till this work is wound up. And yet I often sit up in bed at night, thinking of and wishing for you."

". . . I am silent because I have literally nothing to say. I might indeed repeat over and over again that my life is a pale blank and often a very weary burden, and that the future sometimes appals me; but what end could be answered by such repetition except to weary you and enervate myself?

"*The evils that now and then wring a groan from my heart lie in position; not that I am a single woman and likely to remain a single woman, but because I am a lonely woman and likely to be lonely. But it cannot be helped and therefore imperatively must be borne, and borne too with as few words about it as maybe.*"

But now Papa put his foot down and, with one of his rare but always illuminating moments of insight, summoned Ellen to Haworth. And Charlotte succumbed: "*. . . let me see your dear face just for one reviving week.*"

So for one reviving week sweet Ellen came to her. And Charlotte wrote thankfully to her tried and lasting friend, Miss Wooler, "*she has done me inexpressible good.*" She finished *Villette*, writing with renewed energy and vitality, a fortnight later. Ellen might be shut out from her best friend's work; but when no one else on earth could save that work for posterity, Ellen glided in and saved it.

"*I do miss my dear companion,*" Charlotte writes wistfully and gratefully. "*No more of that calm sleep.*"

It is worth remembering that the awful loneliness of the nights preyed upon her to a degree which belongs to her time. Until Charlotte came home from her interval by the sea following Anne's funeral, she had never come home to a bedroom unshared with a sister. We think, today, of the room and the bed to oneself as an essential, but to the woman of Charlotte's day they were no such thing. E. F. Benson, in one of his family biographies, unique for their social picture as for charm of presentation, describes the family rumpus when his mother, widow of the Primate, in late middle life, could not bear to sleep alone since she had never done so since she married at seventeen. And there was a family quarrel because both her daughter and her adopted daughter wished to keep her company. . . .

There was calm sleep for Charlotte, who suffered terribly from insomnia, when a friend slept beside her; and the voices of her dead did not call at the windows.

Villette was finished. And there was a visit to London, to the Smiths, when Charlotte was taken to see sights of her own choice instead of being on parade at parties. She went to Newgate Prison and the Foundling Hospital. And at Newgate there was pointed out to her a girl who had killed her illegitimate baby: and Charlotte went to her, and took her hand; and was respectfully reminded by the warder that visitors were not allowed to talk to the prisoners. . . . The incident is a reminder of the village girl at Haworth who had been seduced, and whom Charlotte helped and provided for, until she married another man; who "*spent a week of sleepless distress*" when she knew that Charlotte was dying. She also saw the Bank, the Royal Exchange, and other City sights. The practical element in Charlotte found a special·pleasure in the City. Big Business had a fascination for her. In *Villette* she makes Lucy speak of Brussels but it is Charlotte speaking of London:

"*. . . I have seen the West End, the parks, the fine squares; but I love the City far better. The City seems so much more in earnest; its business, its rush, its roar, are such serious things, sights, sounds. The City is getting its living—the West End but enjoying its pleasure. At the West End you may be amused; but in the City you are deeply excited.*" Charlotte's small feet were very firmly on the ground. It was in the same spirit that she complained of a luxurious carriage-outing in the Lakes with the Kay-Shuttleworths, the titled friends who were more of a gratification to Papa than to herself: "*Decidedly I find it does not agree with me to prosecute the search of the picturesque in a carriage. A waggon, a spring-cart, even a post-chaise might do; but the carriage upsets everything. I longed to slip out unseen, and to run away by myself in amongst the hills and dales.*"

(xv)

COMEDY and tragedy are interwoven for Charlotte. Her own acid-pointed humour perceived it. They are so interwoven in her marriage that it is difficult to separate them without blunt-fingered handling.

Arthur Bell Nicholls had been Papa's curate for nearly seven years when he told Charlotte that he loved her, and told her because, although he believed it was hopeless, he could not keep it to himself any longer. A daguerreotype shows him as a

tall and very good-looking man, heavily bearded, with a look of
candour and a most attractive, open smile, buttoned to the chin
in his solid clerical coat. That he had his own sense of humour
is proved for all time by the fact that when he read *Shirley* in his
lodgings with John Brown, the sexton, he so roared with
laughter and stamped his feet on the floor with enjoyment that
Mrs. Brown came running to ask what was to-do. He was
roaring over Charlotte's merciless pictures of the curates; and
especially over his own portrait as Mr. Macarthey, that good
and diligent man whose faults were *"proper, steady-going clerical
faults."*

*". . . The circumstances of finding himself invited to tea with a
Dissenter would unhinge him for a week. . . . The thought of an
unbaptized fellow-creature being interred with Christian rites—
these things could make strange havoc in Mr. Macarthey's physical
and mental economy. Otherwise he was sane and rational, diligent
and charitable."*

It sounds sufficiently dull and hide-bound. But if Arthur
Nicholls was all of that, he was more than that as well. He fell
in love with Charlotte with the shattering and absolute fervour
of a very single-hearted man, and he knew that she saw him
merely as one of the *"highly uninteresting, narrow, and unattractive specimens of the coarser sex."* She said so, and in just
those uncompromising words. He also knew that Papa would
only desire to throw him out of the house, the church, and the
parish, at a hint of such a thing. Papa was torn in two between
his wish that Charlotte should not marry anyone and his even
stranger wish that she should marry in the great world as, he
felt, was no more than her due.

With all this for his own encouragement, Arthur Nicholls
came blundering into the silent parlour where the clock ticked,
goaded to desperation after a particularly trying session with his
vicar, who was pleased to be irritable and sarcastic even though
he had no idea of what was in the curate's mind and labouring
heart. He stood before Charlotte, sitting at her little desk in
her small silk bodice and wide silk skirts, *"shaking from head to
foot, looking deadly pale, speaking low, vehemently, yet with
difficulty, he made me feel for the first time what it costs a man to
declare affection where he doubts response. The spectacle of one*

*ordinarily so statue-like thus trembling, stirred, and overcome, gave
me a kind of strange shock. . . ."*

Charlotte was shaking long before he had finished. She
could give him no answer then, she could only ask him to leave
her alone. She took his arm and half drew and half pushed
him out of the room. And then sat down again at the table and
cried her heart out.

She was overcome from this first strange encounter, by the
utterly unexpected force of the man's feeling. No one had ever
loved her like this. She knew what such a power of feeling
meant; she had experienced it. But to meet it in Mr. Nicholls—
it was as though that ancient bog landslide which was one of the
happenings of her childhood had swept down on the grey stone
house and rocked it to the foundations and smothered the slate
roof.

Papa brings comedy, not to say melodrama, into the scene.
Though it was anything but comic at the time. That hot-
tempered old man promptly played the lowest card in the pack
of every elderly invalid; he flew into such a rage that he nearly
had a stroke and his weak eyes became infected. He poured out
a flood of such abuse on the absent Mr. Nicholls that even his
dutiful Charlotte told Ellen that if she had loved Mr. N., it
would have infuriated her, and that even though she didn't, her
blood boiled. However, as it was a case of Papa bursting a
blood vessel or Charlotte promising to refuse poor Arthur, she
promised.

She was both devoted and dutiful, but she was no fool. She
was a personage in her own right and by her own achievement
and she was mistress of the parsonage; for the first time in the
long-suffering and patient years, Charlotte calls a spade a spade
when commenting on her parent. It makes enjoyable hearing . . .

*"You ask how Papa demeans himself to Mr. Nicholls. I only
wish you were here to see Papa in his present mood; you would know
something of him,"* says Charlotte grimly to Ellen, thereby
revealing that she herself had known something of him a long
time since.

Nor was she going to sit down and wring her hands while
Papa managed her affairs over her head. The vicar sent his

unhappy curate *"a most cruel note"*; Charlotte promptly endorsed it by another saying she had nothing to do with Papa's wounding behaviour. Mrs. Brown, kind soul, reported that Mr. Nicholls had gone off his feed entirely . . . and Charlotte ends a letter to Ellen

"Yours, wishing devoutly that Papa would resume his tranquillity and Mr. Nicholls his beef and pudding——"

She was enjoying herself, a little bit. Papa was behaving atrociously, of course, and poor Mr. Nicholls must on no account expect any hope from her—of course. But the thunderstorm was not without its thrill.

The spectacle unfolds; the vicar and the curate continuing their duties while maintaining a frigid silence, in fact, sending one another to Coventry. And the whole Haworth community suddenly went up in arms and declared for the vicar. Charlotte was their pride; Martha, the younger maid, railed at Mr. Nicholls behind his back for his impudence; her father, John Brown, muttered that he wished he had a gun, he'd learn him. . . .

They could not have helped his cause better. Charlotte could not bear injustice and she had borne such intense suffering in her life that her heart was moved by all sufferers. *"Dear Nell, without loving him, I don't like to think of him suffering in solitude, and wish him anywhere so that he were happier."*

The only person who would speak to him was Anne's old spaniel, Flossie; who was to be seen taking a daily wheezing constitutional at his heels.

It is not very surprising that Mr. Nicholls turned morose and forbidding and that when Papa at long last addressed him at the school-treat he *"did not reply civilly"*. Charlotte censured him, very unfairly, for this manner of his. But revealed herself in so doing: she was turning to him, she was yielding, and she was afraid he might have a bad temper. . . . She had, heaven knows, had enough of living with a bad temper.

Then comes the Sunday before Arthur Nicholls was to leave Haworth. And comedy blows out like a candle, and the taper which rises and shines in its stead is a gleam which may be seen through a shimmer of tears. . . . He officiated at the altar of the stone church; and did not realise until he stood before her

bowed head and screening bonnet that Charlotte was kneeling
among the communicants. He stood transfixed, paralysed, and
without voice. The server whispered to him, and he made a
volcanic effort, pulled himself together, and went on with the
service in a shaking murmur. They were hardheaded north-
country folk, the women of that congregation, but their sudden
sobbing reached Charlotte where she knelt trembling, and she,
too, broke into tears.

"*Papa was not there, thank God!*——" but when he heard, he
surpassed himself for unseemliness by muttering "*Unmanly
driveller!* . . ."

Arthur Nicholls came to the parsonage to take leave—one
wonders what sort of leave—of his unmannerly old vicar. And
Charlotte let him go, and let him get as far as the garden gate.
And then went flitting out into the Maytime dusk, and found
him leaning against the wall, "*sobbing as women never sob.*"
She could not, even then, tell him that she cared; and only he
and she have ever known with just what words she gave him
some comfort. Presently, he was back at Haworth unofficially,
without active church duty, domiciled at the village school.
And Charlotte for the first time in her life of thirty-odd years
would snatch a shawl and go gliding between the tombstones
and across the fields to meet a lover. It is pleasant to picture
those clandestine meetings; they humanise the rigid rectitude of
that upright, tiny figure, they release a something in her which
has a touch of the wild romances of lost Angria. . . . And
really, Arthur Nicholls has earned his right to a Stooping Lady.

So, presently, they are engaged. There is some battling royal
with Papa; but Charlotte has everything under control. It is
represented to him (as to that much more lovable and deserving
father, old Mr. Woodhouse) that he is far from losing a
daughter, he is to gain, not so much a son, as a man about the
house, who will do all the donkey-work of the parish, and put
his curate's stipend into the household pool. . . .

"But, my dear—have you thought where you will put him?
My study——"

"That is all planned-for, Papa. The little back-room where
we used to keep the peat and the firewood . . ."

It does not sound promising? But probably Mr. Nicholls

would have compounded with less or worse, rather than share
his father-in-law's study. And the little back-room was cleaned
and scoured and painted, and Charlotte herself stitched the
pretty green-and-white curtains for it. We may assume that
Arthur, watching her nimble fingers, was more than satisfied.

"*I trust to love my husband. I am grateful for his tender love to
me . . . if . . . I should yield to regrets that fine talents, congenial
tastes and thoughts are not added, it seems to me that I should be
most presumptuous and thankless.*"

She was never more simply and greatly truthful. The whole
matter of her marriage lies in those few sentences. Into the
chill darkness and the terrible silence, and the void where the
clock ticked like a heart beating life away, there had come the
enfolding warmth of a deep human love. A single-minded
human passion. A man in early middle age, profoundly in love
for the first time in a celibate life. There would be no mental
companionship. There would be less than no sympathy with
her work. But a man loved her, beyond reason; and a man who
shared all her narrow precepts and concepts as a churchwoman, who would not uproot her from home, who would
even—and no one else on earth would, and Charlotte knew it—
put up with Papa. She need never be lonely any more.

You may, I think, hear a door close, softly, and a key turn, or
a bolt slide. Charlotte is shutting the door on the Charlotte
Brontë of *Jane Eyre*, and of *Shirley*, and of *Villette*—for the
moment, at any rate. *Villette* has only recently appeared, and is
another best-seller; but it has drawn some rather scorching fire,
and the toil of achieving that last book has been as though she
wrote it in the blood of her own veins. She is infinitely tired.
She has no urge, no compelling desire, to write, just now. Just
yet. All that Charlotte sees is the end of dementing loneliness
and voices calling and sobbing in the winds of winter while she
shivers and weeps in bed. Oh God—it will be wonderful not to
be alone any more.

There will be no driving need, now, to go out into the overwhelming world for company, and come home spent and
stricken from the effort. There will be company at your own
warm fireside. (*Fine talents . . . ? congenial tastes . . . ?* who are
you, to demand everything? Say your prayers, and be thankful.)

Elizabeth Gaskell, when she wrote of Charlotte, took the impregnable Victorian stand with regard to her marriage. Quoting a literary letter from Charlotte to Sidney Dobell, *"which develops the intellectual side of her character, before we lose all thought of the authoress in the timid and conscientious woman about to become a wife, and in the too short, almost perfect, happiness of her nine months of wedded life. . . .*

". . . Henceforward the sacred doors of home are closed upon her married life. We, her loving friends, standing outside, caught occasional glimpses of brightness and pleasant peaceful murmurs of sound, telling of the gladness within; and we looked at each other and gently said . . . 'She is tasting happiness now!' . . ."

This is the Victorian biographer speaking. Nothing by halves, for charming Mrs. Gaskell. She can eliminate M. Héger from Charlotte's blameless scutcheon: vilify Branwell to the extent of landing herself and her publishers in a libel case; and affront old Mr. Brontë—who, with most gentlemanly generosity, forgave her when she visited him in his bedridden days of very old age. She was a lovely woman, of winning manners, and that ancient Irishman was susceptible to the end. But she must wave a flutter of gauze and dew over Charlotte's marriage. It is an odd gesture, coming from her, because Mrs. Gaskell was a married woman with a big family and one of the most successful and popular novelists of her time. One would think that she need feel no necessity for so firmly consigning Charlotte to happy domestic oblivion. . . .

But Elizabeth was, like Charlotte, no fool. She knew, just as well as Charlotte, that this marriage shut, barred, and sealed up the door to Charlotte the writer, the dreamer. She was only more informed than Charlotte, in that she wrote after Charlotte's brief, almost timeless married life had come to its end and Charlotte could scarcely know that the end would come so soon.

But, like most writers of fiction, Elizabeth Gaskell was more than one person in herself. She was "Lily" to her friends; a handsome, racy, indiscreet woman, scarcely to be recognised for the sedate (and always incomparable) biographer. She calls Charlotte "poor soul" in a letter to one of these friends, and says that she herself, visiting Haworth again, would put up at the "Black Bull" rather than be in Mr. Brontë's company—or, as she words it, "so as not to be in Mr. Brontë's road," using the phrase in its north-country sense. In the spring before Charlotte's marriage she stayed with Mrs. Gaskell for shopping, and an old school friend, Catherine Winkworth, paid a call. This friend relates a conversation*—preceded by a whisper from "Lily", "*Say something to her about her marriage . . .*"

Catherine: "*It will be a great happiness for you to have someone to care for and make happy.*"

But Charlotte had had nothing else, all her life, but that unrelaxing task.

Charlotte:—with a touch of spirit:

"*Yes, and it is a great thing to be the first object with anyone.*"

Some decorous chat follows, about Mr. Nicholls being so dependable, and refusing preferment elsewhere because Charlotte would not leave her father.

"*She stopped, and then went on: 'But, Katie, it has cost me a good deal to come to this . . . I cannot conceal from myself that he is not* (underlined emphatically) *intellectual; there are many places into which he would not follow me intellectually. . . .*"

Interrupted by Mrs. Gaskell's coming back into the room, Charlotte continues:

"*Still—such a character would be far less amusing and interesting than a more impulsive and fickle one; it might be dull!*"

"*Yes, indeed,*" said Lily.

"*For a day's companion, yes,*" I said, "*but not for a life's . . . such a character would have the advantage that one might do the fickleness required oneself, which would be a relief sometimes.*"

Lily cries out upon such untimely candour. But Charlotte exclaims:

"*Oh there is truth in it; so much that I don't think I could ever have been so candid.*"

They were married: with Ellen as bridesmaid and Miss Wooler to give the bride away because Papa, troublesome to the last, announced that he felt less well than usual and unequal to the ordeal and took to his bed. He may have had the secret hope that Charlotte would put off the honeymoon . . .

* *Mrs. Gaskell and Her Friends.* Elizabeth Haldane.

but Papa did not realise that his behaviour with regard to Charlotte's bridegroom had opened her eyes inconveniently wide.

"Too bad, Papa," said Charlotte briskly and without the sound of sympathy which he expected to hear. "You must try to rouse yourself for breakfast before we leave for the train."

"You will—be leaving, my dear?" queried the invalid faintly and with implied reproach.

"Of course we shall, Papa. We catch the connection for Holyhead, as you very well know."

Papa groaned in a slight manner and sighed with depth and meaning. But Charlotte had rustled out of the room. Downstairs she found Arthur, who couldn't keep away, standing, and looking very tall and large, in the little room with the green-sprigged curtains.

"What has amused you?" he asked, watching Charlotte's eyes dancing with mischief and a spark of malice.

"Only Papa!" said Charlotte, and her shoulders shook for an instant with voiceless laughter.

"H'm!" said Arthur. He did not find Papa a source of amusement. . . .

So off they went to Ireland, when Charlotte had changed her white muslin dress and white bonnet with the wreath of green leaves for a grey dress and shawl and a bonnet of grey silk with pink roses. She must have looked an endearing little figure, for the fashions of the day were in their final stage of charm before the exaggerated and over-trimmed grotesqueries of the sixties swept them away. Tight, demure bodices, very full, sweeping skirts but no hoops, full muslin sleeves emerging from the stuff of an over-sleeve to a frilled wrist. The hair worn in smooth or rippled bandeaux framing the face, the bonnets frivolous and delicious, worn at the back of the head. And the shawl an art in itself, draped gracefully as a scarf or a mantle. Charlotte can never have looked better than in her going-away costume.

She saw Killarney, and she saw the Atlantic from the cliffs of Tralee. Charlotte, standing above the sea again, asked Arthur to leave her alone with it as she had once asked Ellen, and was half afraid that he might be hurt or offended. But he acquiesced; only, unlike Ellen, he had to come hurrying back because he thought that she was too near the edge. . . . She met his Irish relatives, his clergyman-uncle and guardian, she saw the clergy farmlands at Banagher. It was a mellow time. Charlotte saw her husband among his own people, much loved and warmly honoured. In the articulate Irish way, the servants told her that, glory be to God, sure, she was the lucky lady; hadn't she got one of the best gentlemen in the country, now? . . . Charlotte was surprised, and touched and pleased.

They came back to Haworth, and the "*pleasant peaceful murmurs of sound*" begin.

There was very real happiness for Charlotte.

"*My life is changed indeed: to be wanted continually, to be constantly called for and occupied seems so strange; yet it is a marvellously good thing.*"

". . . *Not that I have been wearied or oppressed;*" (one would hope not, quite so soon . . .) "*but the fact is, my time is not my own now; somebody else wants a good portion of it and says 'we must do so and so.' We do so and so, accordingly; and it generally seems the right thing.*"

It is a little dismaying to see Charlotte arch and bridling, but it is touching as well.

Her mellowing autumnal sunlight reached out to surround Papa; Charlotte was too happy to bear rancour now.

"*May God preserve him to us yet for some years! The wish for his continued life, together with a certain solicitude for his happiness and health, seems, I scarcely know why, even stronger in me than before I was married.*"

There are other murmurs of sound, though. A marriage may totally change a condition or way of life, may flood an in-human state of loneliness with fond, exacting companionship and perpetual demands on time and energy, but when a marriage is made at thirty-eight, it does not totally change a character and a personality. It was only a few months before Charlotte's marriage that Elizabeth Gaskell stayed with her, and recorded some of the most enlightening talks which anyone ever had with Charlotte.

"*I told her of Blank's admiration of Shirley, which pleased her, for the character of Shirley was meant for her sister Emily, about whom she is never tired of talking, nor I of listening. Emily must*

have been a remnant of the Titans—great-granddaughter of the
giants who used to inhabit earth.

The shadow of Emily haunted Charlotte and the need for her.
It was not just the affection of a sister—she felt that, tenderly,
for Anne, but she did not talk for hours about Anne to a
woman of brain and mental attainments, a fellow-writer. She
knew, more deeply and more achingly with every dreary day,
what she had lost in Emily; the company of the greatest brain
and most powerful mind she would ever know. Very far
greater and more powerful than her own. There is a veneration
in her devotion to that sister. A bewilderment, and an awe,
and an element of adoring fear.

Now, hear the voices of Elizabeth and Charlotte on their
"*distant walks*".

"*We talked about the different courses through which life ran.
She said, in her own composed manner, as if she had accepted the
theory as a fact, that she believed some were appointed beforehand
to sorrow and much disappointment; that it did not fall to the lot of
all . . . to have their lines fall in pleasant places; that it was well
for those . . . to perceive that such was God's will concerning
them, and try to moderate their expectations, leaving hope to those of a
different doom. I*" (says happy, successful Elizabeth) "*took a
different view.*"

These long, satisfying talks were taking place when Charlotte
already had her marriage in her mind. When, shrewd, alert,
and dauntless, she was thinking out ways and means to cir-
cumvent Papa, and dwelling constantly in her secret thoughts
on the most appealing side of Arthur Nicholls' character, to
convince herself that such a marriage could be. But, to the one
woman intimate she had, who could enter into her imaginative
and creative life, she could still pour out the pent-up flood of
her worship of Emily's mind and personality, and her dreadful
fatalism under life.

They are strange occupations for the mind of someone on the
brink of a Saint Luke's summer.

Three months after her wedding, Charlotte is maintaining:

"*I believe it is not bad for me that his bent should be so wholly
towards matters of life and active usefulness; so little inclined to the
literary and contemplative.*"

If you can imagine Charlotte whistling—as Shirley did, to the dismay of decorous Mrs. Pryor—this is surely whistling in the dark to keep courage up? It is not left to Charlotte to reveal, involuntarily, how quickly and how deeply she felt the fundamental lack in her kind and loving Arthur. Ellen came to stay, just once, never again, at the house where she had been the most besought and best beloved guest. Arthur was jealous of his wife's best friend. Well, that has happened before and since, and is not of primary importance anyway. Any new-made husband might, if he were as simple, forthright, and tactless as Arthur, be jealous of sweet Ellen. She had been Charlotte's one safety-valve and comfort since their school-days. Arthur's not unreasonable attitude could well have been, I'm here now. But his jealousy really took an ignominious form. Charlotte writes repeatedly and agitatedly to Ellen, that she must promise Arthur never, never to keep a single letter from herself, or he will insist, he says, on supervising every word they write to one another. He has a rooted mistrust of female letter-writing, he says. It is indiscreet, and it may—who knows? fall into the wrong hands. Ellen, who had her own gentle strength and dignity, quite rightly protests. And then comes a plea from Charlotte: "*Dear Nell, give him your promise!* . . ." and Nell gave it. But, *laus Deo*, did not keep it. Instead, she continued to do as she had always done, and kept every letter which Charlotte wrote to her.

They walk on the moors, as they have always done, and Arthur comes too. (If you leave two women alone together, who knows how they may back each other up and whisper confidences?) And Ellen, Ellen who has never taken the smallest part in Charlotte's life as a writer, is moved to ask her friend if she is writing anything just now? . . . It is a question which Ellen has never put, and which takes Charlotte by surprise, coming from her of all people. No, she answers, nothing—just now.

It seems likely—and natural—that Ellen was piqued by Arthur's high-handed ways as a husband. She was not used to being treated so summarily by men. Quite the contrary, in fact. So she shook her pretty head reproachfully, and said: "But you *should*, Charlotte! She mustn't let herself get rusty, must she, Mr. Nicholls?" which was deliberately provoking. And Mr. Nicholls returned (we have Ellen's word for it), in a trumpet-blast: *"I did not marry Currer Bell, the novelist, but Charlotte Brontë, the clergyman's daughter."* He added vigorously: *"Currer Bell may fly to heaven tomorrow for anything I care."*

This is just temper under provocation; and it is not difficult to picture Arthur apologising privately to a flurried Charlotte: "I am sorry, my love. I am, believe me! I did not above half mean it. But that young woman, I confess, does rile me. . . ."

The point is, that nearly always what comes out in a flash of temper is not born of the instant. It is something which has lurked and grown and fermented for some time. And it is not speculation nor prejudice which has established Arthur Nicholls as the one person alive who was actually and deeply opposed to his wife's writing, could not away with the fact that Currer Bell existed at all, and both resented and feared her gift and her fame.

"Arthur says I have no time for writing now, as I must attend to my duties as a clergyman's wife." Charlotte writes this to Ellen. No time; quite possibly. But he had no conception that it was not a matter of time or no time, but a matter of breathing or ceasing to breathe.

Presently Charlotte was writing again. How could she help it? And she read the fragment of a book to Arthur and gave it to him to read, partly because one must share anything with one's husband, but partly in a rather pathetic attempt to draw him into the locked chamber. The only comment which remains from the poor bewildered man is that he told her she was repeating herself and that the plot was too much like *Jane Eyre.*

There is a word of Charlotte's which comes drifting down the years like a blown leaf. One evening as they sat together by the parlour fire she said to her husband with her quiet smile: *"If you were not with me, I should be writing. . . ."*

And it has been taken to indicate the fulness of her content and the contrast in her mind between this cosy Darby and Joan picture and the empty clock-ticking room and its ghosts. Arthur, no doubt, accepted it so, and said a tender word, and pressed her hand.

But it is possible to hear something very different, in the words. . . .

There is honour to be paid to Arthur Bell Nicholls. He bore with Papa and endured living in the same house with him till the old man died, much too late. He refused a better and better-paid living because he would not separate Charlotte from her father. And when her last and lingering illness took Charlotte into its hold, she could write in a faint pencil scrawl words which deserve to be engraved to her husband's memory:

"No kinder, better husband than mine, it seems to me, there can be in the world. I do not want, now, for kind companionship in health and the tenderest nursing in sickness . . . I cannot write more now, for I am much reduced and very weak."

He was the soul of kindness to her in her pain and increasing weakness. She was dying of pernicious anæmia in the task of bearing a child which she could not pretend to desire. *"Medicine I have quite discontinued. If you can send me anything that will do good—do* (underlined). *As to my husband, my heart is knit to him—he is so tender, so good, helpful, patient."*

He had, to remember through all the years of his own long life, her whisper: *"Oh! I am not going to die, am I? He will not separate us, we have been so happy."*

He stayed on in the silent house with the old man until Patrick Brontë died. And would have stayed on still if he had been given the living, but as that did not happen, Arthur Nicholls gave up church duties and went back to his uncle's farm at Banagher. And nearly ten years after Charlotte died, married a cousin. There is a dim old photograph taken of him as an old man, standing in the bleak street of the small Irish town, a white-bearded figure chatting to some of the towns-people and leaning on a stick. There is dignity and benevolence in the figure, even in such an inadequate photograph.

Let it be said quite plainly: he was and would always have been a tender and careful husband to Charlotte the fragile and courageous woman. To Charlotte the writer he should never have been husband at all. He told someone, many years after his own second and comfortable marriage, that his heart was in her grave; and it was surely true. But something else was as surely true. He not only had no vestige of understanding of the second, the innermost Charlotte; he resented her existence.

It is due to his attitude that all the accumulated papers of her own and her sisters' childhood writings were scattered. He did not see them as something to preserve and treasure, however little understood; but as something to be got rid of to the first bidder or applicant.

Charlotte was not entirely mistaken when she foreboded a streak of rancour in his upright nature. He turned his back on the Church when he could not get the Haworth living. He refused to christen a Haworth baby because the parents insisted on naming the boy "Brontë", in Charlotte's memory. This was a serious decision for a man who believed that an unchristened infant, if it died, must be denied burial in consecrated ground! Rancour seems to have worsted Christian duty pretty thoroughly in this instance. Papa summoned the parents and the baby to his room and did the christening, *sub rosa*. And his son-in-law reproached him grimly for going behind his back.

It is futile to speculate on what would have happened if this marriage had lasted longer; but it is impossible not to. . . . Would Charlotte's possession by her own irresistible gift have torn and harried her until she gave way to it once more? Would Arthur's moroseness and rancour have grown until they obscured the tenderness and until he felt bitterly that Currer Bell needed no care from him however much Charlotte Nicholls did?

If she had never married him, she would not have died in exhausted pain because she was carrying his child. And it is out of the bounds of possibility to imagine Charlotte the mother of children. But if she had never married him, she would never have known the warmth and enfolding light of those few months of household happiness after the years in a cold hell of desolation. Even from a practical point of view, Charlotte's reason as well as nerves were not likely to stand much more of that fearful silence and emptiness and brooding.

Perhaps the most compassionate answer is that her death released her from what would have taken shape as a tragic mistake, while the sunlight and the firelight were still warm and bright about her.

Arthur Nicholls was self-evidently a man unburdened by imagination, distrustful of it. But through the six years when he, too, sat alone in the parlour at the end of the day's parochial duties; and officiated in the grey church above her grave; and bore, as best he could, with her old father; one wonders what thoughts came to him and what shadows stole about him and what voices spoke in the winter winds?

Those six years must have been as hard a service given to a memory as ever a man underwent.

She had come to him, flitting across the fields in her shawl, in spite of Papa and the village worthies and John Sexton growling that he wished he had a gun. And she had only been with him for six short months of health and happiness and three of increasing pain and weakness. She had gone back to them, to join them under the stone slabs, to lie beside Emily again, their two wasted and pain-spent bodies emptied of pain and at rest. And—it may be—to the lost splendours of Angria and of Gondal intensified beyond the endurance of human senses? To some fulfilment beyond the reach of human perceptions?

Emily has the last word, after all:

"*I lingered round them, under that benign sky; watched the moths fluttering among the heath and harebells, listened to the soft wind breathing through the grass, and wondered how anyone could ever imagine unquiet slumbers for the sleepers in that quiet earth.*"

Part Two

WHAT THEY WROTE

1

WUTHERING HEIGHTS

WHEN Charlotte set herself to write of Emily, and of *Wuthering Heights*, she dedicated herself to a task which gave her such agony of remembrance that she collapsed into illness under it. She wrote with an incomparable poignancy and with complete integrity. And the task was quite beyond her. With all her devotion, and her belief in her sister's gift, she had no conception of the scope of Emily's powers nor that what she herself saw as a gift was genius.

She feels it painfully necessary to explain Emily, and to apologise for *Wuthering Heights*. And no one is likely ever to explain Emily. And an apology for *Wuthering Heights* would be the height of grotesque comedy if it were not pitiful.

"The immature but very real powers revealed in Wuthering Heights . . . *an original mind (however unripe, however inefficiently cultured and partially expanded that mind may be . . .) Neither Emily nor Anne was learned; they had no thought of filling their pitchers at the well-spring of other minds."*

We may be thankful that Emily, at least, had no such thought.

". . . a secret power and fire that might have inflamed the brain and kindled the veins of a hero; but she had no worldly wisdom. . . . An interpreter ought always to have stood between her and the world."

Quivering with pain and half-blinded by her tears, Charlotte took upon herself the rôle of interpreter. And it should be borne in mind that if she filled it badly, no one else could have filled it at all.

Charlotte was shocked by *Wuthering Heights*. She was made wretched by the thought that it would be held disreputable in Emily to have written such a book. To be capable of writing it. She had to explain it away. Emily had been nursed on the savage traditional stories of ancient Yorkshire; she didn't know life: *"Having formed these beings she did not know what she had done. . . ."* Charlotte goes on to relate that when she herself, while the book was in the making, shuddered over it, Emily would say that she was showing *"affectation"*. That is one of Charlotte's most illuminating pictures of Emily. It is as though one could look through the parlour window into the room with its light of candles and fire and see the scene. Charlotte, shuddering and protesting, pressing her tiny hands to her ears —(she describes the book being read aloud by Emily); Emily towering above her as she sat, staring at her with those unforgettable eyes, amazed, affronted, impatient.

I think that Anne, listening quietly from her seat by the fire, made no such protest. Charlotte says of Anne that she wore over mind and feelings *"a sort of nun-like veil, which was rarely lifted,"* and it is a perfect description, Charlotte using words as she might have set small gems with her elfin fingers; as she did all that laborious and superfine sewing. She does not seem to have remembered that Anne roamed in Gondal with Emily, moving over battlefields soaked in blood, peering through the bars of dungeons and torture-chambers and living in a world of passions on a superhuman scale. Almost everything which they wrote had its roots in Gondal and Angria; but *Wuthering Heights* is a Gondal prose-saga.

Charlotte could find nothing to say for the beings of Emily's creation locked in their death grapple. She was compelled to turn to the homeliness of Nelly Dean, the attachment of Edgar Linton, even the monstrous cartoon figure of old Joseph, to dress the balance. (Think, for one moment, of selecting Nelly Dean, as the redeeming feature of *Wuthering Heights* . . .) There is something infuriating but piteous about this picture of Charlotte; covering her eyes, covering her ears, turning away her face, from a portrayal of passion of the soul rather than of the body which has not its peer in literature . . . ". . . *perverted passion and passionate perversity"*, she named it. She was terrified as well as horrified. She had no eyes, no ears, for the glory and the splendour. She could only frantically maintain that Emily didn't know what she was doing. . . .

But through the blindness and the deafness, her voice utters two clear pronouncements, and one is sheer common-sense and the other is the writer's invincible need. She affirms staunchly that Emily did right in writing down in full such words as *"it has become the custom to represent by the initial and final letter only—a blank line filling the interval . . ." "which strikes me as a proceeding which, however well meant, is weak and futile."* Which, coming from Charlotte, rather takes one's breath away; and merits, in all respect, a salute to a valiant lady, since Charlotte, at heart, was a prude if ever there was one.

And, when she doubts whether it be *"right or advisable to create beings like Heathcliff,"* she goes on to speak her writer's faith; and the words sound a pæan down the years:

"But this I know; the writer who possesses the creative gift owns something of which he is not always master—something that, at times, strangely wills and works for itself."

Much of her working existence was spent in an effort to deny her own faith. But she knew when she was betraying it.

While Charlotte was dismissing and apologising for the heart of the greatness which is *Wuthering Heights*, she had no word of criticism of the flagrant faults which are all that posterity can find to criticise in it. And which are, in their way, a part of the measure of its greatness, since in any other book they would loom tremendous and here they do not matter at all. Emily's one prose work is as much of an outlaw to accepted regulations as is her poetry.

The story opens with narrative by one, Lockwood, who is merely a tenant of Heathcliff's and has no part whatever in the drama. It moves into another and continuous narrative, expounded by the respectable and redeeming Nelly Dean of Charlotte's pathetic approval. Nelly, in fact, relates the whole very long book, the complex history of two generations, repeating conversations, describing incidents, over a period from Catherine's childhood to her daughter's second marriage, with an exactitude which would be striking if they had taken place within the past twenty-four hours. If this were supposed to be taken for fact, the woman must have had the most phenomenal memory in the history of the human race. Nelly is a moorland peasant-child who grew up with Catherine, doing odd tasks about the house and farm, then living in the house as servant, finally as housekeeper. She refers to her status continually; but her speech is fluent, educated, and vivid and she is, supposedly, a profound student of the human character.

But of course this figure, compounded of anachronisms, incongruities, and impossibility, is no more than Emily's pen and the china inkwell sunk in the little slot in that writing-desk on her knee: the tool with which she wrought the story. Just why she chose to use a narrator throughout, no one except Emily will ever know. For pages on end you are oblivious to the fact that the story is being related at all; it unfolds in the accepted way; and suddenly Nelly bounces into the page again and you recollect with a start and a jolt that she is still talking. She talks over a stretch of forty years. . . .

Again, why introduce Lockwood? who gives his first impression of *Wuthering Heights*, and his final one; and between them, sits over gruel recovering from a chill and making Nelly talk. And gives a sudden thumb-nail sketch of his own complex nature by volunteering the account of how he once fell in love but retreated directly the young lady showed signs of response.

And none of it matters. It does not even detract from the greatness of the book. You cannot imagine it other than it is.

There is no possibility of analysing or considering *Wuthering Heights* as you would analyse or consider a novel. It is not a reviewer's piece. There are none of the microscopic touches, the shading, the sublety, with which Charlotte worked, expending them on such immeasurably lesser characters than Emily's. It stands simply as the greatest presentation of a passion welding two human beings which has ever been achieved.

In the Gondal saga there is a bond between a foster-brother and sister who are deceived, ill-treated, and outcast by the all-pervading queen, Augusta, and eventually destroy her in revenge. In *Wuthering Heights*, Cathy and Heathcliff are foster-brother and sister, and the whole book is a story of savage vengeance. And Cathy's witchery, binding Heathcliff; her supine and gentle husband; even the young sister-in-law whom she despises and mocks, and the faithful Nelly; is something of the same spell which Augusta cast like a net.

But when Emily turned from Gondal-in-poetry to Gondal-in-prose, her genius took possession. One of the strangest, the least comprehensible elements in the whole dream-world of the three women is its fantastic remoteness from life. Women day-dream; but not of a pseudo-medieval, barbaric world un-tethered by any actual period in time and charted by imaginary maps. It is hard to grasp that the loves and hatreds of those superhuman or less than human kings and queens could have held Emily and Anne in thrall when they were women in their later twenties and that Charlotte never escaped from the heroic shadow of Zamorna. It stalks across the pages in every book which she wrote. Now, starting from possession by a fantasy, Emily entered into possession by the utmost, the ultimate reality, such as no writer has surpassed. From the fantastic puppets that were Julius and Augusta and innumerable others, known and unknown, in a welter of confused names, she made the loves of Catherine and Heathcliff. It was, in very truth, a genesis.

The fire strikes suddenly, blindingly, in the middle of Lockwood's stilted and pedantic account of his visit to the house. (He calls the interior of the house "*the penetralium*" and makes Heathcliff "*grind his teeth to subdue the maxillary convulsions*", i.e., when they are chattering with cold and shock . . .) From the moment when the child-spirit of Cathy sobs at the window its despairing wail "*Let me in—let me in!*" and Lockwood encounters the "*little, ice-cold hand;*" when he watches his surly host suddenly leap on to the bed and tear open the stiff window, and break down in wild weeping, calling "*Come in, come in! Cathy, do come. Oh do, once more! Oh! my heart's darling! hear me this time, Catherine at last!*" the fire that is the core of the whole book is kindled, and sweeps onward and upward and everything that is redundant, or faulty, or grotesque, is ashes before it and of no account.

Heathcliff, the foundling, grows to a boy in the house of the Earnshaws, Wuthering Heights. Detested and bullied by Earnshaw, Cathy's brother but like a twin to Cathy, the wild, gipsyish little girl whom no one can control. Earnshaw degrades him to the status of the roughest farm-hand, makes a serf of him: but Heathcliff and Cathy are inseparable. Earnshaw, when his loved young wife dies leaving a baby boy, turns savage and a drunkard. *"I could not half tell what an infernal house we had,"* Nelly says.

Edgar Linton, the young owner of Thrushcross Grange, has been fascinated by Cathy since they first encountered each other as children. He is gentle, weak in character, and infatuated with her. And Thrushcross is a sober home of comfort and refinement and peace, in total contrast to Wuthering Heights.

Cathy comes to Nelly Dean in her conflict and indecision: she has accepted Edgar's proposal of marriage and is wretched.

" *'And now,'* " Nelly says derisively and with sturdy commonsense, " *'let us hear what you are unhappy about . . . you will escape from a disorderly, comfortless home into a wealthy respectable one; and you love Edgar, and Edgar loves you. All seems smooth and easy: where is the obstacle?' "*

" *'Here! and here!'* " . . . striking one hand on her forehead and the other on her breast: " *'in whichever place the soul lives. In my soul and in my heart, I'm convinced I'm wrong!'*

" *'That's very strange! I cannot make it out.'* "

" *'It's my secret. But if you will not mock at me, I'll explain it: I can't do it distinctly'* " . . . says Catherine, bewildered and torn two ways at once, and incoherent. She goes on to tell Nelly, a reluctant listener, of a dream in which she was in heaven: and . . . " *'heaven did not seem to be my home; and I broke my heart with weeping to come back to earth; and the angels were so angry that they flung me out into the middle of the heath on the top of Wuthering Heights; where I woke sobbing for joy. That will do to explain my secret, as well as the other.'* " She continues that she has no more right to marry Edgar Linton than to be in heaven. She belongs to the heath, the moors, the heights, and to Heathcliff. Heathcliff she will never marry; her brother has crushed and beaten him so low that it would be degradation. . . .

Heathcliff, sitting in a dark corner of the great kitchen, unseen, hears this far. At Cathy's last words he slips out of the room. And so, never hears her next words:

" *. . . Nelly, he's more myself than I am. Whatever our souls are made of, his and mine are the same; and Linton's is as different as a moonbeam from lightning or frost from fire."*

Nelly tries, awkwardly but staunchly, to explain to Catherine that if she marries Linton she must give up the close connection with Heathcliff which has bound them for almost all their lives. And Catherine breaks out with that flaming innocence which is the keynote of the story:

. . . " 'Who is to separate us, pray? . . . Not as long as I live, Ellen: for no mortal creature. . . . Oh, that's not what I intend— that's not what I mean! . . . He'll be as much to me as he has been all his lifetime. Edgar must shake off his antipathy, and tolerate him, at least. He will, when he learns my true feelings towards him.' "

She reminds Nelly that if she married Heathcliff, both would be beggars; whereas, married to Edgar Linton, she can help him to rise in the world and to escape from Earnshaw's oppression. Nelly, who seems to have more worldly wisdom than her young mistress, scolds her in plain terms and scoffs at the idea. Cathy struggles to put her creed into words, though Nelly is, not unreasonably, quite incapable of understanding and denounces it as nonsense and Cathy as "a wicked, unprincipled girl," at worst, and at best an ignorant little fool.

" '. . . . my great thought in living is himself. If all else perished, and he remained, I should still continue to be; and if all else remained, and he were annihilated, the universe would turn to a mighty stranger: I should not seem a part of it. . . . Nelly, I am Heathcliff! (underlined). He's always, always in my mind: not as a pleasure, any more than I am always a pleasure to myself, but as my own being. So don't talk of our separation again'. . . ."

The incredible innocence of their destroying passion burns through the book to the end. Try as you may, you cannot attribute to them an hour, a moment, even, of bodily fulfilment. They are possessed by it, consumed by it, they destroy each other and themselves by it. The intensity of their uttered words scorches and the bitterness of their tears scalds. But Cathy and Heathcliff are spirit-lovers. And not in any self-denial: they deny themselves nothing. They wreck almost every life with which they make any contact; they are without a vestige of self-control. But that is the only love which Emily could see or could portray: two human beings so blent as one that they betrayed their own souls when they clove themselves apart from one another.

There have been, there continue to be, more theories spun

round Emily Brontë than round any other figure in literature. And of recent years, since anyone who so chooses makes free with a species of claptrap psychiatry, she has been explained, dissected, accounted for, in some very strange theories indeed. The habit is reminiscent of those ephemeral malpractices which spawned among the war-weary youngsters of three decades ago, when people played at drug-taking. The expressed results suggest the trial of Marie-Antoinette and the allegation that she had debauched her doomed little son. To Emily has been attributed inordinate affection concentrated upon each member of her family in turn, with the exception of Charlotte. The most zealous researcher couldn't overlook the obvious fact that she did not even like her elder sister: found her aggravating, limited, and her devotion an intrusive nuisance. It seems odd that no one has reverted to outspoken mythology and suggested that Emily had a fixation for Keeper, her dog. But that may be still to come.

In the face of all such experimental curiosity—and almost all of it is, paradoxically, a tribute to Emily: you can't explain her, you can't get away from her, you have to do something about it and this is what you do—there stands this epic of the soul's passion, so naïve in its ignoring of the flesh that there is something terrible about its god-like simplicity of values. The innocence is more fearful than the savageries. . . . We are not unfamiliar with savagery. The past decade has revealed to us that civilisation is a sufficiently shallow tide. Heathcliff battering Earnshaw to pulp, Isabella worn down to a nervous wreck, the younger Catherine with *"her mouth filling with blood . . . and I sometimes think she can't speak for pain . . ."* these shocked Emily's readers a century ago, and they can sicken a reader today. But we of the nineteen-forties have learned more of what ingenuity of torment can be inflicted upon the human body than Emily had learned from the violent stories of an older Yorkshire. It is the overpowering force of a bodiless love and the fusion of two souls which is beyond our understanding.

Heathcliff vanishes from the moment when he overhears Cathy's flippant dismissal of him as a degraded creature. What happened to him, the convalescent Lockwood demands, while waving away his pills and potions.

" 'Did he finish his education on the Continent, and come back a gentleman? or did he get a sizar's place at college, or escape to America and earn honours by drawing blood from his foster-country? or make a fortune on the English highways?' "

Mr. Lockwood is pleased to be facetious.

To which Nelly returns with her usual solid sense:

" 'He may have done a little in all these vocations, Mr. Lockwood; but I couldn't give my word for any.' "

Cathy shows the first signs of a mind and brain off-balance when, in her despair over Heathcliff's disappearance she has a serious illness, one of those vague "fevers" which occur in all the Brontë books and others of the period.

She recovers; but Mr. Kenneth, the family apothecary, warns Edgar Linton of her delicacy, her excitability; and Cathy is in the fortunate position of the individual who must not be crossed nor gainsaid. (Nelly has some dry comments to make on this . . .) In due course, she marries Edgar, and goes to be mistress of Thrushcross Grange.

Not the least evidence of Emily's supreme power is that she makes Cathy's summer-lightning spell convincing, even through the medium of Nelly Dean's critical un-illusioned eyes. Cathy is a law unto herself, uncontrolled and uncontrollable, but she is love incarnate. Cut off from Heathcliff, the rest of herself, and with something in her wounded beyond cure by his going and by the knowledge that her heedless words have cut her life in two, Cathy responds with all her radiant warmth to Edgar's excessive gentleness and to the orderly tranquillity of her new home.

"She seemed almost over-fond of Mr. Linton; and even to his sister she showed plenty of affection," says Nelly rather sourly.

Then there is the September dusk when Nelly comes from the garden with her loaded basket of apples and lingers in moonlight and etched shadows in the courtyard of the house. In these half-dozen lines there is all the incense and the teeming stir and magic of an autumn evening. Emily did not make such skilled use of word-painting as Charlotte did, who gives you a sunset sky, a wood, a stretch of moorland, with the fine detail of a pre-Raphaelite foreground. But she has cupped a September evening, a high-riding moon, the smell of an orchard, the chill sweetness of the air, all in a walled courtyard, and with hardly a descriptive word.

And Heathcliff's voice says from the shadows:

"*Nelly, is that you?*"

In a book packed to bursting-point with violent scenes, the subdued stillness of the moment of Heathcliff's return comes with an almost physical impact. It is like a touch on the arm.

He is back. And Catherine is beside herself with excitement: "*. . . too excited to show gladness: indeed, by her face, you would rather have surmised an awful calamity.*"

This is significant. From Charlotte onwards, there has been a tendency to assume that Emily wrote rather as though she were working a planchette-board, in the wayward grip of a power which she did not understand that she possessed. That "*unformed writing of a giant's hand*" has dogged her down the years. Her unlessoned genius might—and did—make her oblivious of the shackles of the construction and form of a novel; she did not care about them, she had no need to care about them, because she transcended them. But concerning the persons whom she created, her touch was assured. "*Having formed these beings she did not know what she had done,*" wrote Charlotte. Nothing could be less true or more mistaken. Emily knew to a syllable what she was doing. So, in the hour of Heathcliff's reappearance after nearly four years, there is no brittle gladness from Cathy: it is the "*joy mad with awe*"; the wild and painful ecstasy of a reunion infinitely deeper than the return of a lost love. Cathy's lost self has returned to her. Her numbed, divided soul is awake and complete again. Would such an experience be a matter for easy happiness?

And when, in the middle of the night, she wakes long-suffering Nelly to talk to her, Cathy's unbalanced mind is evident. She is back again in her irrational, mad mood of the night when Heathcliff disappeared; nothing exists but the fact that he has come back to her and Edgar's natural resentment is merely an exasperation. Nelly's warnings are so much wasted breath. Cathy is drunk with exultation and already a little mad with confidence that she has power to handle everyone, settle everything. The radiant insanity of a creature so completed, now, that it feels in itself the attribute of a god.

She slips from Nelly's garret on a note of heady, childish laughter: . . . *"I'll go make my peace with Edgar instantly. Good-night! I'm an angel!"*

Heathcliff is home again. But Cathy has no idea that his reasons for returning are two-fold. He cannot exist out of her sight; but he has also come back to carry out the long, complicated revenge which he has planned ever since her brother, Hindley Earnshaw, made his young life a lost soul's inferno in boyhood. It is a well-planned scheme, down to the least detail: no sudden headlong impulse. Heathcliff lodges at his old home and Cathy's, the house which is now a sort of thieves' kitchen, where Hindley and his companions drink and gamble in the intervals of sodden sleep. And where Hindley's unwanted little son, Hareton, is being turned into such another lost soul as the young Heathcliff. Heathcliff wins everything that Hindley Earnshaw possesses, from him; and encourages him to drink himself to death. And contrives to attach to himself the miserable child, so that, to the end of Heathcliff's life, Hareton loves him. . . .

He could hardly have anticipated the development which lays the uttermost diabolical power in his hands: that Isabella, Edgar Linton's young sister, falls madly in love with him. . . .

Isabella is a slightly-sketched portrait; but even to her least character-study Emily could not help giving life. There are puppets among Charlotte's people; and poor Anne's are more puppet than person at most times; but even Zillah, an uncouth farm-servant who only appears on two or three pages, even Kenneth, the inadequate apothecary, sadly baffled by the dramas and dilemmas of his moorland practice, come to life. Emily, using Nelly Dean as mouthpiece, never gives a minute physical description of any of her characters; yet you see them as though they stood round you. It is partly, perhaps, because the vitality of the conversations is a masterpiece. And partly because Emily never uses verbiage. She writes with an elemental simplicity and forthrightness of words. But why attempt to explain it? Emily possessed the writer's first and best gift in a supreme degree: the creation of living beings.

Isabella is very young, pretty, childish, sheltered and indulged by her brother. Heathcliff comments brutally on her blue eyes:

" '. . . they detestably resemble Linton's' ".   " 'Delectably!'
observed Catherine: 'they are dove's eyes . . .' "

Among the fragments of Emily's poetry there is a lyric:

"A fresh wind moves the clustering roses,
        And through the open window sighs
        Around the couch where she reposes:
        The lady with the dove-like eyes";

There, in fact, is Isabella. Nelly says that she was "possessed
of keen wit, keen feelings, and a keen temper, too, if irritated."
And those keen feelings beneath a pretty, childish appearance
kindle at the first sight of Heathcliff.

Heathcliff behaves criminally over this girlish infatuation.
But Cathy, too, behaves abominably, in her own way. She
shows a fearful clarity of perception of the nature of the man
with whom her own is inextricably mingled; a sudden depth
under her wild, irresponsible seeming:

" '. . . . he might love me if you would let him!' " Isabella sobs
angrily.

" 'I wouldn't be you for a kingdom, then!' Catherine declared
emphatically: and she seemed to speak sincerely. 'Nelly, help me to
convince her of her madness. Tell her what Heathcliff is: an un-
reclaimed creature . . . an arid wilderness. I'd as soon put that
little canary into the park on a winter's day, as recommend you to
bestow your heart on him! It is deplorable ignorance of his character,
child, and nothing else, which makes that dream enter your head
. . . a fierce, pitiless, wolfish man. . . . That's my picture: and
I'm his friend—so much so, that had he thought seriously to catch
you, I should, perhaps, have held my tongue and let you fall into his
trap.' "

Isabella, quite naturally, does not believe her. But we do.
. . . Those two are so interlocked in darkness, as in fire, that
Cathy would throw her fond, pretty sister-in-law to him, if
Isabella were what he happened to want. And she knows him,
now, to the uttermost terrible depths. And it makes no
difference. Heathcliff is devil-possessed, and it never enters
Cathy's head to make any attempt to save him. He is her-
self. . . .

But Heathcliff has no spark of feeling for Isabella. And knowing this, Cathy really does behave like a little fiend, teasing and shaming the girl in front of him, and revealing her pitiful infatuation to him. Heathcliff says rebukingly:

"What did you mean by teasing the creature in that manner, Cathy? You were not speaking the truth, were you? . . . though Isabella Linton may be silly, she is scarcely mad; and in short, we'll dismiss the matter as you advise."

He asks whether Isabella is not her brother's heir; and Cathy, so sure of him that she is not afraid to bait him, and with something of his own cruelty, returns that she hopes not, indeed. Children of her own will be Edgar's heirs. . . .

". . . You are too prone to covet your neighbour's goods, remember this neighbour's goods are mine."

To which Heathcliff answers simply:

"If they were mine, they would be none the less that . . ."

Their one-ness sees no barriers of good or evil and certainly none of good taste. There is, in Heathcliff's words, something which touches while it shocks. He is as impervious to her caustic, provocative raillery as she to his brutality. They are still and always one; even while he is assessing her husband's fortune and she is brandishing her possible children, by that husband, in his face.

Heathcliff waylays Isabella in the courtyard and makes love to her. Cathy reproves him; but it is noteworthy that it is on the same grounds as before: he is not to play with the girl, but if he wants her, he shall have her. *"If you like Isabella, you shall marry her. But do you like her? . . ."*

It is now, and for the first time, that he turns bitterly on Cathy, tells her that she wronged him past forgiveness when she discarded him and that he is determined to be revenged—though not upon herself. Her blank amazement and shocked incredulity at this are completely in character: both exasperating and moving. It is a petulant child protesting: Cathy is without any moral code, and incapable of giving a thought to the effects of her own behaviour. But you perceive at the same time something of the same shattering dismay which bludgeoned Heathcliff when he first realised that she could marry anyone but himself and which drove him out into the darkness. He accuses her of pulling his house of dreams about his ears and offering him (in Isabella) a hovel in exchange; and you realise that in turning to rend her, he has done the same to Cathy.

Edgar, losing his patience, comes into the room and a violent scene takes place and Heathcliff is persuaded, by Nelly—the one person whom he continues to trust and to treat with moderate decency—to leave the house before the men-servants forcibly put him out.

This, following the shock of Heathcliff's rankling anger against herself, unhinges Cathy. She rages wildly and locks herself in her room for three days, at the end of which time she sends for Nelly, who brings her a meal and attempts to reason coolly and even casually with her, but who is horrified by her "ghastly countenance and strange, exaggerated manner."

The convention of a woman in brain fever, especially when she is expecting a child (as Cathy is), is common enough in early Victorian novelists. And the study of an unbalanced woman making wreckage of the life of everyone who cares about her occurs in sufficient modern novels. It is tedious and trifling in them, however skilled the handling. You com-miserate everyone concerned and marvel at their weak-minded patience: and have no difficulty in reminding yourself that it is all straws and cardboard.

One of the hall-marks of Emily's greatness is that even the elements in the book which could be a mistake are infused by her unique power. She makes use of a traditional melo-dramatic situation, and fires it to life as has not been done before or since. Cathy, at her worst, is never trivial and never worth-less. You do not wonder at the patience of the people about her. She is reckless, infuriating, but not only tragic: she is supremely appealing.

"*. . . I've been haunted, Nelly. But I begin to fancy you don't like me. How strange! I thought, though everybody hated and despised each other, they could not avoid loving me. And they have all turned to enemies in a few hours . . . the people here. Isabella terrified and repelled, afraid to enter the room, it would be so dreadful to see Catherine go. And Edgar standing solemnly by, to see it over; then offering prayers of thanks to God for restoring peace to his house, and going back to his books! What in the*

name of all that feels has he to do with books when I am dying?"
It is the same mad innocence as her loving. She loves them all—Nelly, Edgar, Isabella—while she makes their lives hell: and it is beyond her understanding that they could turn against her. But Heathcliff has turned against her. So, her entire world has become her enemy now.

Cathy's madness increases to frenzy; but even her ravings are piteous. It is Ophelia's wild plaintive voice which sounds in the room, as she pulls the feathers from a hole in her pillow and names them as she scatters them on the sheet, and is back on the moors with the birds wheeling overhead.

"Oh, if I were but in my own bed in the old house! And that wind sounding in the firs by the lattice. Do let me feel it—it comes straight down the moor—do let me have one breath!"

She leans from the opened window and though the night is darkness itself and at no time is Wuthering Heights within sight of the Grange, she sees its candle-lit windows: *"Joseph sits up late, doesn't he? . . ."* All the conflict that is rending her life apart is in Cathy's wild outpourings. She is back in her own room *"and there are two candles on the table making the black press shine like jet."* But there is no black press in her luxurious bedroom at the Grange, and so Nelly reminds her roundly.

". . . Nelly, I'll tell you what I thought, and what has kept recurring and recurring till I feared for my reason. . . ." She thought she was a child again; and as her memory cleared, all the unhappiness in the dream *"was swallowed in a paroxysm of despair. I cannot say why I felt so wildly wretched: it must have been temporary derangement; for there is scarcely cause . . ."* Cathy is bewildered, not when she is dreaming but when her mind grows lucid. Because—why should she be overwhelmed with despair, here in her own sheltered household, where her every whim is law and her husband lives to indulge and take care of her. And then from her breaking reason and her breaking heart there bursts the groping cry: *"But, supposing at twelve years old I had been wrenched from the Heights and every early association, and my all in all, as Heathcliff was at that time, and been converted at a stroke into Mrs. Linton, the lady of Thrush-cross Grange, and the wife of a stranger: an exile and outcast,*

thenceforth, from what had been my world—you may fancy a glimpse of the abyss where I grovelled. . . ."

It was Sir Thomas Browne who wrote "We call sleep a death; but it is the awakening that kills us and destroys those spirits which are the house of life."* For Cathy, the awakening is death. She has cast herself out into exile from the only world whose air she can breathe. Heathcliff is still, and for ever, her all in all. She has no place, no reality, as Mrs. Linton, the lady of the Grange. She is a ghost among ghosts there. And the patient, sorrowing husband is still a stranger.

It is to be supposed that the very word, psychology, was unknown to Emily. But she has left an unparalleled picture of a nature racked by such a conflict that the body is disintegrating under it. And Cathy is not a fragile creature. The harassed apothecary says irritably:

"Nelly Dean, what has there been to do at the Grange? A stout, hearty lass like Catherine does not fall ill for a trifle . . ."

It comes as something of a jar to hear this being of flame and witchery and dark gypsy loveliness described as a stout, hearty lass. But, as Nelly remarks, Mr. Kenneth is *"a plain, rough man"*; and before Cathy became a fine lady, she grew up in a home as primitive and comfortless as a medieval keep and spent most of her waking hours out on the moors.

In the middle of all the household turmoil over her illness, the news is brought that Isabella has eloped with Heathcliff. . . .

With spring, what is left of Cathy is just able to move from her bedroom to the parlour and the room next to it is turned into a bedroom since she has an invincible horror of the one upstairs. A desperate letter from Isabella sends Nelly plodding over the moor to Wuthering Heights; and Heathcliff compels her to carry a letter from him to Cathy and swears that he will see her. It is a spring evening, a Sunday evening, with bells ringing in the valley and the beck running free in music, when Nelly manages to lay the letter gently on Cathy's knee as she sits by the window. But she is past reading it; or even of taking in its urgent message. Only the reproduction of Emily's own words could convey the broken stillness, the lifeless gentleness, which lies on her, sitting there in her white gown and shawl

* *Religio Medici.*

with her hair, cut during her illness, combed back like a little girl's hair.

Heathcliff is keeping watch in the garden, as he has done by night for hours at a stretch during her illness: now he makes his way into the room. He drops to his knee and has her in his arms.

"Oh, Cathy! Oh, my life! how can I bear it?" Nelly hears at the end of the long embrace and the frantic kisses.

Cathy reproaches him bitterly, with a last flickering of ebbing vitality, and he answers with a still more violent and desperate bitterness. Till she breaks him, by a sudden unbearable return to her old, childish pleading; and Heathcliff is in tears more terrible than his upbraidings, and, in Nelly's words, *"they were locked in an embrace from which I thought my mistress would never be released alive. . . ."*

". . . Why did you betray your own heart, Cathy? . . . I have not broken your heart—you have broken it; and in breaking it, you have broken mine. . . . What kind of living will it be when you— oh God! would you like to live with your soul in the grave?"

" 'Let me alone, Let me alone,' sobbed Catherine. 'If I have done wrong, I'm dying for it. It is enough! I forgive you. Forgive me!'

" '. . . I forgive what you have done to me,' " he tells her, but how to forgive what she has done to herself? And ends with his despairing cry: " 'Kiss me again; and don't let me see your eyes! . . .' "

At midnight, Cathy's daughter is born: and Cathy dies. And Nelly goes out in the dew of daybreak to find Heathcliff still on guard under the trees.

" 'She's dead!' " he said. " 'I've not waited for you to learn that. . . .' "

So little remains to us of all that Emily wrote that none for whom her work has any value would willingly forgo any fragment of it. If the inequality of her verse is any guide, much of it probably had no other value than being Emily's. But you wade through the lengthy ballads and you ponder the odd wisps that are like blown leaves, not because they have any intrinsic worth; because you are still searching for Emily. I suppose that it will never be possible to assess exactly how much of the silence which has closed over one of the greatest writers in literature is due to Charlotte. How much, in her inflamed loyalty and scrupulousness and terror of misunderstanding, she destroyed. I cannot help feeling that Emily's two microscopic *"birthday papers"*, folded to the size of a sixpence and wedged into a tiny box, only escaped for posterity because Charlotte, knowing nothing about them, never thought to look for them.

But I never re-read *Wuthering Heights* without wishing that Emily had given Heathcliff his tremendous dying, on the heels of Cathy's departure from life. That she had let him—having torn the locket with Edgar's hair from her dead throat; and broken open her grave to look on her dead face; and rent one side of her coffin so that his body might eventually mingle with hers when he was buried—finish with life. Because the rest of the book is one long waiting for that final fulfilment. And something of the fire and the power have ebbed; and only rise again, rending the veil of the temple, in the time of his dying, and afterwards.

Isabella escapes from Heathcliff and lives in the south, where she bears his son. Heathcliff is master at Wuthering Heights, and Hareton Earnshaw is growing up there exactly as he did himself. But Hareton, for whom Nelly, once his nurse, retains a tenderness, is not wholly ruined by his diabolical upbringing. He is uncouth and primitive, but there is a deep-hidden core of gentleness in him, and he has an inexplicable feeling for Heathcliff which is the nearest to affection that the boy has ever known.

Young Catherine Linton is a golden child, loving and loved, with something of her mother's spirit and pride but nothing of Cathy's sorcery of charm nor cruelty. It is noted that both she and Hareton Earnshaw—who is her cousin—have Cathy's dark eyes, though Catherine has the Lintons' soft, gold hair. When Isabella dies her son, Linton, is brought to Thrushcross Grange. Linton is a puny, peevish boy, ailing and spoilt; but Catherine loves him. Heathcliff demands his son; and having terrorised him into a pitiable, broken creature, kidnaps Catherine and gets them married. This is his revenge on Edgar Linton, who is devoted to his young daughter, and is dying.

Thereafter, the story is heavy with sickness and violence. Heathcliff hates his son, and Catherine; and their lives are a savage torment until Linton, very soon after the marriage, dies. Heathcliff then summons Nelly Dean to Wuthering Heights and bids her establish herself there with his son's young widow and keep themselves out of his way. They settle down to a cloistered existence that is comparatively peaceful; and young Hareton Earnshaw is falling in love with Catherine. Something of Cathy's diablerie springs up in the girl, now; she treats him with hurtful contempt and makes unkind fun of his laborious efforts to read some of her books. Nelly scolds her; and Catherine's own innate sweetness—which has somehow survived her ghastly life since her marriage—comes into play like sunlight in that black house. She wins Hareton to friendliness, and helps him with his reading, and coaxes him to help her plant a little flower garden.

. . . The power is creeping back. Emily makes a live and lovable idyll out of this coming-together of the two hapless young things. There is a blessed lull in the storm of savagery and horror which has raged through the second part of the story.

Heathcliff is at first enraged as he sees Catherine and Hareton drawn to one another; then, in the middle of an access of rage, Nelly sees him stare down into the girl's face, and suddenly lay his hand over her eyes that are Cathy's eyes. . . .

There is a warm, firelit picture, seen through Nelly's honest vision, of the two reading together. And a rather remarkable revelation of the not wholly extinct good that is in Heathcliff and the warmth of heart and generosity in Hareton, when the young man tells Catherine firmly that he will hear no criticism of Heathcliff, even from her. ". . . *if he were the devil, it didn't signify: he would stand by him: and he'd rather she would abuse himself, as she used to, than begin on Mr. Heathcliff.*"

Nelly sits at her sewing, watching them in placid content, when Heathcliff enters unexpectedly.

"*Well, I reflected, there was never a pleasanter or more harmless sight; and it will be a burning shame to scold them. The red firelight glowed on their two bonny heads, and revealed their faces animated with the eager interest of children. . . .*"

Heathcliff does not "scold" them—a rather mild term for his usual violence of speech and hand. He motions to them to leave the room, and presently opens his tormented heart to Nelly. *"It is a poor conclusion, is it not?"* he asks her wearily and with a quietness that is almost unknown in him. He has spent most of his life in undermining and destroying the houses of Earnshaw and Linton; and now, when the last representatives of each are finding happiness and peace in one another, he does not even wish to raise his hand against them. . . . *"I have lost the faculty of enjoying their destruction . . ."* Hatred and bitterness, resentment and violence, are receding like a tide. Nothing is left but the intolerable longing to be one with Cathy which has haunted and ridden him for eighteen years since she died. The likeness of her daughter and her brother's son to herself tortures him. But it is the least of the torture.

". . . for what is not connected with her to me? and what does not recall her? I cannot look down to this floor but her features are shaped in the flags! In every cloud, in every tree—filling the air at night, and caught by glimpses in every object by day—I am surrounded with her image! The most ordinary faces of men and women—my own features—mock me with a resemblance."

He has spoken of a change that is approaching him. *"I'm its shadow at present. I take so little interest in my daily life that I can hardly remember to eat and drink."*

Nelly, out of her depth, enquires prosaically enough if he feels ill, and if he is afraid of death. He tells her his only dread is that he, with his iron constitution, may live still longer.

"And yet I cannot continue in this condition! I have to remind myself to breathe—almost to remind my heart to beat! . . . I have a single wish, and my whole being and faculties are yearning to attain it. They have yearned towards it so long, and so unwaveringly, that I'm convinced it will be reached—and soon—because it has devoured my existence. . . . Oh God! it is a long fight; I wish it were over!"

A few days later, a strange, unrecognisable state of happiness descends upon Heathcliff and takes possession of him. He is white, and his great frame is shaking, uncontrollable even by his invincible will, but he is happy.

They are all baffled by such an unprecedented condition. Nelly observes *". . . to see the master looking glad would not be an every-day spectacle."* He is unable to take food, which troubles Nelly, who spends the last hours of his life pursuing him with unwanted meals. . . .

And there comes the spring night, *"so still that not only the murmur of the beck down Gimmerton was distinguishable, but its ripples and its gurgling over the pebbles, or through the large stones which it could not cover."*

The beck is at its music; as it was on the last night of Cathy's life.

". . . I'm too happy; and yet I'm not happy enough. My soul's bliss kills my body, but does not satisfy itself. . . . By God! she's relentless. Oh, damn it! It's unutterably too much for flesh and blood to bear—even mine."

But she is near relenting now. She has haunted and beset him and kept him hungering for eighteen years, and her face has come between him and every other sight under heaven and the sense of her presence has touched him, sighed in his ear, and fled before him as he rushed to grasp it. But not any longer. He is dead, in the morning, under the swinging lattice where Cathy's little cold hands tapped and bled, with the rain beating on his face and one of his own hands resting on the sill to meet hers.

The superfluous Lockwood has a final glimpse of the two young people, rambling in moonlight and coming back to Nelly and the preparations for their wedding. And he stands by the three graves, and muses on the quiet of the sky and the heath and the harebells above those driven and tormented sleepers who now lie so still. But the ultimate word, the enduring word, comes from the shepherd-boy whom he encountered *"crying terribly"*:

"There's Heathcliff and a woman, under t'nab," he blubbered, *"un I darnut pass 'em"* . . .

II

THE PROFESSOR

I READ *The Professor* for the first time as a schoolgirl; and at the end I felt nothing but almost incredulous surprise that Charlotte could write "such a dull book" . . . I have read it many times since then; and, between one reading and another, learned her own deliberate reason for writing it. ". . . *I had got over any such taste as I might once have had for ornamented and redundant composition, and come to prefer what was plain and homely.*" (She referred to her unpublished writings: this is her first actual book.)

Yes—well: it is one thing to emerge from the flourishes and roulades of one's green attempts at writing, and quite another to be devoid of life. Later, Charlotte learned her lesson, and very painfully. It is the only "dull book" which she wrote. Elizabeth Gaskell, while admitting that *"the plot in itself is of no great interest,"* affirmed that Charlotte never did better work than in some of the characters, *"Nor in grace of womanhood, ever surpassed one of the female characters there described."*

She was a very loyal and deeply admiring friend to Charlotte; and she was writing this comment when *Jane Eyre* and *Villette* had made Charlotte famous and had also brought down on her head a certain amount of bludgeoning disapproval. The charming writer of *Cranford* was relieved that Charlotte could and did write one book which could shock none of her contemporaries. I doubt whether anyone today would agree with her.

That dreary and wooden young man, William Crimsworth, is cast off by his titled relatives because he will not come into line with their notions of a career proper to a member of the family who is penniless and under patronage. Tries business—or, as he terms it, "trade"—— under his elder brother, a Gestapo-figure who abuses and humiliates him. Goes to Brussels and turns teacher. Finds, teaches, and marries a little Swiss lace-mender,

Frances Henri. They set up a joint school; and prosper. Return to England and a modest country property.

It certainly would not matter in the least that this story was humdrum in itself. In essence, it is a sketch of the canvas which became *Villette* and the outline of *Villette* is no more arresting or remarkable. But *Villette* is crowded, pressed, with the interweaving dramas of personal lives and the marvellous interplay of human characters and temperaments. In spite of Mrs. Gaskell, the people in *The Professor*, except for one or two scenes, never come to life. William is prosy and sententious and condescending. When he finally asks Frances to marry him, he informs the reader complacently that it was never his way to be tiresomely demonstrative, and proceeds to give her an English lesson. He comes back to his lodgings and indulges immediately in a bout of what he calls "*hypochondria*" and which the puzzled reader diagnoses as some form of nervous dyspepsia. He is sunk in depression, has gloomy visions of death, and doesn't see Frances for a week. Charlotte lets loose a jet of allegory in this connection; and one can only retain patience by remembering that she is describing, in William, torments and miseries of her own experience.

But what a time to choose!

Frances herself is virtuous, oppressed, and enduring. She lives in poverty but also in dignity and fastidious neatness. There is one scene when the book very nearly comes to life; when William brings his cynical Radical friend, Yorke Hunsden, to meet Frances in her exquisitely tidy lodgings, and Hunsden, who had expected Mimi and the attics of *Bohème*, is surprised and impressed. He launches into a provocative argument against the conditions in England, his own native country, and Switzerland, and Frances, who had an English mother and a Swiss father, suddenly shows a fiery spirit and argues back. She quotes from Milton: "*and it was when the word 'hell' twanged from off her lips with a somewhat startling emphasis, that Hunsden deigned to bestow one slight glance of admiration. He had never before heard a lady say 'hell' with that uncompromising sort of accent and the sound pleased him from a lady's lips. . . .*"

Singular taste? But even Hell-said-the-duchess cannot do very much for the scene. It twitches with some action; it never fully stirs with life. Hunsden has his vigorous moments: it is amusing, if surprising, to hear him call William *"an essential sap . . ."* (just as it is amusing to read Emily's diary-note where she says of the Haworth school-project that it was *"no go . . ."*) But it takes more than some fluent diatribe and an occasional touch of slang to make a human being.

The Professor, though an immeasurably better book than Anne's *Agnes Grey*, must stand beside it on the shelf; a book which one would never read if anyone but Charlotte had written it. . . .

HAVING written her prim, dull book, Charlotte produced a book which for vibrant intensity of feeling had not yet been equalled in published English fiction. It need not be surmised that she made this perfectly acrobatic *volte face* because *The Professor* was refused by every publisher. Anne's *Agnes Grey* was primmer and duller and without any of the occasional spurtling of the embers which redeems *The Professor*, nor was it in any respect a good piece of work, which, in its limited way, Charlotte's is; but *Agnes Grey* had been accepted. It is nearer the truth to feel that Charlotte wrote *Jane Eyre* because she had learned, as far as she was ever to learn it, the lesson of her credo: do not gainsay the spirit; write as it moves you. Never mind whether the result is commercial failure or success. Never mind whom you shock or displease.

> "Biting *a truant pen,*
> Beating *myself for spite;*
> Fool! *said to me my soul,*
> Look in thy heart and write."

She learned in theory, by way of her first flat book. She was never equal to learning it entirely in practice. And even so, it was not the thought of rising or falling sales, nor even the wounding brickbats, which held her back, but her own imprisoned self which could not break wholly free.

It was an astounding woman who could follow Frances Henri by Jane. The first plain heroine in fiction. The first woman to be both passionate and invincibly respectable. When, a century later, a film was made of the book, the part of Jane was played by a notably pretty actress who skimmed about like a mouse with her great eyes swimming in tears . . . Jane, the spitfire, with her insignificant small body and the plain face which was Charlotte's challenge, her sandy hair and her green eyes. The story, as a story, shocked numbers of people while it became a best-seller overnight. But if daring and originality were its chief claim to fame, who would read it now? The book lives by the pulse which beats through it, universal, and burningly alive; not as a museum-piece.

Dickens himself has not surpassed and hardly equalled the study of a miserable and tormented child which opens the book. Jane's bewildered wretchedness in the Reed household, unable to understand why she can do nothing right, is, in its way, a subtler piece of drawing than the brutal bullying of the boy, John, or even the memorable nightmare of terror when she is locked into the Red Room. It is difficult to read that description even now without a shudder of compassion and indignation. It is akin to the account of Smike, pounded near to imbecility and almost to death (I admit to being unable even to re-read that part of *Nicholas Nickleby:* I skip it every time . . .)

The question of how far the terrible school of Lowood was, in fact and in detail, the school of Cowan Bridge may be left to rest, after all these years of vehement discussion. Charlotte was aware of her own vindictiveness when wronged and driven to desperation. Little Jane has the same taint; and when questioned by the just and kindly Miss Temple says of herself *"I infused into the narrative far less of gall and wormwood than ordinary."* Charlotte recognised her own use of gall and wormwood. This part of *Jane Eyre* brought a flurry of denial and support from various contemporary persons which makes the only comic element in the whole hideous and tragic affair. Pupils writing to say that the picture was only too true to life; pupils—one pious lady in particular squawking like a furious fowl—writing to deny it *in toto* and proclaiming the Rev. Carus Wilson little less than a saint and a lover of little children. . . . One pupil disgusted by an anecdote of how she vomited after having senna tea forced down her . . . vomit denied, and the senna tea was delicious bread-and-milk. . . .

The matter may well be left, now, with the pained and dignified words in which Charlotte's widower-husband gave it decent burial.

In spite of all indignant and squeamish protests, the picture remains, not in *Jane Eyre*, but in attested fact, of little Maria Brontë dying under physical torment and harassed by wordy cruelty. A child's figure, weak and sick from a blistered side, trying to stand on the icy floor of a dormitory and to drag on her clothes, having been pulled roughly out of bed by a furious teacher; and begging her weeping schoolfellows not to make a fuss as it would only mean more punishment for her.

It is enough!

In the back and forth of accusation and counter-accusation, there has been a tendency to overlook the superb writing which Charlotte put into Lowood. The crowding cold, indoors and out. The undermining, never-satisfied hunger. The moors in frozen winter under the *"mists chill as death"* and the trees *"ranks of skeletons"*; the moors in spring, breaking into green and lit with primroses; the bare garden-plots inside the grey stone walls of Lowood coming into flower, just in time to strew the graves of the children who were dying in the bleak dormitories *"while rooms and passages steamed with hospital smells"* and the smell of death. (Which was no less the smell of death because Charlotte had to call it *"the effluvia of mortality"*.) Your own hands and feet go numb as you read. There is a sick feeling at the pit of your stomach. You may shudder before the coarse horrors of Dotheboys Hall but you shake with cold and are sick with hunger at Lowood.

And the unfolding of the child Jane is a subtle piece of character-study. Lowood v. Cowan Bridge should not be allowed to submerge her. The hunted little creature who comes to school wild and terrified but driven so frantic that she is ready to bite and tear (figuratively, not literally). The longing for tenderness which breaks out in her cry to Helen: *". . . if others don't love me I would rather die than live—I cannot bear to be solitary and hated, Helen."* Her exultant surprise when she discovers that she really is a bright pupil and *"learned the first two tenses of the verb Etre, and sketched my first cottage (whose walls, by-the-by, outrivalled in slope those of the leaning tower of Pisa), on the same day."* And when she ponders the ambitious possibility, on the strength of the verb Etre, of being able some day to translate a little story-book which the French teacher has shown her.

So, as all the world knows, even those who have never read the book, Jane goes out into the world as a governess, and to

Thornfield Hall. *"When I got to Thornfield, I could not stop,"* said Charlotte. And the reader wishes that she had got to Thornfield sooner. Her dynamic joy in writing this part of the book may well be accounted for, in part, by the tediousness of Jane's apprenticeship.

"How long were you there?" Mr. Rochester asks her. *"Eight years." "Eight years! You must be tenacious of life. I thought half the time in such a place would have done up any constitution!"*

There was another and deeper reason for Charlotte's happiness when she *"got to Thornfield"* and the rapid flow of her writing. She was back in Angria. She had discarded scruples and self-discipline for the moment, the heavenly, satisfying, moment. It is not only that much of the drama—melodrama, even—in *Jane Eyre* has its original version in certain Angrian fragments, situations and even an occasional phrase. Charlotte was, for this time of writing, given over again to the spell of Zamorna, the dark-browed and overwhelming lover who dominated her mind, and the intriguing situation of passionately devoted women who loved him. But now she knew something of her own powers. She was experiencing the heady delight of bringing those maturing powers to bear on the daydream from which she was never to escape. Consider for a moment what this could mean. You have lived with daydreams always. As you began to grow up, you saw them as a snare, indeed, as a sin. A time comes—gradually or suddenly, who can tell?— when the realisation breaks upon you that your gift, which is from God, and your dreams, which you have come to believe are a temptation of Satan, are not divisible nor opposed: they are one and the same. Your dreams are the clay in your hands. You have only to work the clay and breathe life into it. Could there be a more transforming and exultant discovery? Don't fight them; ride into the heavens in that gorgeous pageant. Don't stop: you need not! . . . In fact, you cannot. . . .

The power was greater than the dream. Charlotte buried herself in a story that was an assemblage of certain treasured stories belonging to her younger years, and turned an inchoate mass of raw melodrama into a great book. Inevitably, she was least successful with her darkling hero. It is a little too easy to find Rochester comic. I was once present in a provincial

theatre at a play made from *Jane Eyre*. The casting, unlike that
of the picture, was very good, as far as Jane and Rochester were
concerned; Jane a spirited, nondescript little creature in a
mouse-coloured, Quakerish dress, Rochester subtle and without
bombast, and, incidentally, an actor who was well-known to, and
highly popular with, the audience. He could fill that large old
theatre all or any days of a week. But at the crucial moment of
his big love-scene, the audience, who were there because he was,
not because of the play, broke into helpless laughter which
drowned the words. They loved their favourite; but Rochester
was too much for them.

It is something less than justice. In Charlotte's hands
Rochester has moments of reality. They owe something to her
exquisite treatment of the setting for a scene. The winter
evening on the moor at moonrise with the blue smoke of the
village chimneys wavering into the air and the silence filled with
the sound of running water from the hidden becks. The sound
of the becks haunted Emily and Charlotte. And out of the
silence Rochester comes riding, the big dog, Pilot, bounding
ahead. The horse slips on the frozen ground and throws him;
Jane comes from her seat on the stile to offer her help, in her
*"black merino cloak, a black beaver bonnet; neither of them half fine
enough for a lady's maid."* So they encounter one another for the
first time. Rochester, curt and imperative and yet courteous,
speaking with directness, and Jane answering with simplicity and
also with her own imperturbable stubbornness:

*"I cannot think of leaving you, sir, at so late an hour, in this
solitary lane, till I see you are fit to mount your horse."*

Jane worsted by his horse, which won't let her catch it by the
bridle. Rochester laughing, and compelled, apologetically, to
limp to his mount, clutching Jane heavily by her small shoulder.

The orchard in the summer night with its branches bending
with apples and its tangle of sweet-smelling flowers and its
fruit-bushes; and Jane trying to slip away unseen.

*"A great moth goes humming by me: . . . he bends to examine
it . . . As I crossed his shadow, thrown long over the garden by the
moon, not yet risen high, he said quietly without turning:*

" 'Jane, come and look at this fellow.' "

He is as aware of her flitting presence as **she of** his visible figure. And so, from the casual, intimate words to the cat-and-mouse scene (taken direct from Zamorna and his patient Mina Laury, this——) where Rochester pretends that he is dismissing her before he marries Blanche Ingram, and wrings from her, through her vehement sobbing and the sound of the nightingale (*"Jane, do you hear the nightingale? Listen!"*) the core of her tortured heart; her love and her shining, unabashed pride in the admission of it.

The deserted manor-house, Ferndean, sunk in its woods, where Jane finds him, blinded and maimed, after the fire has wrecked Thornfield. So buried in a dark green twilight that she loses her way even within the park gates, *"still as a church on a week-day"* except for the cascade of the *"small, penetrating rain"* through the dense leaves. There is nothing high-flown nor exaggerated in the picture, yet it reads like an account of a buried city of Ang-Kor. Here it is that Jane watches him come out on to the single step, and lift his hand to feel whether it is still raining and try to grope his way across the grass.

But what gives the figure of Rochester life is Charlotte's extraordinary gift for vivid conversation. In *Jane Eyre* her people speak for themselves more fluently and more copiously than in any other book which she wrote. There is too much close-packed narrative both in *Shirley* and in *Villette*; in *Jane Eyre* there is page after page of natural talking.

She could well have called both her later books by other titles than the ones which she chose, but *Jane Eyre* is inevitably named. The book is Jane from first to last. It takes something more than even a powerful talent to create a live being from nothing; to work without a lay-figure of any kind. This Charlotte attempts in Rochester. But in Jane, she had herself for a foundation . . . Jane, quietly and comfortably established at Thornfield with her small pupil, Adèle, and the pleasant old housekeeper, Mrs. Fairfax, who is a distant relative of Rochester's; restless and disturbed by daydreams and straining towards *"the busy world, towns, regions full of life I had heard of but never seen."* Pacing the corridor of the attic floor *"backwards and forwards, safe in the silence and solitude . . . and best of all, to open my inward ear to a tale that was never ended—a tale my imagination created, and narrated continuously; quickened with*

*all of incident, life, fire, feeling, that I desired and had not in my
actual existence.*" And there follows a manifesto on behalf of
women in their limited lives, the manifesto which rose to a
pæan in Caroline's reflections in *Shirley*.

In that first meeting with Rochester, alone on the moors in
the dusk, Jane says "*I had no fear of him, and but little shyness.
Had he been a handsome, heroic-looking young gentleman, I should
not have dared to stand thus questioning him against his will and
offering my services unasked. I had hardly ever seen a handsome
youth; never in my life spoken to one. I had a theoretical reverence
and homage for beauty, elegance, gallantry, fascination; but had I
met those qualities incarnate in masculine shape, I should have
known instinctively that they neither had nor could have sympathy
with anything in me, and should have shunned them as one would
fire, lightning, or anything else that is bright but antipathetic.*"

Rochester was almost ugly and his manner was abrupt, and
he is more often frowning than not. So Jane doesn't fear him—
which most young women of Jane's period would have done.
She doesn't fear him because she need not steel herself against
the weakness of losing her heart to him. . . . In *Villette*, Lucy
loses hers, first, to gay, handsome John Bretton while knowing
that it is contrary to nature that he should care for such a one as
herself. In life, Charlotte had to arm herself against the genial
charm of George Smith, her publisher, younger than she was,
but certainly sufficiently in love with her to make his mamma
uneasy. She shrank from attractiveness in a man because of her
besetting consciousness or belief that she had none. The day of
the *jolie laide* had not yet dawned—in England, at least. The
fact of five known suitors in her fantastically cloistered existence
was never sufficient to convince her that, however plain, she
possessed a charm of her own. By way of a dry jest from Fate,
the man whom she eventually married was remarkably good-
looking . . . but his cloth, apparently, rendered that fact
antiseptic. And in any case, his best friend and well-wisher
could not attribute any dangerous charms to that ultra-
orthodox, unyielding clergyman, Arthur Bell Nicholls.

But there it is: much too important to be unstressed. Jane
comes to love Edward Rochester with all her passionate heart
and upright soul, because nothing warns her that such a state of

things could happen to her. She is only afraid of mythical men who look something between a masculine fashion-plate and the Duke of Zamorna. Lucy braces herself taut against the lovable child of fortune, John Bretton, only to succumb to the brilliant, irascible gnome that is Paul Emanuel. Charlotte breaks her heart and her life on the stolid rock, Constantin Héger, erudite and most able teacher, encrusted domestic barnacle. There was no green light for danger, for either Lucy or Charlotte. The primeval simplicity of their emotional values was an unconscionable time a-dying; it lasted well into the twentieth century, when female film-addicts had a pathological cult for the smooth charm of such an actor as Rudolph Valentino. Not the least of the shattering audacity of *Jane Eyre* lies in the fact that it had an ugly and ungallant hero. To match a plain-faced heroine, who neither faded nor declined but pealed her innocent passion from the housetops. That Jane all but brings herself to death, when she runs from Thornfield and a mock marriage on discovering that Rochester's wife is alive and a madwoman, did nothing to condone her immodesty. She admits her passion, in one of the simplest and the greatest love-themes to be found in the English language; and that, more than anything else in the book, drew the comment from one reveiwer that if the writer were a woman, under the hermaphroditish pen-name of Currer Bell, she must be an abandoned female. . . .

The story unfolds, like the huge panels of a tapestry, where the spectator is perpetually astonished, dumbfounded, by the life-likeness of the scenes, and the exquisite workmanship of the minutest details. Jane, with her fire, her rectitude, her restrained composure, is indispensable to Rochester before she discovers that he is her life and her world. She is governess to the little girl who is his ward, and who, he tells Jane, is his illegitimate daughter. He recognises in Jane, from the first time of meeting, a creature utterly out of the common, bound by no conventions, only by the code of her own valour and integrity. Their companionship is exhilarating for her, healing and regenerating for him. "*My thin crescent-destiny seemed to enlarge; the blanks of existence were filled up; my bodily health improved; I gathered flesh and strength,*" she says.

What Charlotte drew was not only the picture of a love-affair:
it was the most finely-wrought conception imaginable of "the
marriage of true minds." Who had been concerned with that
in prose and poetry since Shakespeare wrote his sonnet? . . .
It was Charlotte's obsessing dream and unfulfilled quest. She
was accustomed to see marriage considered as a woman's need
for a provider and a man's for a bedfellow. Now she depicted
an enthralling mental communion mingled with a passionate
physical love. Jane brings an impish humour to play on
Rochester's surging emotions. His ever-riding, imperious
friendliness delights her, because he meets her on an equal
footing, equally without exaggerated courtesy or condescension.
She loves his rugged physical traits but she has no delusions
about them, and she tells him so.

No love-scene in the book goes deeper to the root of the
matter than one which is no love-scene at all: Jane, who has been
at Gateshead to see her dying aunt and to learn the secret of
being her uncle's defrauded heiress, is walking up to Thornfield
from the coach-stop when she sees Rochester sitting on the
stile. He scolds and teases her humorously and Jane remains
outwardly impassive and annoyingly sedate until

". . . he smiled at me with a certain smile he had of his own,
and which he used but on rare occasions. He seemed to think it too
good for common purposes: it was the real sunshine of feeling—he
shed it over me now;

" 'Pass, Janet,' said he, making room for me to cross the stile:
'go up home . . .'

". . . something in me said for me, and in spite of me:—

" 'Thank you, Mr. Rochester, for your great kindness . . . and
wherever you are is my home—my only home.' "

The happy state of things is broken up by the house-party
which has borne down upon Thornfield, and the centre of it is,
of course, the fabulous Blanche Ingram who is scheming to
marry Rochester and to whom he pays an elaborate, artificial
court. Blanche Ingram and the social scene in the crimson and
gilt drawing-room have been held up to ridicule often enough;
there is no need to labour the point here. When Charlotte is
being vindictive she invariably sinks to exaggerated cartoon-
level, and here her ladies and gentlemen are grotesque. She had

no knowledge of drawing-rooms. Blanche with her jet ringlets and amber scarf, addressing her mother as *"Baroness Ingram of Ingram Hall——"* and telling Rochester's footman to *"Cease that chatter, blockhead! and do my bidding"*, is too frightful to be amusing. But I have always enjoyed Jane's dry comment on the rococo charade of Rebecca at the well, where Blanche appears to gorgeous advantage: *". . . the camels only were wanting"*. . . .

But if Blanche's flourishings and flauntings are nonsense, Jane's anguish of jealousy is real. And it is Blanche's antics and Rochester's tormenting teasing which bring from Jane her most memorable outburst:

"Do you think, because I am poor, obscure, plain, and little, I am soulless and heartless? You think wrong!—I have as much soul as you—and full as much heart! And if God had gifted me with some beauty, and much wealth, I should have made it as hard for you to leave me, as it is now for me to leave you . . . it is my spirit that addresses your spirit; just as if both had passed through the grave, and we stood at God's feet, equal—as we are!"

The book takes a turn into melodrama with Jane's wedding interrupted at the altar-rail by the revelation that Rochester's mad wife is alive and under guard in the attic regions of Thornfield, and by the sight of her, grovelling and growling; and by Rochester's long recital of how he was deluded and trapped into the marriage. It is still melodrama throughout the struggle of wills and of words between Jane and himself. I think—though admittedly this is no more than a personal opinion—that it only moves into its powerful and gripping reality again when Jane slips away from Thornfield in the daybreak carrying her shoes and silencing the door-lock with a feather dipped in oil. . . . She wanders and starves and is rebuffed and humiliated for three days and nights, and finally drops on the step of Moor House, and is taken in by St. John Rivers, the clergyman, and his sisters Diana and Mary.

Now the book takes on a new power. It is, in some respects, more subtle than the earlier part, in that Charlotte creates a subtler conflict here. St. John Rivers appears at first encounter too rigid a classical statue, and certainly Charlotte's sense of humour is rather out of sight in her first presentation of him.

It is not the happiest introduction to a man that he should stand
at the foot of the bed where you are lying apparently in a state
of coma and remark:

"She looks sensible, but not at all handsome."

*"Ill or well, she would always be plain. The grace and harmony
of beauty are quite wanting in those features. . . ."*

But this is only Charlotte the woman intruding and elbowing
Jane out of the way. She has created a young man as beautiful
as he is fanatically good: so she must stress the point that he
found Jane wholly unattractive.

St. John at first does seem repellent. He seems, in fact, a
stick—however handsome a stick. Jane's chance remark *"I am
not ambitious,"* touches a spring.

*"He started at the word 'ambitious'. He repeated 'No. What
made you think of ambition? Who is ambitious? I know I am: but
how did you find it out?' "* And a little later, he opens his mind to
her. Tells her that he has all but died of misery because his life
as a minister of the church is so narrow. That he felt within
himself talents, powers, desires, which were killing him with
their pent-up forces. And that he has found peace in choosing
the career of a pioneer missionary in the East.

While they are still standing at the gate of Jane's cottage
—he has given her the tiny village school in charge—there
appears like a vision the lovely girl, Rosamund Oliver, who
is in love with him; and Jane is the silent witness of her
engaging and artless entreaty that he will come home with
her to dinner at the Hall, where her father will be glad to
see him. And of St. John's face, unmasked and working with
emotion and suffering. *". . . he looked nearly as beautiful
for a man as she for a woman,"* Jane says. He refuses, politely
but relentless, and goes his way. And Jane remembers his
sister's words: *"You would think him gentle, yet in some things he
is inexorable as death."*

There is an unfortunate amount of stilted phraseology
in Charlotte's handling of St. John. She seems to fall into
a form of words which she assumes to be in key with his
lofty temperament—and both are occasionally highly exasperating to the reader. But the language cannot detract
from this study of a man in an anguish of self-denial and self-

frustration. St. John's pain is as real as Rochester's, buried alive and forcing a way, shattering the stone that he has laid upon it.

There is almost always a quality of bludgeoning simplicity and directness in the emotions which Charlotte portrays. In the feeling of Jane for St. John Rivers she uses a finer touch than anywhere else. Jane, discovered by St. John to be the missing heiress to her West Indian uncle's fortune, and cousin to himself and his two very human and lovable sisters, is now on an intimate family footing in the household. And in Plain Jane he sees the helpmeet for a pioneer missionary which Fair Rosamund could never be. He tries to persuade —or more truly, to bully—Jane into marrying him. And her vehement, repeated refusals are based, not only on the knowledge that he has no atom of love for her; but on the dread, the realisation, that she herself could come to care for him. . . . She has cut herself off for ever from Rochester, as she believes. She is terribly, dangerously drawn to this man with his façade of steel mail and his banked-down inner fires. She sees herself living in the hell of the undesired woman who could, just conceivably, give an unwanted love and break her heart upon a stone. Heartbreak twice over for Jane.

She is saved, just in time, by the spirit-call of Rochester's voice speaking her name. She breaks away and goes to him, finding him, freed at last from his maniac-wife, blind, and utterly dependent upon her love. And so to *Reader, I married him.*

But I must always feel that in the St. John-Jane theme Charlotte threw away a superb story. She had to discard from strength, of course; Jane and Rochester must have their Happy Ending. The truth is, her teeming creative brain had too much material to hand. The whole part of the book which belongs to the Rivers family is swamped by Rochester, and Moor House is lost in the sinister shadow of Thornfield. But it is far too good to be merely an episode.

And I think that Charlotte knew it. *Jane Eyre* ends with a last message from St. John, who is dying at his eastern post and realises it. It is a slightly embarrassing resolving chord, because Charlotte gives way to one of her pious outbreaks of Biblical quotation. But it is still St. John who has the last word.

III

SHIRLEY

"I took great pains with 'Shirley'," Charlotte wrote. It is possible that she took too great pains, and in doing so, sinned against something which was her fundamental belief as a writer. She wrote to George Lewes, after *Jane Eyre*, that she was half-resolved to write a quieter and more finished book, but only half-resolved.

"When authors write best, or at least when they write most fluently, an influence seems to waken in them, which becomes their master. . . . And should we try to counteract this influence? Can we indeed counteract it?"

She questioned whether it were *"right or advisable"* to write as Emily had written in *Wuthering Heights:* but went on to assert that a writer is possessed by his or her gift, driven by the impulse, and cannot gainsay it.

She never wrote such an unequal book as *Shirley*. And it is doubtful whether anyone else has. It contains the most incongruous elements. The maddening flaws stand out all the more violently because, whenever the mastering influence struggles to the surface, battling for breath, and takes Charlotte in hand, her people spring to life, as always, unforgettable. But it is fairly dumbfounding, the way in which they are alive on one page, and on the next are made to mouth perorations which you know that they could never have uttered—sometimes it is not even a matter of the next page, it is the next sentence.

There is an appalling amount of stilted artificiality in *Shirley*. And when live simplicity takes its place, you realise that Charlotte is creating in fits and starts, and that the rest is mechanical, without life, the creative fire has died down. It never gutters out, we may be thankful for so much; it spurts into flame again and again, from first to last. But the mingling of fire and cinders is bewildering.

It is remembered and sometimes offered in excuse that when

Charlotte was about two-thirds through *Shirley*, Branwell died, Emily died, and Anne died. And that, by her own admission, the figure of Shirley was a fanciful portrait of Emily. That she wrote the remainder wrenched and shattered from loss.

The very fact that she was absorbed in such a piece of work made it a task almost intolerable to continue. There was Shirley, the picture of health and vitality, rich, independent, free, mistress of herself, her fortune, and her estate. And while Charlotte laboured on, behind Shirley in her gown of purple satin, her gold ornaments, her rose-trimmed bonnet (it's a formidable picture, as drawn by poor Charlotte!) rose the sights which haunted her day and night. Emily gasping her life away, Emily's body, wasted to skin and bone, under the church floor. But actually, the chapters (XXIV and XXV) which Charlotte wrote as soon as she could write anything after Emily's death contain traces of harrowing simplicity, the voice of Charlotte's stricken heart. The artificialities and rolling periods can hardly be laid to the account of tragedy in Charlotte's life. Such elements are not, as a rule, the outcome of personal tragedy.

She wrote the whole book under stress, and part of it under anguish. But it was never Charlotte's lot to write any book in tranquillity, fenced round with care and consideration. Certain parts of the book show signs of having been written when the spirit flagged so wearily and hopelessly that Charlotte simply couldn't be bothered. But those are its weaker, not its worst patches.

She planned the book on something of an heroic scale, with a background of the Napoleonic Wars and the industrial riots and the Orders in Council which checkmated the Yorkshire wool trade. They are vigorous, stirring scenes; the figures of Joe Scott, the foreman, and William Farren, spokesman for the weavers thrown out of work, are thoroughly alive, and their homely, energetic speech is never out of key. When it comes to the war, and to Napoleon and to Wellington, Angria takes hold again, bursting suddenly and rather overwhelmingly into the homely and realistic scene. Wellington, after all, had been Charlotte's very first hero. Her publishers understood that, when they sent her a copy of his portrait with her own portrait by Richmond; and very old Tabby peered at it and pronounced it a bad likeness of Papa. Robert Moore and the hard-headed old rector, Helstone, indulge in a wordy battle, each declaiming through two solid pages of ardent rhetoric on behalf of their opposing heroes:

". . . this wooden-faced and pebble-hearted idol of England . . . the most humdrum of commonplace martinets . . ." fulminates Robert, who is half-Belgian and a French patriot in exile.

The rector retorts with "besotted Imperial France" as being no worse than "bloody republican France," and launches into a choleric sermon where the English troops are compared to the Israelites "standing dryshod on the Asiatic side of the Red Sea" and the French to "a set of pampered Ethiops about as strong and brutal as the lions of Libya." When the book comes to its end in a carillon of peace-bells and wedding-bells, Angria fairly stalks across the scene.

. . ."We are now in the heart of summer—in mid-June—the June of 1812. . . . The nineteenth century wantons in its giant adolescence: the Titan-boy uproots mountains in his game, and hurls rocks in his wild sport. . . ."

The slightly stunned reader surmises that the Titan-boy must be the Little Corporal? But the following paragraphs relegate him to allegory; he is, in fact, the young nineteenth century. . . .

"This summer, Bonaparte is in the saddle: he and his host scour Russian deserts. . . . He marches on old Moscow: under old Moscow's walls the rude Cossack awaits him."

He, the "Barbarian stoic!", is not deterred by the rude Cossack, however. ". . . his allies are the elements—Air, Fire, Water."

An instant later, Charlotte is into a welter of religious fervour, when the allies so described turn into avenging arch-angels, "stationed before the throne of Jehovah . . . clothed in white, girdled with golden girdles; they uplift vials brimming with the wrath of God . . ."

Whenever she is carried away by these tides, Charlotte pours out Biblical quotations. Her extraordinary memory was crammed with such books of the Bible as even the devout believer seldom pores over. Her excerpts from the minor prophets are so unfamiliar that only the quotation marks distinguish them from her own imagery.

"In this year, Lord Wellington resumed the reins in Spain: they made him Generalissimo for their own salvation's sake. In this year——" (there follows a roll of the Peninsular victories).

Then Charlotte lets herself go on the subject of Wellington.

"Lord Wellington is, for you, only a decayed old gentleman now: I rather think some of you have called him a 'dotard' . . . Scoff at your ease—your scorn can never break his grand old heart."

This is Angria with a vengeance. (Or Verdopolis, the world which preceded Angria, if you prefer; it does not matter essentially: it is the same encircling and enduring fantasy.) This is the atmosphere of Lord Charles Florian Wellesley, Marquis of Douro, etc.

So often, Charlotte's deepest feelings are voiced in arresting simplicity and almost perfection of words, in a letter: and in deplorable verbosity in a book. Compare these declamations with a letter to Miss Wooler, of March 1848:

"I have now outlived youth; and . . . certainly many things are not what they were ten years ago: and, amongst the rest, 'the pomp and circumstance of war' have quite lost in my eyes their fictitious glitter. I have still no doubt that the shock of moral earthquakes wakens a vivid sense of life, both in nations and individuals; that the fear of dangers on a broad national scale, diverts men's minds momentarily from brooding over small private perils, and for the time gives them something like largeness of views; but, as little doubt have I, that convulsive revolutions put back the world in all that is good, check civilisation, bring the dregs of society to its surface; in short, it appears to me that insurrections and battles are the acute diseases of nations, and that their tendency is to exhaust, by their evidence, the vital energies of the countries where they occur."

This could hardly be bettered. It is timeless and boundless.

Again, about six years later, she writes to a friend:

"I say nothing about the war; but when I read of its horrors I cannot help thinking that it is one of the greatest curses that ever fell upon mankind . . . it really seems to me that no glory to be gained can compensate for the sufferings which must be endured. This may seem a little ignoble and unpatriotic; but I think that as we advance towards middle age, nobleness and patriotism have a different signification to us to that which we accept while young."

It is evident from *Shirley*, as will be shown, that Charlotte

was impressed and troubled by the horrors of poverty and
unemployment. And once again, in a letter to Mr. Williams,
always the most understanding of her correspondents when her
mind, not her emotions, was in play, she shows a length and a
breadth of sight which is startling as you read the words. In
Shirley, her compassion, her uneasiness, and her disapproval of
harshness in the employer, is transparent. To Mr. Williams
she goes further than, it may well be, she dared let herself go in a
book. He had described to her a *"model man of business"*, the
typical go-getter, whose ruthlessness they both deplored:

*". . . the marked tendency, I fear, of the day produces, no doubt,
cruel suffering. Yet, when the evil of competition passes a certain
limit, must it not in time work its own cure? I suppose it will, but
then through some convulsed crisis, shattering all around it like an
earthquake."*

Among the uncompromising people of their Yorkshire home
the three sisters were remembered with tenderness for their unvarying kindness and courtesy, not only of manners but of
heart, to all those who, in the language and thought of their
day, would be named their "inferiors". And in the books of
Charlotte and of Anne, the blackest characters are always drawn
as being rude or inconsiderate to them. Drawn, it must be
admitted, with the vehemence of a moral cartoon. But
Charlotte knew that courtesy and charity, however copious and
freely bestowed, were not enough. She even ventured to hint
her uneasy belief that there should be no place for charity in a
justly-ordered scheme of life. To Mr. Williams she went
further still. To us, living in the necessary and essential earthquake, her words ring with a remarkable sound, coming from a
sequestered woman of almost a century ago.

Charlotte never wrote a book without paying off an old
score. Lesser writers do it, but escape notice. And there is this
to be said for the practice; it is cathartic. It was well put in
"Stalky", where the harried Beetle says of a malicious master,
what does it matter if King scrags him, he can always do a
poem about him, can't he? . . .

But it is to be deplored when a writer sacrifices some integral
goodness of work to this prickling and melting of the wax
figure. And this Charlotte did in *Shirley* when she wasted an

opening chapter on caricatures of The Curates. She was definitely allergic to curates. She flagellates them all through the book, and with such exaggeration that the portraiture is not amusing, merely tedious and wholly unconvincing. She was heavy-handed in her treatment of them and only once does her wit break through; when she says of the curate, Donne:

"*The outside of the cup and platter he burnished up with best polishing powder; the furniture of the altar and temple he looked after with the zeal of an upholsterer—the care of a cabinet-maker.*"

As Charlotte wrote of the mill-riots, her attitude to the men concerned is strong and clear:

"*As to the sufferers, whose sole inheritance was labour, and who had lost that inheritance—who could not get work and consequently could not get wages, and consequently could not get bread—they were left to suffer on; perhaps inevitably left; it would not do to stop the progress of invention . . . the war could not be terminated, efficient relief could not be raised: there was no help then; so the unemployed underwent their destiny—ate the bread and drank the waters of affliction.*"

There is a penetrating, controlled bitterness here; and at the end, a sigh of hopelessness. And there are no flourishes. There never are when Charlotte is writing from her heart. There is a terrible amount of flourish throughout *Shirley*; and there are fanfares and declamations to beat the band. Those two fatal weaknesses of Charlotte, so deeply enjoyed, Allegory and Rhetoric, are given their heads. There is a constant addressing or adjuring of the reader.

"*I am aware, reader, and you need not remind me. . . . It seems to me, reader . . . Yes, reader, we must settle accounts now. . . . I think I now see the judicious reader putting on his spectacles to look for the moral.*"

The last sentence comes in the paragraph which closes the book and is an echo from Thackeray, whom Charlotte so profoundly admired.

If the book is so packed with faults, and all of them faults which date it, and which are particularly annoying to modern readers, what makes it timelessly readable, memorable and anything but a museum-piece?   The answer lies surely in

Charlotte's immense power of making her people real. So real that, when she stumbles, and turns one of them into a mouthpiece for a stream of her cherished rhetoric, you want to twitch her sleeve and urge "He—or she—would never have said that. You know they wouldn't!"

She had, too, and to a supreme degree, the novelist's gift of caring intensely about the people whom she created, and of making the much-adjured reader care. She loved some and disliked others; you can always tell what Charlotte felt about any of her people. She was incapable of feeling indifferent towards any of them.

And finally, for anyone to whom Charlotte herself means more than any character of her creation—and they are legion— *Shirley* has the fascination of tracing Charlotte as she intrudes into its pages, slips, glides into them, making havoc—or even hay—of some page as she does it.

It is rather too long before Shirley herself, the central figure, comes on the scene. We meet nearly everyone else in the book before she appears at all. When the curates have been thrashed and disposed of, the book gets under way with Hollow's Mill, a night-attack on the new machinery which is to throw so many of Robert Moore's men out of work, Robert Moore himself, and Hollow's Cottage, his bachelor home with his trying spinster sister, Hortense. Hollow's Cottage is a picture of scrupulous, over-scrupulous, neatness and cleanliness—and comfort.

"Two doors covered with crimson baize, a strip of crimson carpet down the steps (stairs), contrasted with light-coloured walls and white floor made the little interior look clean and fresh."

You hear Elizabeth Gaskell's description of the parsonage as she first saw it:

". . . It is a cold country and the fires were a pretty warm dancing light all over the house. The parlour had been evidently refurnished within the last few years, since Miss Brontë's success has enabled her to have a little more money to spend. The prevailing colour of the room is crimson, to make a warm setting for the cold grey landscape without."

Shirley is set in the pleasant Calder Valley, not among the moors which Elizabeth Gaskell conveys in one sentence: *"up above the whole world, and the very realms of silence."* It is full of green fields, and the scent of hawthorn blows across its pages, time and again. But Charlotte gave to Hollow's Cottage her own ideal of cosiness. . . .

Robert Gérard Moore, the half-Belgian exile, the mill-owner, really is, in Mr. Bumble's words to Oliver, "an orphan that nobody can't love. . . ." He is a most unlikeable man! May Sinclair summed him up as "that unspeakable man of business", which is strong but not much too strong. Except that he is very good-looking, and that Charlotte, who made him, Caroline, who loved him, and his waspish sister, Hortense, who more or less exists for him, unite in assuring us that he is gentle, considerate, and charming in his home—"*nowhere so perfect a gentleman as at his own fireside*"—— there appears to be no reason why Caroline should spend her heart upon him. He may be a lamb on the hearth but he is certainly a tiger in the counting-house. Obsessed—he admits it—by the idea of making a fortune, and adamant to the wretched, starving men who would prevent him. In fairness, it must be added that he is labouring under the burden of his dead father's bankruptcy, due to the war; and that, however harsh to his workpeople, he is incapable of revenge, refusing to bring to justice the crazed fanatic who half murders him and paying for his funeral when he comes to what we may be allowed to call a sticky end without benefit of rope. In one of her apostrophes to The Reader, Charlotte "*is happy to inform him that neither Mr. Moore nor his overlooker ever struck a child in their mill.*"

Which, The Reader may concede, is something.

But you never feel that Charlotte likes him, any more than you do. She expends a weighty amount of devil's advocacy on him, but that is all. He is, of course, one of her Masterful Men and, with the exception of William Crimsworth (*The Professor*), the least pleasant. . . . And Professor Crimsworth hardly counts, since he never comes to life at all.

Hortense is one of Charlotte's heavy-handed caricatures. Her place is obviously in the Pension Héger.

" '. . . *apathy is what I cannot tolerate in those who have the benefit of my instructions; besides, one should not be apathetic in studying standard works.*' "

". . . '*I will give her a system, a method of thought, a set of* opinions: *I will give her the perfect control and guidance of her feelings.*' "

" '*Be sure you do, Hortense,*' " says Robert ironically; " '*here she comes.*' "

And here comes Caroline: the young cousin who is the rector's niece and ward.

It is sometimes said that Charlotte used her beloved Ellen as a lay figure for Caroline, and it is probably as near truth as any such allegation can be. There is more of drawing from the model in *Shirley* than in any other book which she wrote. It is a standard example of that perennial question, How Did the Picture-Man Know? A question which no reader, and, I think, no writer, can ever answer completely. She drew Caroline with great tenderness, and with delight in every touch. But there is an incalculable difference between Ellen as we know her and Caroline as Charlotte made her. Ellen was very pretty, pious, flirtatious in a mild and beguiling fashion, very loving. A *simple Yorkshire girl*, remember? That rather odious phrase of Charlotte's is forgivable only because it was an unconscious cry of her desperate need of a mind which could be a companion to her own and which, except for rare intervals, she never found. Not even in Emily, since Emily's mind ignored the avid reading and the exhilarating discussions which were the bread of life to Charlotte's. Ellen, it is safe to assume, was not gifted with imagination. She was one of the "tender and untortured souls." In a placid, charming way, she was robust.

Caroline is very pretty, too. Charlotte dwells on her prettiness fondly; her lovely face and graceful figure, her quantities of brown curls, her sedate, becoming clothes, always very simple but with an elegance of simplicity. Charlotte took a deep, fastidious pleasure in clothes. It scintillates from her letters, time after time, it is borne out by descriptions from anyone who knew her. *Dainty as to the fit of her boots and gloves,* said Elizabeth Gaskell. And there is that letter to Ellen explaining that she prefers dark or grey fur (tippet and cuffs) to brown or yellow. And her letter to Elizabeth Gaskell regretting that she had not that handsome friend's help when shopping in Leeds, and the wistful little episode where she chose a black satin in place of an extravagant pale or light silk, and wished that she hadn't.

And she took pleasure in pretty people. Morbid and weighed down by her own plainness, she had the wide generosity of a plain woman who receives other women's beauty as a gift.

You can see Charlotte's hovering smile of absorbed enjoyment while she was writing the long, very detailed description which ushers in Caroline.

It has been rather too easy to see Caroline Helstone merely as a lovelorn maiden who pines to the point of death for love of her hard-headed cousin, submits meekly to humiliating treatment from him, and, still meekly, accepts him in the end. There could not be a more distorted picture of her. She has great courage, and dignity, and even in her unhappy love she is no daguerreotype, she is alive and appealing. It is a most universal study which Charlotte makes of Caroline as a girl in love. It is not ephemeral; nor febrile; nor boring; which is more than can be said for the same subject in innumerable lesser hands. And when Caroline is on the scene, whether with Robert or with Shirley, Charlotte wrote some of the most natural, most fluent, least stilted conversation to be found in any of her books. Even Caroline suffers now and again from the germ of rhetoric which breaks out through the book in a perfect rash. There is a really lovely miniature of the cottage parlour in firelight and lamplight, with "*its best—its evening charm*", and Caroline, wearing that evening charm as attractively as the knot of pink ribbon at the collar of her brown merino dress, demands that he shall read some Shakespeare aloud.

"*And you are not going to be French, sceptical, and sneering? You are not going to think it a sign of wisdom to refuse to admire?*" she adjures him warningly. (How many of us have suffered from that aggravating habit on the part of a superior being. Robert, you see, is one of your carping highbrows, in spite of Hollow's Mill and his cloth-weaving.)

"*I don't know.*"

"*If you do, Robert, I'll take Shakespeare away; and I'll shrivel up within myself, and put on my bonnet and go home.*"

Now, if you can ignore the bonnet, this is the kind of thing which any one of us might say and most of us have, times beyond number. But Charlotte has to inflate it by making Caroline say:

"*Your heart is a lyre, Robert; but . . . it is often silent. Let glorious William come near and touch it. . . .*"

(Glorious William. God give us patience.)

When Caroline first recognises that she is in love with her cousin, she is naïve, candid, and confident. She is not afraid to admit that she loves him, and she is certain that he loves her. There is a poignant simplicity of utterance in her reverie, no high-flown phrases, nothing artificial. She saw, Charlotte says, "*the visions we see at eighteen years.*" And now Charlotte gives way to a ringing peal of allegory.

"*Before that time, we sit listening to a tale, a marvellous fiction; delightful sometimes, and sad sometimes; almost always unreal. Before that time our world is heroic; its inhabitants half-divine or semi-demon; its scenes are dream-scenes: darker woods and stranger hills; brighter skies, more dangerous waters; sweeter flowers, more tempting fruits: wider plains, drearier deserts, sunnier fields than are found in nature, overspread our enchanted globe. . . . As to our sun, it is a burning heaven—the world of gods.*"

This sounds a piece of pure exaggeration; Charlotte, as usual, cantering away on her Pegasus-hobbyhorse which has got out of hand. Until you realise that this is not allegory with the bit between its teeth. It is Angria. She is making a gift to Caroline of her own dream-world. It is quite out of character, she would never have woven daydreams of that order. She put her dreams into words, and they are of being Robert's devoted wife, studying his comfort, making him happy and telling him of his faults—which she does already . . . Even in the hour of "happy ending", that is still the theme of Caroline's daydream:

"*I love you, too, Robert, and will take faithful care of you.*"

And that hard individual is sufficiently moved to remark that it will be like a rose sheltering a block of stone; in which you agree with him.

It seems strange that Charlotte should bring the tumult and surge of Angria into contact with Caroline and not with Shirley. Shirley was at least created with Emily in her mind and in her heart.

Robert is irresistibly drawn to this lovable cousin with her prettiness, her gentleness, and her courage and her strong desire to escape from the purposeless vacuum of her comfortable and protected life. (*"I should like an occupation; and if I were a boy it would not be so difficult to find one . . . I could be apprenticed to your trade—the cloth-trade: I could learn it of you, as we are distant relations."*)

But he cannot allow himself to take a wife until he has retrieved his fortunes. One would think that it was no impossible matter to tell this to Caroline, who would wait for him until Doomsday. But instead, he keeps her on a perpetual seesaw, yielding to her sweetness and his feeling for her at one encounter, and withdrawing into frozen discourtesy at the next. When Shirley appears, Robert sets out on a deliberate campaign to acquire a rich wife. And it is impossible not to suspect that such an aim was always at the back of his mind.

Soon after the idyll of firelight and glorious William, Caroline meets Robert and is received by him with what amounts to a slap in the face. She behaves with a dignity which is touching and, going home, tries with all her might to occupy herself instead of brooding. It is one of Charlotte's most real and living pictures, this one of a girl struggling valiantly to accept heartbreak and not to give way, while the door-bell rings time after time, and at every ring she inevitably thinks that Robert has come to the Rectory. There is a stream of maddening visitors including all the curates, and at long last Robert comes to see the rector and she is found by him alone in the empty dining-room. This time, he tells her straightforwardly and with real tenderness that she would do better not to think of him, and why. And Caroline's answer is honest and valiant, with a note of childish candour.

"I know it is your duty to try to get on, and that it won't do for you to be romantic; but in future you must not misunderstand me if I seem friendly. You misunderstood me this morning, did you not?"

This could hardly be bettered for true character-drawing.

Robert—the man really is something of a cad—having brought her to this desirable state of mind, sees his cake slipping through his fingers and hastily grabs it, kissing her good-night several times over.

*"One minute only—put down the candle an instant—good-night.
I kiss you because we are cousins. . . ."*

His logic seems open to question.

Charlotte allows herself, in her own rôle, the writer addressing the reader, a tirade of vehement and passionate bitterness
such as Caroline never felt. And not only on Caroline's behalf.
She is crying aloud on behalf of all slighted women; and most of
all, on behalf of herself. She ends it with:

*"There may be apathetic exhaustion after the rack; if energy
remains, it will be rather a dangerous energy—deadly when confronted with injustice."*

No one knew more than she, of that dangerous energy.

There is still no sign of Shirley; instead, Charlotte suddenly
introduces a conversation-piece on a grand scale, the Yorke
family at Briarmains. They have so little to do with the story—
and next to nothing whatever, with Shirley—that it seems as
though she drew this large family-group for the sheer enjoyment
of it. She did a peculiar thing. The Yorkes were taken from the
Taylors, the household where Mary and Martha, her schoolfellows, were her friends—Mary her only close friend besides
Ellen Nussey—and where she was a frequent visitor and even
more frequently in request. She drew a rather magnificent
figure in Hiram Yorke, the rich manufacturer, who is a combination of the despotic Yorkshireman of those legends and
local histories which gave Emily the material for *Wuthering
Heights* and a man of outstanding culture with a love of the
arts. He alternately speaks French, educated English, and the
Yorkshire *patois* of his own workmen; and he has a humour of
his own. When Robert Moore answers his friendly question
"What has gone wrong?" with a burst of metaphor concerning
the *"machinery"* of his being and the *"boiler which I take to be the
heart"*—Mr. Yorke, lapsing into his native speech, says:

*"That suld be putten 'i print: it's striking. It's almost blank
verse. . . . If the afflatus comes, give way, Robert, never heed me:
I'll hear it this whet (time)."* Nicely calculated to prick the
afflatus.

Rose and Jessy Yorke are Mary and Martha Taylor, and here
Charlotte was carried away by the memories of that happy
friendship and the poignancy of Martha's early death and her

own loss when Mary emigrated to the other side of the world. She makes such a live, intriguing study of the two girls, Rose, the serious rebel, Jessy, the enchanting little child, fearless, audacious and lovable, that they throw the book off-balance for the time being. She describes their looks, analyses their characters, foretells their futures; the lament for Jessy is one of the most haunting threnodies ever written. There is too much narrative, which is a fault of the entire book, but the few scenes when Rose and Jessy speak for themselves are so alive that you hardly know whether you are reading *Shirley* or listening to Mary and Martha in the garden at Roe Head and round the cottage piano at Haworth. Which, actually, you are doing. Rose and Jessy are intruders into the book; but they give a picture of Charlotte happy in a young friendship, which is treasured—the word is not too strong—by anyone who cares for her. There is a scene where Rose is poring over one of Mrs. Radcliffe's romances with Caroline reading over her shoulder: *"Rose showed her the attention of asking, ere she turned a leaf— 'Are you ready?' Caroline only nodded."* They talk of foreign travel.

"It makes me long to travel, Miss Helstone . . . I mean to make a way to do so if one is not made for me . . . I am resolved that my life shall be a life: not . . . a long, slow death like yours in Briarfield Rectory."

"Like mine! What do you mean, child?"

"Might you not as well be tediously dying, as for ever shut up in that glebe-house—a place that, when I pass it, reminds me of a windowed grave. I never see any movement about the door: I never hear a sound from the wall: I believe smoke never issues from the chimneys. What do you do there?"

And a little later Rose affirms:

"I feel monotony and death to be almost the same."

This is Mary and Charlotte. The potatoes in the cellar; the perpetual exasperated effort from Mary to make Charlotte break free from bondage.

There is no record that Charlotte ever fell foul of Mrs. Taylor and the fact that she was a constant visitor would seem to make it unlikely. But she made Mrs. Yorke a monstrous figure, as monstrous as her huge, fantastic caps. A domestic juggernaut, hysterically jealous, insulting and mean in mind. It is no wonder that Mrs. Taylor protested when *Shirley* was published. And even if Mrs. Yorke is no more than an invention, it was an odd thing for Charlotte to do: to introduce such a *mardi-gras* absurdity into a family-piece where her two friends were drawn with loving and detailed craftsmanship—exactly as she might have painted their miniatures. The boys of the Yorke family are pure Cain and Abel. They belong to the world of *Wuthering Heights.* Even young Martin's calf-love for Caroline has cruelty in it. It is noteworthy that both Rose and Martin describe the same trait in Caroline's face: all her face, Rose says, looks *"somehow, what I call clear."* And Martin: *"—something so clear in her face."* Little Jessy prattles a thorough, detailed description which gives a delicious picture of Caroline, adding *"—and when I am as tall as she is, I mean to be like her."* And you see, not the Yorkes and the Helstones, but the covey of girls streaming over the moors, and filling the Haworth parlour with music and laughter and the bedrooms with whispered talk and laughter. And you remember that Ellen was the prettiest of them, and that they all loved and admired her. But that it was Emily's beauty which Ellen saw and remembered vividly when she herself was an old woman. And knew that ignored, uncared-for beauty for something infinitely above and beyond her own.

At last there is Shirley. She has come into her fortune and her unassuming country estate (*"my modest Grange"*), and she and Caroline become close friends. Whenever Charlotte lost herself between Shirley and Emily, there is discrepancy, there is a falling-off, which comes as a shock. When Shirley is the creature of Charlotte's own making, pure and simple, she is enchanting. When Charlotte is straining to mould her into a magnificent figure-head in Emily's likeness, the results are sometimes disastrous.

One sees Emily smile when poor Charlotte saw her likeness in so many impossible faces: her own portrait by Richmond; the face of George Lewes, whose portrait shows him as an early Victorian Adonis with a touch of the dandy quite in key with the period. My poor dear—you think everyone looks like me. . . .

Shirley is the most unequal piece of creation which Charlotte ever achieved. And at times, and in places, the greatest. She is enchanting. Even her gown of purple satin worn with a rosebud bonnet cannot diminish her. . . . She is intensely self-willed, warmhearted, hot-tempered; a warmly hospitable mistress of a house, a practical young woman of business, a relaxed, happy dreamer. *"In Shirley's nature prevailed at times an easy indolence . . . moments when her thoughts, her simple existence, the fact of the world being around—and heaven above her, seemed to yield her such fulness of happiness that she did not need to lift a finger to increase the joy."*

Shirley, unknown to anyone and unrecognised by herself, has given her untamed independent heart to Louis Moore, the brother of Robert and tutor to her young lame cousin with whom she was brought up. When she takes up her residence at Fieldhead, she has business dealings with Robert Moore— (*"Half my income comes from the works in that Hollow"*)—is particularly kind and winning toward him as Louis's brother, and lends him a large sum in order to save his business. Caroline quite naturally assumes that Shirley is in love with him; and sees from the first that Robert intends to marry her. This tangle is wrought and worked out by Charlotte with a masterly subtilty. Misunderstanding; the significance of a speaker's words translated by the hearer; the whole familiar and romantic bag of tricks, is used by Charlotte with the sleight of hand of a magician. Just at this time, the rector, having quarrelled with Robert Moore on political grounds, sends The Cottage to Coventry and forbids Caroline any contact or communication. Shirley says:

"By the way, you must miss that Cousin Robert of yours very much, now that you and he never meet."

"I do."

"And he must miss you."

"That he does not."

". . . If he is, and always was, as indifferent to you as you say, why did he steal your hair?"

"I don't know—yes, I do: it was my doing not his. Everything of that sort always was my doing."

Charlotte makes one or two distressing blunders with

Shirley, those queer lapses from good taste which occasionally befell her. When Shirley plans to take her friend on a sea voyage and Caroline is delighted,

"*Shirley rubbed her hands. 'Come, I can bestow a benefit,' she exclaimed. 'I can do a good deed with my cash. My thousand a year is not merely a matter of dirty bank-notes and jaundiced guineas' . . .*"

We squirm a little. Until we remember that Shirley couldn't be vulgar if she tried: and that Charlotte has merely missed step.

Again: when Shirley has lent five thousand pounds to Robert to replace his wrecked machinery, the starvation and misery of the men thus thrown out of work is giving rise to the menace of some outbreak. Shirley confides to Caroline

"*. . . my conscience is quite uneasy, as if I had committed or was going to commit a crime . . . I have fallen under a stern influence which I scarcely approve but cannot resist. Something will be done ere long, I fear, which it by no means pleases me to think of. To ease my mind, and to prevent harm as far as I can, I mean to enter on a series of good works. Don't be surprised, therefore, if you see me all at once turn outrageously charitable.*"

Shirley is twitting herself, with a quizzical eyebrow raised and a twitch of her lips; she often does. But the whole gesture of her ample almsgiving is out of key, when she confides that it is being done in order to pacify the possible rioters before they riot—it is Charlotte again, lapsing from taste, from common-sense, and from character-drawing. And when Shirley offers a sort of apology with

"*What I want to do is to prevent mischief. I cannot forget, either day or night, that these embittered feelings of the poor against the rich have been generated in suffering: they would neither hate nor envy us if they did not see us so much happier than themselves——*" that is the truer Shirley speaking. Charlotte had some uncertainty and uneasiness about the whole episode. She headed the chapter *Shirley Seeks To Be Saved By Works.*

Her humour is sometimes vitriolic, and still more often heavy-handed; but it plays upon Shirley with a delicate charm. When the two girls are discussing the sea voyage, Shirley teases Caroline, making light of her own anxiety for Caroline's heart-ache and sinking health:

"Will you think of Fitful Head, now, when you lie awake at night; of gulls shrieking round it, and waves tumbling in upon it, rather than of the graves under the Rectory back-kitchen?"

"I will try," Caroline says, docilely. And goes on to release a perfect deluge of high-wrought imaginative pictures of the sea. The pictures are essentially Charlotte's, and Caroline lets herself go entirely:

". . . a herd of whales rushing through the livid and liquid thunder down from the frozen zone . . . wallowing, flashing, rolling in the wake of a patriarch bull, huge enough to have been spawned before the flood. . . ."

To which effusion Shirley returns dryly:

"I hope our bark will meet with no such shoal, or herd, as you term it, Caroline . . . I should not like to be capsized by the patriarch bull . . ."

And Mrs. Pryor, her prunes-and-prism ex-governess, now her companion and duenna, interrupts:

"My dears, does it not strike you that your conversation for the last ten minutes has been rather fanciful?"

This is neither Shirley nor Caroline; it is Charlotte, laughing at herself, making a joke at her own expense. No one but Ellen had entered into her passion for the sea. It seems possible enough that Emily, who wanted nothing but her moors, had sometimes derided it. So: let Caroline be parched for the sea, and Shirley amuse herself by dismissing the patriarch bull—and really, Caroline asked for that, by her unrestrained hyperbole—and draw a mocking, terrifying picture of a siren-mermaid.

Shirley, facing squarely her household account-books, tells Caroline:

"I know we never get up illuminations at Fieldhead, but I could not ask the meaning of sundry quite unaccountable pounds of candles: we do not wash for the parish, yet I viewed in silence items of soap and bleaching-powder calculated to satisfy the solicitude of the most anxious enquirer after our position in reference to those articles. . . . Caroline, you may laugh at me but you can't change me. I am a poltroon on certain points—I feel it."

And when Mr. Donne exhibits a craven spirit, attacked by Tartar, Shirley's mongrel bull-dog and familiar spirit,

" 'There are other visitors coming,' observed Shirley, with

that provoking coolness which the owners of formidable-looking dogs are apt to show while their animals are all bristle and bay."

You can see Emily taking exactly that line when one of Papa's clerical visitors fell foul of Keeper.

Robert brings a note from the Home Secretary, no less, concerning the industrial unrest in the neighbourhood, for Shirley to read. He finds Caroline with her, and escorts her home. Charlotte seldom showed a more delicate power than in her handling of the whole situation of which this is an incident: the rich young woman, conferring with the business man who is her tenant, her colleague and, incidentally, her debtor; while the girl who is nothing but his mute lover sits by, looking on, listening quite outside that inner circle. It could all be so noveletteish or mawkish-romantic; it is nothing of the kind. After all, apart from industrial riots, the strong, bold drawing of the Yorkshire types, and the grinning caricatures of the impossible curates, the story of *Shirley* is as simple as anything chosen by Charlotte Yonge, or by Jane Austen, whose simplicity and subjects Charlotte despised. A glorious girl, free and wealthy, in love with the family tutor and wrestling with her own feelings not because of difference in station or in fortune but because freedom, independence, and a certain endearing gypsy-lawlessness are the breath of life to her, and she literally panics before the thought of surrendering them.

"*A still, deep, inborn delight glows in her young veins; unmingled—untroubled, not to be reached or ravished by human agency because by no human agency bestowed: the pure gift of God to His creature, the free dower of Nature to her child. This joy gives her experience of a genii-life.*"

Those words of Charlotte's describing Shirley surpass, as a portrait of Emily, anything that anyone else, or even that she herself, has written of her sister. Then, a gentler girl, with depths of character and courage, in love with an ambitious man. And a warm, devoted friendship between the two girls in spite of the fact—or supposition—that there is, apparently, a man between them. Charlotte was magnificently equal to creating the conflict of passion in *Jane Eyre* and the embittered torment of *Villette*; *Shirley* is in a so much milder and simpler key; it is possible to overlook the extraordinary talent which she shows in making its very simplicity throb with reality.

There is a universal quality in it, all through. When Robert—who can't leave poor Caroline alone, confound him!—tells her that he has her in his eyes, that he sees her wherever he goes, *"Lina you will haunt me."* That he imagines her, in her white party dress, in the cottage window-seat; even among the *"buxom lasses in pinafores"* in his mill. Who hasn't been hag-ridden by such likenesses? When Caroline tries to work off her restless unhappiness by long walks in the countryside, and always ends up at a slope above the cottage and the mill where she can see the lighted windows, unseen. When she rebuffs Shirley, unable to bear the sight even of her friend since her friend, she believes, is her rival; and Shirley flatly refuses to be rebuffed, takes off her bonnet and demands her tea, and goes off into a fit of temper because *"that six feet of puppy-hood makes a perpetually recurring eclipse of our friendship . . . ever and anon he renders me to you a mere bore and nuisance . . . you will wish me at Jericho tomorrow, Lina."*

And Caroline gives way to that rare piteous, outcry:

" 'Love hurts us so, Shirley . . .' "

" . . . 'We really are friends, then, Lina, in spite of the black eclipse?' "

" 'We really are,' returned the other, drawing Shirley towards her, and making her sit down, 'come what may.' "

" 'Come then, we will talk of something else than the Troubler,' " says Shirley briskly.

Shirley's relatives come to stay with her, bringing the little lame cousin, Henry, and his tutor, Louis Moore. Now the story moves into a species of dance; advance, retreat, beckon, dismiss: glide in a pavane or a gavotte; whirl in a dizzying folk-dance. . . .

Charlotte is happier in her treatment of Shirley in contact with Louis than she is in her handling of Louis himself. The brothers Moore are not fortunate in their presentation as lovers, it must be admitted . . . Louis is quite insufferable. He is desperately proud and very poor. Shirley has been his pupil with her young invalid cousin. Now she is his regal and un-approachable hostess, with whom he is hopelessly in love.

Which is all very harassing for the unfortunate young man, but he is so cocksure, and carries such a load of chips on his shoulder, that it is hard to sympathise with him.

Also, Charlotte uses that artificial and too-easy medium, the private diary, to eke out the devious unfolding of the romance. Louis is forever sitting down to scribble in his notebook, and he discusses his state of heart and Shirley's state of mind and behaviour with the cool logic of a casebook. He hardly speaks or writes a natural word. He is—I am sorry!—the stuffed shirt of stuffed shirts.

The charm of this whole *motif* lies in the delicious scenes where Shirley invades the schoolroom, becomes a schoolgirl again, toasts oatcake before the fire, is tender to the lame boy who adores her and a half-docile, half-rebellious pupil to Louis.

Caroline, dear nitwit! believes that Shirley dislikes the unfortunate tutor and pleads with her to be courteous to "*Robert's brother*". She admits regretfully that he isn't as fine-looking as Robert nor has so good an air . . . and Shirley laughs sarcastically:

" '*Well, well,*' " *was her comment.* " '*On the plea of the man being . . . Robert's brother, we'll just tolerate his existence, won't we, Cary?*' "

Really, for a moment, you hear an echo of Emma's indignation when the besotted Harriet said of Frank Churchill: " 'Only to be sure it was paying him too great a compliment, but she did think there were some looks a little like Mr. Elton.' Emma restrained her indignation and only turned from her in silence."

This ordeal by visiting relations wipes out Shirley's and Caroline's plan of a summer tour. They are nicely described as "*a genteel foraging party besieging Shirley in her castle and compelling her to surrender at discretion.*" And it is when Caroline is thrown back on her own solitary company and in her disappointment, and having fretted herself to the brink of a serious illness, that she gives voice to that long monologue on the misery of single women debarred from an absorbing work which is so far out of place in a novel and yet so memorable an apologia. Too much is out of place in this latter part of *Shirley*.

There is a horrifying amount of rhetoric and declamation from everyone concerned. There is too much narrative instead of conversation, which weights and deadens the reality. And when there is conversation, it is artificial and melodramatic, with tantalising flashes of truth and simplicity to make it the more aggravating.

There is no need for melodrama or pomposity, when Louis is claiming Shirley, knowing that she loves him as he loves her. When Shirley is facing her furious and ridiculous uncle. And when Robert askes Caroline to marry him. But there it is. As though Charlotte had let go some control.

The contrasts are dumbfounding. She never wrote a more living scene than the chapter which she called "A Summer Night", where Shirley and Caroline keep each other company at the Rectory while the rector and Robert are out to deal with the mill-riot. The two girls over their supper of bread and milk, Shirley with old Helstone's pistols beside her on the table (" '*Cock them before you go to bed,*' " he reminds her coolly), and Caroline with the carving-knife . . . (" '*a lady's knife, light to handle, and as sharp-pointed as a poignard.*' ")

"*They both sat under the window, and both leaned their arms on the sill, and both inclined their heads towards the open lattice. They saw each other's young faces by the starlight, and that dim June twilight which does not wholly fade from the west till dawn begins to break in the east.*"

Caroline says: " '*Shirley, I hear the beck in the hollow.*' "

They sit there, murmuring together. Earlier in the day, during the great school-feast and school-procession, they have seen the redcoats riding towards Briarfield and heard the jingle of the accoutrements and the sound of horses' feet. Now they hear the muffled tramp of the rioters growing louder and drawing nearer.

It is a faultless picture. Tension, and growing danger; young valour; and the smell of flowers in the warm night and the tranquil sound of the running stream. Nothing mars it.

And there is another scene, where reality breaks through the stilted artifice, or rather, alternates with it, and leaves you startled and marvelling. We owe to whatever streak of finer

feeling there is in Robert Moore that he himself confesses to
Yorke his degrading offer of marriage to Shirley, and spares
himself nothing in his shame and self-reproach.

". . . *She started up, walked twice fast through the room in the
way that she only does and no other woman, and ejaculated 'God
bless me! . . . She stopped and looked at me.*

" '*God bless me!' she piteously repeated, in that shocked, indignant, yet saddened accent. 'You have made a strange proposal.
. . . You spoke like a brigand who demanded my purse, rather than
like a lover who asked my heart.' *"

Robert blurts out that whatever his own feelings might be,
he had believed that she loved him. . . . Whereupon Shirley
hurls herself into the fray and tells him exactly what she thinks
of him. She tells him with declamation and adjuration and
works herself up into a frenzy of oratory, and Moore, not to be
outgunned, invokes "*the ghost of Judas*", etc.

And then, still weeping, and just as he is tip-toeing from the
pink drawing-room, hat in hand,

" '*Oh Moore!' said she: it was worse than 'Et-tu-Brute!' *"

That sigh from Shirley lingers in the mind, when all the
oratory has been laughed at and shuddered at and forgotten.

And so to what Charlotte called "The Winding-Up".
Happy endings were in favour with novel-readers of the time,
and Charlotte knew it. More important, she meant *Shirley* to
end happily. And in so far as the facts are concerned, it does.
Jack has his Jill and all shall go well. But the fever of oratory
was upon her, and she could not escape into an atmosphere of
simple happiness. She was never adept at conveying happiness.
She had too little experience of it. So Louis battles with
Shirley in a sort of zoological fugue—he names her leopardess,
she pats his hand and calls him Tartar, her dog's name. Even
Robert is impelled to call Caroline his dove. . . . Humour goes
by the board and so, alas, does any sense of reality. You regret
the Shirley of the schoolroom toasting-fork who breaks out
when summoned to receive callers that she envies a savage
" '*in that she has no drawing-room duty to perform, but can sit at
ease weaving mats, and stringing beads, and peacefully flattening her
picaninny's head in an unmolested corner of her wigwam.' *"
(Geography is not Shirley's strong point.)

The book ends with a picture of the green Hollow turned into *"the manufacturer's daydreams embodied in substantial stone and brick and ashes . . ."* and the contrasting picture, given by an old Yorkshire woman, of the place when it was " *'a lonesome spot . . . and a bonnie spot—full of oak trees and nut trees'* ", where her mother saw " *'the last fairish (fairy) that ever was seen in this countryside'* ", " *'just at the edge of dark.'* "

Charlotte concludes by telling the reader, that overworked individual, to look for the moral, if any. The reader of a later day might, possibly, find it where she could not: in her own turning from the live green wood to the sounding brass and the smothering stones of Babel, in this, the book which yet holds more of sheer beauty than any other which she wrote.

IV

VILLETTE

THROUGH the last years of her life Charlotte emerges in a gentleness that is something to wring the heart when you remember the cause. The gentleness of a nature so flayed by sorrow and loss, suffering such a slow death by unimaginable loneliness and starvation of mental needs, that the fires of life have died down. Not enough left of vitality; only a fathomless weariness.

Which makes it all the more surprising that *Villette* should be a book saturated with acerbity. A mind spent with suffering and immured in an unnatural solitude could, conceivably, produce a book which held fierceness, bitterness, anything you like, but not, one would expect, a corrosive acid. *Villette*, considered by generations of critics to be Charlotte's best book, reminds one, irreverently, of that brilliant excerpt from a popular radio-programme: ". . . that dear old lady, filling her scent-spray with vitriol . . ." Not that Charlotte was an old lady by any means; she was in her thirties. But the scent-spray is filled with vitriol, all the same. And this is the book which she wrote with such heartsick exhaustion and hopelessness that she was in a panic lest she should never finish it at all.

The book, of course, has suffered badly from being the bone of contention between critics who flatly denied that Paul Emanuel was taken from M. Héger and Lucy's love for him was Charlotte's for M. Héger, and the critics who asserted the opposite. Well—the publication of Charlotte's letters to Héger have answered that question for ever.

There is nothing, ever, to be gained, from the partisanship which maintains that one book or another is a writer's "best book". It must always be a matter of opinion. I could not, personally, choose any one of Charlotte's books as her best. The balance, in each of them, tilts and rises and falls from start to finish, and the same book excels in certain elements and comes off badly in others. There is no steadily soaring chart of progress in her work: how could there be, in anything so dynamic? There is less of it than is generally assumed, in the work of any established writer, at any time.

Villette is a masterly piece of work; and a mastering one, if the word may be allowed to pass. George Eliot, reading it when it first appeared, said *"There is something almost preternatural in its power."* Perfectly true; but equally true of any book that Charlotte wrote, except *The Professor*. It is so gripping a book that any attempt to express the power sounds exaggerated. The more so because the scene, the events, could hardly be more limited in scope: a girls' school in Brussels. . . . Pupils, teachers, a doctor. One girl, only, who is not a pupil of that school but who is bound by a childhood intimacy to one of the teachers. And all this in 1852; when the school-scene was not yet a happy hunting-ground of vice for writers. . . . Could anything have, in the words of Ginevra Fanshawe, more of a *"bread-and-butter-eating, school-girl air"*? But out of this, Charlotte made a masterpiece.

The book has all the faults which she never relinquished, and some of them in full cry. But in one respect it does outstrip any other book of hers: the development, the unfolding of character. In *Jane Eyre* and in *Shirley* the people could not be more alive, but they are completed when Charlotte first brings them on to the stage. There is no difference between Jane Eyre, the passionate, unhappy child maintaining her ember of pride through all ill-treatment and craving to be loved, and Jane Eyre, the passionate young woman, whom even starvation and beggary cannot humble and whose love determines her whole way of life. Shirley is strong, wilful, and warmhearted, Caroline is sweet, loving, and self-disciplined, from first to last. Rochester is Rochester from the moment when he comes riding out of the mist to *"Reader, I married him."* The brothers Moore are men of wood all though the book. In *Villette*, Charlotte has mastered character-in-the-making. The novelist's craft can go no further. Her people grow and change, gradually and before you.

Lucy, waiting from hour to hour for a last sight of Paul Emanuel, calls *"suspense—a worse boon than despair."* But suspense is among the best boons to a reader, and in this book Charlotte has brought it to concert-pitch. In plain words: you have to read on, you simply must know what's happening. A recent Brains Trust of intelligent older children, it may be remembered, condoned the "twopenny comic" as devoured by their younger brothers and sisters for that reason: the children, they said apologetically, had to see what happened next. . . . Thereby stating at least one of the fundamentals of fiction. Incidentally, this fundamental as supremely used by two of the Brontës has just received startling, somewhat dismaying recognition: a popular and inexpensive magazine for women has run *Wuthering Heights* as a "strip". . . .

One other quality in *Villette* is perhaps the most surprising of all, when you remember that Charlotte wrote it in such a state of illness and exhaustion that she had to drive herself to the work: her fresh humour plays over it like summer lightning. There is deep bitterness in this book, and caricature, and exaggeration; but there are perpetual touches of delicious wit, the phrase here and there that is Charlotte using the perfect word.

It is a book of dizzy contradictions. Character-drawing in which she surpasses herself; tense interest; brilliant touches of humour. Allegory and Rhetoric dragging and clanking their heaviest chains—(I'm sorry! it is contagious)—and a new be-setting sin, the Harangue. Charlotte preaches in *Villette*. She mounts her father's pulpit and launches into evangelistic sermons.

But, here as elsewhere, now as always, the glaring faults, while they nettle you, serve to show up the incongruous splendour of the whole achievement.

The chief puzzle, to me, at least, has always been that she could choose Lucy Snowe. She said that she did not like her. It would be difficult for anyone to like her, that vinegarish young woman. You pity Lucy, you suffer with her, and toward the later part of the book you may even admire her, but like her you cannot. And it seems a strange choice for Charlotte to spend a year of her life in the unremitted company of a being whom she disliked as she created her.

At the outset, Charlotte appears to drop a stitch which she

never picks up. She told her publishers that it was done on purpose and with no intention of picking up. The results remain unsatisfactory, even so. There is Lucy Snowe, staying in the delightful house of her widowed godmother, Louisa Bretton; and Mrs. Bretton's attractive schoolboy son, John Graham Bretton. The house springs vividly to life (Charlotte loved interiors), Louisa Bretton is vigorous, handsome, kind, and Graham is one of the nicest and most natural schoolboys in English fiction. Then, Lucy is removed, vaguely planted upon nameless relations where, indirectly, you are given to understand that she was not happily placed. Still vaguely, some family influence cuts her off from all communication with the Brettons. She is companion to an elderly invalid. She takes herself to Belgium and the capital city, Villette, and the Pension of Mme. Beck. And then, and only then, the story begins to move. And nowhere in it is there ever any explanation of the hints concerning Lucy's girlhood. They would have been better omitted if the dim less-than-sketch were not to be enlarged.

The beginning of the book wavers in another manner as well. A little girl, Paulina Mary Home, called Polly, comes to stay in the Bretton household until her widower father, who is going abroad, shall send for her. This portrait of Polly is one of the most delicate and finished pieces of work which Charlotte ever did. An intensely sensitive, deeply loving little creature, with the precocious gravity and independence of a child who has been her father's close companion, and a hundred quaint and comic ways. She idolises her father, becomes devotedly attached to Graham, who treats her with alternate good-humoured indulgence and a boy's impatient carelessness. She senses that the frigid and critical girl, "Miss Snowe" does not love her, and is very distant towards Lucy. Until the night before Polly is to leave, when the little creature is so miserable that she creeps into Lucy's bed for comfort. Lucy shows in a most unattractive light. She has that acid streak which makes her censorious of any happier creature. She considers Graham spoilt and Polly too sensitive and too much indulged by the boy and by his mother. And yet—such is Charlotte's paradoxical gift—it is Lucy (the whole book, like *Jane Eyre*, is written in the first person), who presents the exquisite picture of the child to whom she is coolly unsympathetic.

The picture of the little Paulina is so finely drawn, and in such microscopic detail, that it is impossible not to feel that Charlotte was more absorbed in her than she meant to be. You hear no more of Polly, you do not see her, for many years. This is not the first time that Charlotte's own superabundant power of creation has run away with her and that she has made a subsidiary character almost too interesting. But in this case, she has expended a wealth of detail which is unmistakably loving detail. Paulina, both as a small child and later as a young girl, is drawn with the minuteness, the tenderness and the loveliness, which you find in the decorations to a missal. The colouring is of liquid jewels and gold-leaf. To convey a child's talk is a snare for any writer, and it was not an element in which Charlotte might be expected to excel. She had been an unwilling nursery governess. Her portraits of the pupils at the Pensionnat de Demoiselles are spiteful. But there are pages of perfectly natural, spontaneous chatter from Polly which are as endearing, as moving, and as comic as the talk of any intelligent small child can be. But she sweeps Polly from the board like a very dainty ivory pawn; we hear no more of her for over ten years. And she resolutely moves Lucy Snowe into play.

Now we are in the Pensionnat; and Charlotte is living in the Brussels years again, and all the cankering hurt and bitterness and humiliation are laboratory phials in those small, terribly powerful hands of hers as she draws Madame Beck. And all the influence of Angria and the force of her own feeling for Constantin Héger are creating Paul Carlos Emanuel. These two figures have been so obscured by their prototypes that it is worth stressing what subtle, complete creations they are in themselves. It is a thousand pities to permit Mme. Héger and her worthy husband to stand in their way. . . . Madame Beck is much more than a revengeful caricature. Lucy hates her, as Charlotte hated Madame Héger; but Lucy does her justice. She is a supremely shrewd, competent, unscrupulous woman, decorous to a degree, worldly-wise to the point of genius, completely imperturbable until Lucy stands between her and the cousin and colleague whom it is her intention to marry. She steals, *"shod with the shoes of silence,"* even into a page of *Shirley*, where she has no business to be, exactly as she stole through the dormitories and the class-rooms and the deep, walled garden, and peered into Lucy's drawers and read her letters and kept every thought and every secret and every possession of her pupils and her teachers under that all-pervading *"surveillance"*. . . . In *Shirley*, Charlotte is merely speaking of Shirley's penetrating smile, and observing that men don't like to be read too clearly: women should be *"endowed with a soft blindness."* And suddenly, she breaks forth:

"I remember once seeing a pair of blue eyes that were usually thought sleepy, secretly on the alert, and I knew by their expression—an expression which chilled my blood, it was in that quarter so wondrously unexpected—that for years they had been accustomed to silent soul-reading. The world called the owner of these blue eyes 'bonne petite femme' (she was not an Englishwoman): I learned her nature afterwards—got it off by heart—studied it in its farthest, most hidden recesses—she was the finest, deepest, subtlest schemer in Europe."

Only, here, it is not so much Madame Beck whose memory pricks Charlotte into a burst of venom that has no part in the story in hand. But Maria Héger. . . .

Lucy says:

"I say again, Madame was a very great and a very capable woman." She says (and with considerable astuteness) that she could have conducted a far greater enterprise than a girls' school. She could have led a parliament, run a police force. *"Wise, firm, faithless; secret, crafty, passionless; watchful and inscrutable; acute and insensate—withal perfectly decorous—what more could be desired?"*

Charlotte's weighing of words is almost awe-inspiring. No woman writing ever had such a tireless mastery of exactitude and *value* in words. She can never have written a careless line; she certainly never wrote a slipshod one. Even in her shocking bursts of oratory, even in her reverberating allegories and her harangues, she handles each word, weighs it, and puts it down in place. And when it comes to Madame Beck, her words are not something which she manipulates: they are slow, deliberate drops of acid. The scent-spray has become a syringe.

". . . . *No private sorrow touched her.* . . . . *Not the agony in Gethsemane, not the death on Calvary, could have wrung from her eyes one tear.*"

Dr. John Bretton, settled and practising in Villette, is called in to attend a sick child at the pensionnat. Almost at once Lucy recognises in this handsome, debonair, and thoroughly attractive man, the boy, Graham Bretton. And from the first, his attitude toward her is made clear by Charlotte in a few brilliant strokes. He not only does not recognise her. ". . . *according to my presence just that degree of notice and consequence a person of my exterior habitually expects; that is to say, about what is given to unobtrusive articles of furniture, chairs of ordinary joiner's work, and carpets of no striking pattern.*"

And here Lucy takes a step forward under our eyes. That remarkable character-development shows movement. Lucy, so acid, so unamiable, so whaleboned in her insular prejudices that she is virulent and almost vulgar in her comments on the Belgians, and crude in her vehemence against every manifestation of Roman Catholicism: is wounded, and quivers, and reveals herself as terribly vulnerable. And, poor girl! She is to reveal herself so at every turn, as the book goes on. She disapproves of "sensibility". She was cold and repellent to a six-year-old-child because Polly was hypersensitive and showed an unusual capacity for deep feeling. But in herself, Lucy Snowe is "like a heart without a skin". And with the entrance of splendid John Bretton, this becomes apparent.

Shortly after he has become an *habitué* at the pensionnat, Lucy is relaxing in the garden late in the evening. And suddenly a desolate nostalgia for her lost childhood comes over her and finds utterance in a single cry. (We are still told nothing about this childhood. Charlotte maintains her stubborn and mistaken silence here, and it is vexing.) In this hour of slipping armour, she says:

"*I had feelings: passive as I lived, little as I spoke, cold as I looked, when I thought of past days, I could feel . . . And in catalepsy and a dead trance, I studiously held the quick of my nature.*"

I think that Charlotte left Lucy's childhood a blank and a hint because it was her own. There is so very much of herself in Lucy; herself, not as she was seen by other people but as she was in her own eyes. And I am not thinking of the Héger situation. Lucy's excruciating self-repression, Lucy's deadly fatalism and acceptance of an arid lot in life, Lucy's perpetual and cruel showing-up of her own appearance, her lack of grace and looks. Even the things in Lucy which she approved in herself: her rabid Protestantism, her detestation of her Belgian pupils.

Now she ponders her own susceptibility to wind and weather. She remembers a thunderstorm and the schoolgirls in a panic, telling their beads. But *"As for me, the tempest took hold of me with tyranny: I was roughly roused and obliged to live."* The electricity in the air pierced, broke through, Lucy's armour of self-restraint. That sedate young woman describes how she opened the window, sat on the ledge dangling her feet to the jutting roof of a lower part of the building. And for twenty-four hours afterwards, ached with restlessness for a wider, more exciting life. *"This longing, and all of a similar kind, it was necessary to knock on the head"*; Lucy describes that she did this, as Jael drove a nail through Sisera's temples; and gives such a picture of physical torture as you can hardly bear to read.

There was no need for Lucy Snowe to bury alive her straining feelings, her ambitions, her longings. She was young, she was alone in the world, she had courage and energy. She could have worked and fought her way to a larger life. Her deathly acceptance of a drab fate is incongruous. But Charlotte was not free; nor, by the standard of her time, very young. She was shackled by ill-health, by a wrecked nervous system, and above all, by her allegiance to Papa. There are times, many times, throughout the book when Charlotte speaks with Lucy's voice.

And this, the first sign of roused sensibilities within Lucy, comes after John Bretton has walked into the conventual and overcharged atmosphere of a girls' school. . . . It is admirably done.

That evening, she comes upon Madame going through her drawers. She is more or less indifferent to the system of espionage, because, she says with a dreadful, quiet bitterness, she has nothing to lose. *"Lover-less and inexperienced of love, I was as safe from spies in my heart-poverty, as the beggar from thieves."*

But the spying was due to the fact that Madame has seen Dr. John talking to Lucy for a few minutes in the garden. And that night, Lucy first laughs and then cries.

"I never had felt so strange and contradictory an inward tumult as I felt for one hour that evening: soreness and laughter, and fire, and grief, shared my heart between them. I cried hot tears: not because Madame mistrusted me—I did not care twopence for her mistrust—but for other reasons. However, that turmoil subsided: next day I was again Lucy Snowe."

The hardest sort of kicks without the ha'pence: to be credited with a love-affair which you knew to be one-sided. . . .

Charlotte was dissatisfied with her own handling of the character of John Bretton; she told her publishers as much. Except that she uses too much narration when building him, tells the reader too much and ignores the fact that his words and actions are a complete and finely-drawn presentation in themselves, there seems no obvious reason for her dissatisfaction. She loads *Villette* with narration. She calls herself *"the faithful narrator"* and the over-taxed reader could wish for less faith. The reason for her comments on John Bretton, one feels, is deeper than obvious. Into *Villette* Charlotte wrought the two loves which ever possessed her; that is now so widely known and so incontestably accredited that one need not add one more discussion to the many.

So, in Brussels, Charlotte learned to care for her Belgian tutor with her entire being. She was then a diminutive nobody, merely an avid scholar. In London she came to fall in love, no one will ever know exactly to what extent, with her handsome and gallant young publisher, George Smith, and he with her. She was then his star author, his mother's famous guest, the Currer Bell who had taken London by storm. She knew better than to marry a man years younger than herself, a man of fortune, of position, of crowded social life. Perhaps George Smith knew better, too. . . . But she saw him, beyond all these practical considerations, as a figure standing in the sun; she emphasises the *"brightness"* of his lot; it seems, through her eyes, to surround him in a golden downpour. And with such, her shadowed, sick life could have nothing to do.

And when it comes to Lucy, Charlotte entangles her two loves. Lucy spends her passionate, hopeless heart on the sun-god, John Bretton. And later, is drawn to the fierce, intolerant, noble little man, Paul Carlos Emanuel. But Charlotte spent her heart on Constantin Héger. And only knew the tremors and excitement, the gratification of the wise, resigned denial, of a brief passage of the emotions, with George Smith. Her own letters make that clear.

Hence, or so I believe, her dissatisfaction with her own work in the matter of Dr. John. He looms too large (for Charlotte), and Lucy loves him too deeply. He—and Lucy—have got out of hand.

Professor Paul Carlos Emanuel appears at first as a horrible little man, and Lucy's patience and amusement at his ape-ish tricks seem incredible. He is intensely conceited, intolerant, bad-tempered, and insolently rude. Only when he chooses to inveigh against Englishwomen in a school lecture does Lucy lose her temper and fire back. "He fumed like a bottled storm," is one of her neat descriptions of him. He exists on a pendulum, this little man with his ugly, sallow face and his black unruly hair and his burning blue eyes. One minute he is so offensively rude, so childishly self-centred, that he is unbearable: the next, his generosity, his warmth, and yes, his tenderness, disarm you as they disarm Lucy. He scolds and harasses her; he helps and comforts her.

" 'Donnez-moi la main,' said he, and the spite and jealousy melted out of his face, and a generous kindliness shone there instead. 'Come, we will not be rivals, we will be friends;' he pursued . . . 'instead of vexing and hindering, as I felt half-inclined ten minutes ago—for I have my malevolent moods; I always had from childhood —I will aid you sincerely. . . . Pauvrette!' "

He is the only one to guess Lucy's secret, her hopeless love for Dr. John; and he is diabolically jealous. Lucy does not see, for a long time, that his violent and insufferable behaviour to herself is because he is irresistibly drawn to her. That she never, or hardly ever, resents it; that she finds it only comic; indicates the slow growth of what she eventually comes to feel for him. The whole expanding of this interplay of the two natures, indissolubly meant for one another, is marvellously worked-out.

There are so many moments when Charlotte steals into the picture behind Lucy's subdued skirts.

"About nine o'clock A.M., an important functionary, the 'coiffeur' arrived. . . . I took my turn with the rest and could hardly believe what the glass said; the lavish garlandry of woven brown hair amazed me——"

Charlotte had copious and beautiful hair. It was her one beauty. And there is a description of her at a London party, when, unable to believe that she possessed even one beauty, she had added an artificial braid which was only too palpably "brown silk" . . . Lucy's new dress for the school fête is *"a crape-like material of purple-grey—the colour, in short, of dun mist lying on a moor in bloom."* Charlotte had a morbid dread of bright colours. They are her label for beauty; Shirley wears the shot silks of a peacock's tail, Blanche wears amber, the preposterous glamour-girl, Ginevra Fanshawe, wears crimson velvet to set off her milky blondeness. When Lucy has found her kind, domineering godmother again, and is staying with the Brettons in their *"quiet little chateau,"* surrounded with warmth and light and comfort and happiness, Mrs. Bretton insists on giving her a gown of pale rose-colour, muted by black lace. At the State Concert she catches sight of herself in a mirror:

"No need to dwell on the result. It brought a jar of discord, a pang of regret; it was not flattering, yet, after all, I ought to be thankful; it might have been worse."

Lucy is literally dragged by Paul Emanuel into the school play, and has a success. She discovers that she enjoys acting! . . . *"but it would not do for a mere looker-on at life."* She never allows herself to act again.

You long to shake Lucy, the resigned, stubborn martyr. Like Mrs. Elton she is "bent on neglecting her music": she insists on making life a dumbklavier. Until you remember that here it is Charlotte speaking. A woman with life and hope battered out of her, not a morbid girl.

Lucy's nightmare of a summer vacation, spent in utter solitude and in attendance upon an idiot-girl left in her charge, brings her to a nervous breakdown. And how piercingly

Charlotte's cry tears through her words now. Her fearful dream, too terrible for Lucy to relate, and the black depression which drowned her on waking. The worst part of the nameless dream:

"... *the well-loved dead, who had loved me well in life, met me elsewhere, alienated ...*"

And you catch the echo of Charlotte's dream at school, at tranquil Roe Head, when she saw Maria and Elizabeth, the little dead sisters, and they had become haughty and fashionable and were very critical of the comfortable school parlour. ... Worse than any nightmare fantasy. Imagine any one of the Brontës suddenly turning worldly and condescending. ... It left a scar in Charlotte's mind as her gloomiest and most awful visions could not do.

In her desperate plight, Lucy, the rabid Protestant, wanders into a church and tries to confess her misery to an elderly priest. And Charlotte did that, when she was alone in Brussels and frantic with pain over Constantin Héger. She confided this wild venture to Emily in a letter, and warned her (unnecessarily, one would think?) not to tell Papa. ... It is Lucy who gives her reason for a distraught action when reason was rocking.

"*That priest ... was naturally kind, with a sentimental, French kindness, to whose softness I knew myself not wholly impervious.*"

She will not go back to him for instruction as he invites her; because, in her aching need, she might—it is just conceivable, she feels—enter his Church, for its comfort, its tenderness, its gentleness.

"*Without respecting some sorts of affection, there was hardly any sort having a fibre of root in reality, which I could rely on my force wholly to withstand.*"

Charlotte—and Lucy—are vehement, and sometimes tasteless, in their diatribes against Roman Catholic ritual. And the reason lies less in their obdurate Protestant dogma than in an hour of utmost agony when Charlotte crept guiltily and like a thief in the night to the feet of the Mother of Sorrows; and could never quite forgive herself. ...

Lucy faints in the street; and it is Dr. John who rescues her and takes her to his mother. And now the whole atmosphere warms and brightens; and Lucy's embittered frigidity thaws. Her humour comes to life. She describes Mrs. Bretton as "*preferring all sentimental demonstrations in bas-relief.*" She describes a visit from Madame Beck, who is pleased to find that her humble English *gouvernante* has such fine friends. "*She came in and went out, quite a living Catherine wheel of compliments, delight, and affability.*" She gives a gradual, really charming picture of John Graham Bretton with his mother, whom he teases with the affectionate impudence of an adored son. As when he points out to her a particularly Juno-esque beauty and suggests bringing her home as a bride: Mrs. Bretton, bristling up at once, talks of "*the height, bulk, and circumference of that mighty doll in wood and wax, and kid and satin*"—she herself being a woman of ample proportions. And John says winningly:

"*Mamma, she would fill your blue chair so admirably!*"

On another occasion,

" '*The sensible, admirable old lady! Mother, you are better to me than ten wives yet.*'

" '*Don't be demonstrative, John, or I shall faint, and you will have to carry me out; and if that burden were laid upon you, you would reverse your last speech, and exclaim, Mother, ten wives could hardly be worse to me than you are!*' "

The whole atmosphere lightens and brightens as Lucy slips back into the enjoyment and comfort of the Bretton home. But is not all happiness.

" '*Do not let me think of them too often, too much, too fondly,*' I implored, '*let me be content with a temperate draught of this living stream: . . . quite tranquil!*'

"*Still repeating this word, I turned to my pillow, and steeped that pillow with tears.*"

It is hardly surprising that she cannot be tranquil; with John Bretton infatuated with her pupil, Ginevra Fanshawe, and making Lucy his reluctant confidante and bespeaking her good offices at every turn. Here Charlotte failed. Ginevra is an exaggerated and venomous caricature of a heartless and witless gold-digger, and is as impossibly unreal as Blanche Ingram. And John Bretton would never have been deceived by her for a moment. The entire picture of Dr. John in love with this sawdust creature is out of character and out of key.

But the daily study of John Bretton under Lucy's eyes is, otherwise, admirable. He was a good-humoured, charming schoolboy, thoughtless, and in his young egotism sometimes unconsciously cruel. He is exactly the same as a young man. Lucy drives this home in pages of steady, one might say, thumping narration. She disapproves of him as much as she succumbs to him. Poor Lucy has to disapprove of nearly everybody, and infallibly of anyone whom she loves. He is vain and careless and not over-sensitive to other people's feelings. He is too kind and endearing to Lucy; and too carelessly cruel. One day, he begins to call up reminiscences of his boyhood when she was in his mother's home.

"He had assumed a bantering air: a light, half-caressing, half-ironic, shone aslant in his eye. . . . Graham could devote to others the most grave and earnest, the manliest interest, he had no more than raillery for Lucy, the friend of lang syne."

She tells him, and with truth,

" *'In manner you were almost the same yesterday as today.'*

" *'What am I today? What was I the yesterday of ten years back?'*

" *'Gracious to whatever pleased you—unkindly or cruel to nothing.'*

" *'There you are wrong; I think I was almost a brute to you, for instance.'*

" *'A brute! No, Graham: I should never have patiently endured brutality.'*

" *'Why, had I been Nero himself, I could not have tormented a being inoffensive as a shadow.' "*

No wonder that she remembers it long after: and repeats it to herself when Paul Emanuel scolds her for the frivolity of a pink gown and some rosebuds in a bonnet. Brutality would have been less wounding.

He is much more than a charming and sometimes thoughtless young man. He is a *"beloved physician"* to the poorest of his patients. He is a man of culture and knowledge which Lucy prizes; he knows all the treasures of Villette, famous or obscure, and makes her free of them. Just so, George Smith offered London to Charlotte and Anne as he might have offered a bouquet. He is cured of his infatuation for Ginevra, and the process of the cure is in character and credible, as the infatuation never was. Ginevra, and John Bretton in connection with Ginevra, belong to Ouida rather than to Charlotte. "That mealy-winged moth," Lucy calls her; and is apter and neater in that single phrase than in all Charlotte's overloaded descriptions, and impossible conversations attributed to her.

Lucy goes back to the pension and "from the passionate pain of change to the palsy of custom," and waits for a promised letter.

" 'I'll write—just any cheerful nonsense that comes into my head— shall I?'

" '. . . you'll not have time.'

" 'Oh! I will find or make time. Good-bye!' "

There is a fearsome release of Rhetoric over this, while Lucy reminds herself that she must never by a written word betray her real feelings, and a flood of Allegory: several pages, in fact, which anyone might be pardoned for skipping . . . and then, from this welter of imagery there emerges a poignant and universal picture of a woman living for a letter. It is almost unbearable. Charlotte's own letters to Constantin Héger do not give a more vivid picture of those years of craving and crumbs at Haworth after her final return from Brussels.

"I suppose animals kept in cages, and so scantily fed as to be always on the verge of famine, await their food as I awaited a letter. . . . My hour of torment was the post-hour."

Professor Paul Emanuel has shown himself fanatically jealous of Lucy and Dr. John. He is the only individual to guess her secret—which is straining belief rather far, on Charlotte's part—and he behaves very badly indeed.

"Never was a better little man, in some points, than M. Paul: never, in others, a more waspish little despot." He is completely disarming in his rare moods of apology when he realises that he has wounded as well as angered Lucy; and Lucy treats him with spirit and an impish humour. He is beginning to attract her by his very ferocity as it dawns upon her that this eccentric little man sees her as something other than "Quiet Lucy," the creature "inoffensive as a shadow . . ." that he is intolerant, unjust, violently rude, and deeply contrite, because, to him if to no one else, she is important. . . .

"*You are well habituated to be passed by as a shadow in Life's sunshine: it is a new thing to see one testily lifting his hand to screen his eyes, because you tease him with an obtrusive ray,*" she tells herself.

That, then, is the first reason for Lucy's seeing the little professor as something other than a diminutive circus clown. But very soon there are others in abundance. The true Paul takes shape, elbows out of the way the splendid and towering figure of Dr. John, as he once does in a concert crowd, almost knocking Lucy down in his furious rush past. No quotation can convey the fiery strength and reality and appeal of Paul Emanuel completed. This is no Rochester, striding and ranting, and no wooden Indian of a Robert or Louis Moore. If there were no other achievement in *Villette*, the character of Paul Emanuel would make it unforgettable.

"*I used to think . . . that he had points of resemblance to Napoleon Buonaparte. I think so still.*"

He does not like learned women; but Lucy is ignorant, intelligent, and eager for scholarship. He works with her, unsparingly, keeps her supplied with books, shares his mental life with her.

"*What quiet lessons I had about this time! . . . How sweetly, for the jealous gibe, and the more jealous, half-passionate eulogy, were substituted a mute, indulgent help, a fond guidance, and a tender forbearance which forgave but never praised.*"

"*M. Emanuel was not a man to write books, but I have heard him lavish, with careless, unconscious prodigality, such mental wealth as books seldom boast; his mind was indeed my library and whenever it was opened to me, I entered bliss . . . I used to think what a delight it would be for one who loved him better than he loved himself, to gather and store up those handfuls of gold-dust, so recklessly flung to heaven's reckless winds.*"

He can sit in peaceful, unburdened silence with Lucy now. "*Il est doux, le repos! Il est précieux, le calme bonheur!*" says this little savant who has never before been known to rest peacefully for an hour.

And there comes an evening when he joins her in the garden, and takes her hand, and, instead of an ordinary, friendly greeting, says softly " '*Douce consolatrice*' . . ." The unusual

words, and the look in his ugly little face, give Lucy her first
knowledge that he loves her. And then, as a matter of course,
they are interrupted; and deliberately. Madame Beck and the
old priest, Père Silas, who is Paul's old tutor and pensioner,
come out into the garden. . . .

The obsessing figure of Dr. John is receding.

"*What was become of that curious one-sided friendship which was
half-marble and half life; only on one hand truth, and on the other
perhaps a jest?*"

Lucy does not quite know. But it is finished. And in its
place, and for always, there is a kindly friendliness on both
sides. Lucy is no fool; and her acidity is ebbing now that life
holds some good. She knows that, as she puts it, there will
always be a small, inconspicuous room in Dr. John's house of
life which is Lucy's Room. It was not so one-sided a friendship,
after all. . . .

But Paul Carlos speaks:

"*I was conscious of rapport between you and myself. You are
patient, and I am choleric; you are quiet and pale, and I am tanned
and fiery; you are a strict Protestant and I am a sort of lay Jesuit:
but we are alike—there is affinity between us. . . . Yes, you were
born under my star!*"

There, in a word, you have Lucy and Paul Emanuel. And
there, in Charlotte's conviction, you have Charlotte and
Constantin Héger.

Meanwhile, a charming, small picture is hung beside Lucy's
wide and storm-skied canvas. Little Polly and her melancholy
father suddenly re-appear. Mr. Home has inherited a Belgian
property and title; he is now the Comte de Bassompierèe and
Polly, at seventeen, is a fairy-like creature, the little Countess.
Dr. John rescues her in the panic when a theatre catches fire,
and Lucy is with him. There is a re-union of the households of
the Brettons and the Home de Bassompierèes and Lucy is in her
usual mouse-like rôle of trusted confidante in white linen, in
pointed contrast to Paulina's white satin. . . . The picture is
one of Charlotte's masterpieces in miniature. Paulina is
delicious; all her childhood traits remain, with the extra gift of
a sense of humour.

" . . . *since he (Papa) grew into a Count, he has needed so*

much attention . . ." as her father clamours for his breakfast.
And when she describes her first going to school:
"What was the result? In the most admirable manner, Papa came to school likewise: every other day he called to see me. Madame A. grumbled, but it was of no use; and so, at last, Papa and I were both, in a manner, expelled. . . ."

It is really no wonder that John Bretton's susceptible heart comes to anchor. In his sincere love for Paulina, the best in him comes into full play. Especially as Lucy, who now has her own life, shows a spurt of spirited defiance and flatly refuses to play go-between when that thick-headed young man appeals to her yet again. In Charlotte's hands, the golden lad and girl come, not to dust, but to a happy ending ever after. John Bretton and Paulina embody her fatalistic creed that certain human beings are born to good fortune and others are doomed throughout life.

Lucy and her professor are doomed for Charlotte. After every obstacle has been manipulated by Mme. Beck—(*"I knew she secretly wanted him, and had always wanted him"*) and Père Silas, Paul Carlos storms through them all, as he might be known to do. And on the night before he is to sail for the West Indies on a matter of family property, he and Lucy are betrothed in utter content and happiness. He leaves her established in a little school of her own, and he is to return in three years and marry her.

It would be obvious to any reader that Charlotte never intended a happy ending for these two. Otherwise, what was to hinder them from being married on the spot and going to the nebulous West Indies together? We know from Elizabeth Gaskell that it was Papa Brontë who could not endure the idea of an *un*happy ending: and it is amazing that Charlotte conceded as much as she did. It is not a very blind-folding concession after all: one wonders whether it even satisfied Papa?

In the autumn of Paul's return, there is an epic storm at sea: *"It roared frenzied for seven days. It did not cease till the Atlantic was strewn with wrecks . . ."*

And the reader is permitted by Charlotte to take his choice: either Paul survived or was among the drowned. Either Lucy knew "*the delight of joy born fresh again out of great terror*" or she was among those for whom "*when the sun returned, his light was night.*"

We know only too well that the sun never shone for Lucy.

AGNES GREY *and* THE TENANT OF WILDFELL HALL

IT has been rather generally accepted that Anne, as a writer, was a shadow, eclipsed by her great sisters. But one thing is certain: as a person, she lives. Gentle, lovable in goodness (which is not invariably a trait in good people), calmly poised in emergency, and full of courage. Her last spoken words, uttered almost in the act of dying, were *"Courage, Charlotte, courage!"* She, who was delicate in body all her life, was the embodiment of the words "In steadfastness and quietness shall be your strength."

So much so that, at the distance of a century, one feels grieved to say anything harsh of Anne's work: apologetic to her gentle shade. . . .

But there is really nothing to be said for her first small book, *Agnes Grey*, other than as a curio, something which one of the Brontës wrote. I happen to possess several bound volumes of a girls' magazine belonging to the period, or very shortly after; any one of its serial stories might be *Agnes Grey*. And any one of its steel engravings might illustrate that artless and extra-ordinarily lifeless story. And this cannot be put down to the conventions of the time. Where were they, anyway, those conventions? Charlotte Yonge was writing books concerned with teeming clerical households and infused with staunch clerical piety which are beloved and read and sought for and collected today; because her people are alive. Only Arthur Ransome has equalled her for living schoolboys and school-girls. Rossetti was writing smouldering poetry. Thackeray was castigating the upper classes; and calling a spade a spade in his lectures on the Four Georges, to which London society flocked. Dickens was opening the sewers which ran below the solid comfort of early Victorian existence.

Anne wisely restricted herself to the world that she knew: the daily life of a governess. But in this tepid little story, no one comes to life at all. There are villainous little children, and parents who crush young Agnes almost out of existence. There is a frivolous coquette, and a rector who tells a troubled old woman of his parish, crippled with rheumatism:

" 'It'll do your rheumatiz good to hobble to church,' he says: 'there's nothing like exercise for the rheumatiz'." And when she tries, haltingly, to explain that she is as troubled in spirit as in bones, tells her that if going to church doesn't satisfy her spiritual needs "it's all up" and that hell is probably her destined portion. . . . To offset this shepherd of souls there is a curate, Mr. Edward Weston, a forbidding-looking man, but he is patient and sympathetic with old Nancy and kind to the cat (which the rector smacked when it jumped on his knee . . .) and adopts the little dog which Agnes's employers will not allow her to keep. Anne, like Emily, and unlike Charlotte, loved animals. To make his virtues quite clear, Anne reproduces verbatim his prolonged evangelical homily to old Nancy. And a labourer "in the last stage of consumption" speaks movingly of his practical goodness:

" 'That's his way, Miss Grey; when he comes into a poor body's house a-seein' sick folk, he like notices what they most stand i' need on; an' if he thinks they can't readily get it theirseln, he never says nowt about it, but just gets it for 'em.' "

There is a wistful shadow of Willy Weightman here. But Mr. Weston has nothing of his high spirits, his humour, or, perish the thought, his susceptibility. Mr. Weston, you feel, has never sent a Valentine in his life.

Agnes's trials come to an end when she goes home to rejoin her widowed mother and start a school for young ladies. Mr. Weston is providentially appointed to the same watering-place. And even when he asks the happy Agnes to be his wife, on the cliffs and at sunset, Anne goes no further than

" 'You love me then?' " said he, fervently pressing my hand. " 'Yes.' "

And that is all. What in the world has happened to Gondal?

Agnes Grey found a publisher. Even though he delayed in bringing out the book by Acton Bell until Currer Bell's Jane Eyre had set the Thames on fire. They were not to know that

What they knew was that little Anne had written a book and the book had been accepted. Quite naturally, with this encouragement, she wrote another. She wrote *The Tenant of Wildfell Hall*.

Charlotte was almost as much distressed by Anne's second book as by *Wuthering Heights*. She said in her Biographical Note that Anne's motives were *"pure, but, I think, slightly morbid."* She maintained that Anne's gentle, melancholy nature was so much oppressed by the sight of Branwell doing himself to death through drink and general excesses that she flogged herself to write *Wildfell Hall* in the nature of a temperance tract.

This simply is not true. At best, it is a less-than-half-truth. That Anne's horror over Branwell gave her the idea is quite likely, is almost a certainty. No one in the family knew as much about Branwell's mad love-affair as Anne did. She was a witness of his *"daily troubled joy"* in the Robinson household, she was the Robinsons' governess. And the book is written in the sedate, precise style in which she wrote *Agnes Grey*; in which she probably tried to instruct her young pupils. But even if she began this piece of work in didactic mood it soon got the better of her. It is a melodrama, it is a moral story, if you like; but it is alive and it has passion. There is no known fragment of Gondal to which anything in *Wildfell Hall* can be attributed; but the spirit of Gondal surges through it. It is the only piece of work by Anne which even begins to make comprehensible her close companionship with Emily in the world of Gondal. This is the Anne who went to York and *"was"* half-a-dozen Gondal personages throughout that short visit. She is censorious throughout the book, it could not be otherwise. Just as Charlotte is censorious of wrong-doing in every book that she wrote. Only Emily stood outside and beyond judgment; she never found it essential to condemn where she created. But *Wildfell Hall* is a robust book; and robustness is odd to connect with fragile Anne. Some part of her mind must have corresponded to the unconquerable valour of her spirit, stronger than the frail body.

It is surprising that Anne, writing in the first person, wrote as a man, Gilbert Markham. Even Charlotte did not venture on

that, since William Crimsworth. The Markhams are a Yorkshire family who own an ample manor-farm; the widowed
mother is a managing, affectionate, dominating woman, rather
suggestive of Louisa Bretton. Gilbert is the eldest son, and
there is a pert, cheery sister, Rose, and a vigorous younger
brother, Fergus, who is restless in leading-strings, and wants to
go to sea or into the army, no matter which. Wildfell Hall has
been taken by a new tenant, a young widow, Mrs. Graham, and
the neighbourhood is curious and thronging to call. Indeed,
this opening scene at tea in the parlour is a reminder of the
opening of *Pride and Prejudice*. Rose is urging her mother to
call; and Fergus says gravely:

*"And, pray, be quick about it; and mind you bring me word how
much sugar she puts in her tea, and what sort of caps and aprons she
wears, and all about it, for I don't know how I can live till I know."*

Nobody laughs at this schoolboy humour. But Fergus is so
pleased with it that he chokes over his tea and has to rush,
snorting and strangling, into the garden.

Gilbert is bored by all the feminine curiosity and chatter.
Also, he is half in love with Eliza Millward of the vicarage. He
sees Helen Graham for the first time in church: like all-Highbury
and Mrs. Elton; like the Yorke family and Caroline Helstone;
church was the scene of so much satisfied curiosity in the books
of the first half of the nineteenth century. A tall young woman
in black, with long dark hair in glossy ringlets, and a slightly
haggard face with too much strength of will in it to please him.

He comes upon the Hall a day or two later in the course of
rough shooting; Anne's description of the steep, sheer country
and the half-deserted Elizabethan house in its overgrown garden
is almost worthy of Emily. It had stood enclosed in privet
hedges and boxwood and laurel cut into fantastic shapes that
are now either mangy or sprouting wildly. A little boy, trying
to climb the wall, slips, and is caught by Gilbert. Helen Graham
rushes from the garden and snatches the child from him: and
apologises, stammering and colouring, when Gilbert explains.

He encounters Mrs. Graham on various social occasions, and
has a strong argument with her about her perpetual care and
over-anxiety with regard to her small boy, Arthur. Helen is
strong and independent in her views; and she is equally

vehement in asserting that girls should not be brought up in shielded ignorance nor boys thrust into the rough-and-tumble of existence too soon. There is a definite antagonism between herself and Gilbert.

He sees Helen sketching out of doors, and walks home with her. A few days later he meets his sister, the rector's daughter, Eliza, and his young brother, all bound for the Hall. Fergus solemnly informs him

"... *you're not fit to associate with ladies and gentlemen like us, that have nothing to do but to run snooking about to our neighbours' houses, peeping into their private corners, and scenting out their secrets; or picking holes in their coats when we don't find them ready-made to our hands. You don't understand such refined sources of enjoyment.*"

Now, this may not be very light-handed humour, but humour it is, of a sort. And that Anne could sketch a school-boy with his tongue in his cheek is worth noticing.

Scandal buzzes round the mysterious young lady who chooses to live alone with her child and one old servant in a few rooms of the old, deserted house. Gilbert, who is now in love with her, is enraged; and asks her to marry him. She repulses him gently, and tells him that tomorrow she will make all mystery clear. At the gate, he looks back; sees Helen come out accompanied by a young man, Frederick Lawrence, the squire and actual owner of the Hall. He hears them talk intimately and sees them embrace. He rides home demented, and when he meets Lawrence on horseback next morning, knocks him down.

Gilbert goes back to the Hall, has a scene with Helen; who hands him her private journal which is to explain everything.

This, of course, is pure melodrama and the only interest in it lies in the surprising fact that Anne is writing. The homely scenes at the farmhouse, the scandal-mongering women and whispering girls, are very well done. The vignette of Eliza and her plain, hardworking sister Mary might almost have come from Charlotte's hand. Mary, who "*was trusted and valued by her father, loved and courted by all dogs, cats, children, and poor people, and slighted cnd neglected by everybody else.*" Anne, in short, could write. . . .

The diary tells the story. Helen was a young heiress, brought up by an aunt, and she is a skilful painter. Frederick Lawrence is her brother. (Anne really danced a fling with melodrama here.) She loses her head and her heart to a fascinating rake, Arthur Huntingdon, and insists on marrying him. He is a drunkard and a gamester, fills the house with his debauched companions, and tries to ruin the child-character of his little son as Earnshaw had tried to ruin Hareton. He leaves Helen alone in the country for long periods, but she is still too much in love with him not to forgive him whenever he comes back. His friend, Hargrave, loves and pities her and would willingly elope with her; but Helen sends him away.

Huntingdon finally causes Helen to revolt, when he makes love outrageously to her friend (sic) Annabella, whose husband, Lowborough, is blindly devoted to her. Helen flies, with her child and Rachel, her old nurse, now her maid. And takes shelter under the name of Graham at her brother's house, Wildfell Hall.

Now, all this is sufficiently highflown romance and, once more, the only point of interest might well lie in the fact that it is gentle, melancholy Anne who writes it. But this is not the case. There is fire in this piece of work; authentic fire. Helen may preach at her erring husband, but her anguish of disillusionment is real and her torture of jealousy over Annabella is a heart laid bare. There is a scene when Helen overhears two of the hard-drinking guests complain that Huntingdon is going to clear the house of them all to please his wife. Thankful, and generous, she goes into the garden in the moonlight to find him, and throws herself into his arms.

"First he murmured 'Bless you darling!' and returned my close embrace with a fervour like old times; and then he started, and in a tone of absolute terror, exclaimed,—'Helen! What the devil is this?'"

He scolds her for running out *"in your light evening dress this chill autumn night,"* and Helen answers gaily and happily *"It is a glorious night!"* He sends her indoors, and she kisses him again and runs back to the house. And a day or two later, prompted by Hargrave, goes out to the shrubbery, where she finds Huntingdon and Annabella in one another's arms. She

leans against a tree, half-fainting, and learns that when she flew
to her husband in the moonlit garden, it was Annabella whom
he expected. And hears him declare that he has not a jot of
feeling left for her but "*You know I must keep straight with her as
long as I can.*"

Helen remains with her husband in order to save little
Arthur, and keep him as much as possible with herself and old
Rachel. Huntingdon decrees that it is high time the boy had a
governess; and brings a demure and musical young woman into
the house who turns out to be his mistress. On which Helen
escapes with her child and Rachel.

There the diary ends.

There is a terrifically rhetorical scene between Gilbert and
Helen, in which she admits that she loves him and says that they
must never see one another again. She offers him in a handsome burst of pulpit-oratory the prospect of meeting in heaven
. . . which is quite in key with Anne and what you might
naturally expect.

Gilbert's not unreasonable retort is,

" '*But can you, Helen, contemplate with delight this prospect of
losing me in a sea of glory? . . .*' "

And really, in all this bookful of surprises, nothing is much
more startling than that—coming from Anne. . . . It is only, I
think, equalled by the interlude when Helen is pouring tea for
Mr. Grimsby, who is solemnly and ponderously in his cups:

" '*Did you ever hear such nonsense as they talk, Mrs. Huntingdon?
. . . They can't take so much as a bottle between them without its
getting into their heads——*'

" '*You are pouring the cream into your saucer, Mr. Grimsby.*'

" '*Ah, yes, I see, but we're almost in darkness here.—Hargrave,
snuff those candles, will you?*'

" '*They're wax; they don't require snuffing,*' said I."

Grimsby waves his hand solemnly, and continues "*with the
same strange uncertainty of utterance and heavy gravity of aspect as
before,*" to censure his host and his friends for their inability to
carry their liquor.

" '*I think you will find a sensible result produced on that tea,*' interrupted Mr. Hargrave, '*by the quantity of sugar you have put into it.
Instead of your usual complement of one lump, you have put in six.*' "

Whereupon, Mr. Grimsby, still solemnly, empties the over-sweetened cup into the sugar-basin by mistake for the slop-basin, and "*is constrained to trouble you for another.*"

Charlotte would have you believe that Anne wrote this, and other scenes, under duress of a sense of duty and with Branwell before her eyes. I take leave to doubt it. The writer in Anne was in the saddle, as she wrote. She was a grieving sister; she was certainly not a humorous writer or a humorous person; but she could write a really funny scene round a drunken man and a cup of tea.

Helen is summoned back to her husband who is dying. She nurses him—and sermonises him—and there is no death-bed repentance (which Branwell experienced). Anne was too much of an artist, with all her faults as a writer, to make use of that stage-prop. And it must have cost her pious and tender heart something, to refrain. Instead, she gives Huntingdon a few outbursts of very genuine feeling. His friend Hattersley observes awkwardly:

" '*I say, Huntingdon, I would send for a parson of some sort. If you didn't like the vicar, you know, you could have his curate or somebody else.*' "

And Huntingdon, clutching Helen's hand, returns:

" '*No; none of them can benefit me if she can't.*' "

And admits bluntly:

" '*I can't repent; I can only fear . . . except that I'm sorry to have wronged you, Nell, because you're so good to me.*' "

He dies. And Gilbert Markham waits in hope for Helen's return. When he is maliciously and flauntingly informed by Eliza that Mr. Lawrence has gone to be present at his sister's wedding to a Mr. Hargrave.

Gilbert rounds on her; and dashes to Lawrence's house, Woodford, for authentic news. The manservant tells him with a meaning simper that "*Master went yesterday to Grassdale . . .*"

Gilbert posts away to Grassdale, to find a wedding in process at the church—but it is Lawrence who is being married to Hargrave's pretty sister.

This, one would think, should unravel the coil. But he learns that Helen has inherited her uncle's rich property and is now the owner of half the country round. . . . This pleasing information is given him gratuitously by two fellow-passengers in the coach, who *"kindly came to his assistance and brought him low enough"* by enlarging on the timber, the game, pointing out Helen's woods and preserves with an umbrella and remarking jocosely that the widow, *"quite young yet, and uncommon hand-some"* will doubtless marry a nobleman.

" *'Fraid there's no chance for uz'* (*facetiously jogging me with his elbow as well as his companion*), *'ha, ha, ha! No offence, sir, I hope?'* (*to me*)."

This is novelette of the first water: but how unexpectedly that demure, dry humour of Anne's slips in again. One feels positively sorry for Gilbert.

This, then, he feels, is the end. You do not marry heiresses when all that you have is a Yorkshire farm. He stands under a tree—one of Helen's trees, confound it—and looks across the park at her stately mansion.

And then, need we say? a carriage rolls past, and little Arthur, from within, squeals for joy at the sight of his old friend, Mr. Markham. And Helen calls to the coachman to stop. Her aunt is with her, and they bear him off to the house. Gilbert, like the frog-butler, is very proud and stiff; and Helen is baffled and hurt.

He is as stiff as a ramrod; but Helen is warmly human and impulsive and—in short—standing no nonsense. She offers him her worldly goods and herself—and a rose—and he clasps her in his arms (but even in that blissful moment has to say *"Have you thought of your aunt?"*) Little Arthur now trots in with a picture-book; and everyone is happy.

A thorough, early Victorian romance, with the lovers kept apart by every machination of malice and of fate until the last page. A moral but forcibly melodramatic study of a Rake's Progress. An etching, inset, of a homely Yorkshire household; and a neat, dry study of a gossiping circle of men and women in a country district. A picture of the torment of jealousy in a girl's impetuous and disillusioned heart, which pulses with real pain. Some admirable, live conversation in a quantity of verbiage, like flickers from an embedded coal-fire. A good deal of homily; and some redeeming jets of humour. An appealing, sensitively-drawn figure of a woman with warmth of heart and grace and dignity, especially in the final love-scene and *éclaircissement;* Helen is fit to stand among the loved heroines of Victorian fiction, and she deserves to be better known than she is. Trollope might have drawn her, except for her tendency to preach. . . . A book that is entirely alive, despite its naïve defects.

The stuff of the Brontës is in Anne.

Part Three
PERSONAL WORD

PERSONAL WORD

BALLET FOR PUPPETS: A FANTASIA

THE stage stretched immense in emptiness, and the back-drop was a fugue of shadows, racing, weaving, rearing and sinking; their perpetual movement was a rushing of winds.

". . . horses with flying manes and thin legs, hunters and ladies and gentlemen on horseback.

" 'These are only dreams,' said the crow, 'they are coming to carry the high masters' thoughts out hunting.' "*

Below the tornado of shadows, sweeping and intermingling, was a plate-glass window of that concave glass which appears to be none, so that you feel you could stretch your hand and touch the objects shown. And there were gauze curtains lowered so that the figures behind them showed mistily; dummies in a plate-glass window? no, puppets, life-size, hanging limp on their wires.

The puppet-figures thronged about Emily in a tapestry of movement, Heathcliff a dark torch streaming, Cathy a dancing flame. It was triple flame that wreathed and soared as they two stretched hands to Emily and danced about her. The overhead lighting ran up and down the fine wires which manipulated those balanced limbs and joints and rayed in a web above the two dark heads. Their rhythm quickened, grew faster still, they were spinning, floating, against the cavalcade of the shadows; the wires snapped, drifted in a broken cobweb, vanished, the puppets took on life. The misty shapes of Linton, of Hareton, of the younger gold-headed Catherine, circled and drifted, mingling in the dance, but they were dimmed before the blasting force of the two who were welded by one invincible fire. While they danced, the rushing shadows swept high above them, and bore down upon them, and the sweeping robes brushed them in passing, went between them like a blade. Suddenly Cathy stood, swayed, flung her arms wide to the dark

* From *The Snow Queen*. Hans Andersen.

241

figure of Heathcliff, who snatched her to him. They retreated into the dimness of the hanging gauzes.

Emily did not move while her puppets closed upon her and receded. But when she stood alone, her sombre bodice rose and fell with her deep intake of breath and her nostrils widened to a harsh, keen air. In the instant of fusion, as her vision bore down upon her and possessed her, Emily's gaunt body arched backwards, arms lifted and outflung, vibrant with ecstasy, and gave one soaring leap that was a cry rendered by the straining flesh in place of voice.

Anne glided across the stage, fragile, graceful, in a sprigged dress, and her little company of people came about her. In the plate-glass window, through the gauze curtains, some puppets hung visible but motionless; no manipulation could set them dancing. Anne's pale Agnes Grey and her curate were limp and dangling against the wall and other puppets hung in a row beside them. There was a blank, neat doll in a lilac gown and a black silk apron, and a clumsy male puppet with a wooden face and large steel spectacles. Beside Frances Henri hung a pair of dangling dolls which should lie on divan-cushions or cover a telephone; one with black floss-silk ringlets and a robe of rather dingy white satin and a tarnished gold sash. Blanche Ingram, painted crudely as a Dutch doll, reduced to hanging beside the meek little lace-mender, her cherry mouth fixed in an unchangeable curl of haughty scorn, unable even to turn a bared shoulder and puffed satin sleeve on humble Frances. And next to her, a pink-faced, pouting doll in red velvet and glittering beads wound round her limp neck and stiff arms, yellow curls like barley-sugar cascading over her shoulders, a soiled lace handkerchief stitched to one hand. Ginevra had tilted sideways against Blanche, while beyond her a prim, solid puppet hung apart, plump as a pillow in a black gown, with bright chestnut hair tightly braided round the head. Mrs. Pryor's painted eyes stared fixedly before her, her painted mouth was pursed in dismay; mercifully, her wires were tight: she need not rub shoulders with the distressing company in which, poor blameless lady, she found herself.

But figures from Wildfell Hall moved about Anne, and their wires snapped and frayed into nothing. (This occurred throughout, whenever a puppet came to life.) Helen in pale dark beauty, Huntingdon and Gilbert Markham, broke from the wires into bludgeoning reality. The rake and charmer confronted the honest, bewildered lover, the solid northern farmer, baffled and wounded by the intricate mass of melo-dramatic situations and intrigues. Gilbert's sore heart beat through the sawdust. The dance of the two men was a duel of hate and contempt with something elemental in its vigour. And Helen, sinking to the ground between them in a passion of desperate weeping, was touched with life.

Huntingdon disappeared; and Gilbert stood, leaning against the old tree, looking down the green reaches of the park to the towers and the windows of Staningley, molten in the sun. And Helen came to him, in her black robes, the drenching black veil put back from her beautiful face and framing it, and the rose in her fingers. They danced, the advance and retreat of that culminating hour, the man rigid with pride, pacing with measured steps, the woman sweeping to him on a winged, spontaneous movement, retiring, rebuffed and resentful; turning, coming to him again in a swift, dauntless figure, confident, laughing at his scruples and his proud pain. They went out, together, his arm about her, her black draperies drifting across him. Anne stood, her pretty head bent in reverie, her bonnet with pink ribands hanging from her hand; and the air about her pensive, drooping figure pulsed with the melodramatic virility which her transparent fingers had evoked. And in the air was the sound of a whisper of laughter; a faint chuckle. The imp of humour that lurked in Anne, making itself heard. . . .

There was *The Dance of the Two Charlottes*. The puppet-Charlotte wore a dress of dark, plaid stuff, the folded necker-chief of Branwell's lifeless portrait and stiff, frizzed ringlets, as she trod across the stage with little steps and an occasional jerky lift and dip of the wires. She paced sedately back and forth, a book held close to her down-bent eyes, and every now and again lifted her head and glanced beyond the ring of light in which she moved with a nervous, abrupt gesture of appre-hension sharpening to fear. One stiff, minute hand went to the breast of the sober frock in a startled movement.

The figure which crept upon her had no wires: Charlotte, her ugly little face lit by the burning brown eyes, her lovely hair smooth and gleaming in a heavy net on her shoulders, a gown of pale silk whispering about her in full, soft folds. She caught the first Charlotte's arm, gazed urgently into her face; the first Charlotte stared at her in dread, snatched her arm away, and quickened her pace. They wove into a dance of pursuit and retreat; the live Charlotte following the puppet-figure like a shadow, murmuring at her ear, linking a bare arm in hers, waylaying and besetting her.

The prim puppet snapped from the wires and the dance was a conflict: Charlotte, the hypersensitive, shackled creature, fearfully drawn by the spell of her own gift and the tumult of her own passionate being, shrinking, repulsing, and beating down the other with blows of her tiny hands. The second Charlotte laughed, tossed back the glossy load of her hair, caught the small, frantic hands and spun her enemy into a pulsing waltz.

The shadows on the wall thronged, quickened into a frenzy, beat about the head of the first Charlotte like wings, blinding her. She jerked this way and that, to evade them, tore herself from her partner, and fled.

The other Charlotte lifted her silken skirts and danced like a swallow dipping and wheeling in the ring of light, still laughing to herself. Presently, the first Charlotte crept back and they stood facing one another. She clasped her hands, crushed the knuckles against her mouth, her small body quivered and stiffened. Her hands dropped to her sides, her head rose, she stood like a wooden soldier at attention. Then wheeled, and moved slowly away. The other Charlotte lifted her shoulders, shook her head, sank in a half-mocking, half-despairing curtsy, with a liquid movement of indescribable grace, and was blotted out by the curtain.

No Room For Death. On the stage Emily stood alone, closing in her unrelenting grapple with her invisible enemy that was not death but life holding her back. Alone, but the stage was peopled, crowded to suffocation, by the defiant challenge, the torment, the agony of that dying. As she stood, rigid in her chosen and fanatic isolation, her body incapable of further movement, a puppet-Shirley stole beside her and hovered; the

handsome, wilful figure that Charlotte's heart-wrung devotion
fashioned in Emily's likeness and which, at Emily's side, must
remain no more than a puppet. Out of Emily's presence,
sparkling with a vitality of her own, but beside her, of no more
actuality than Jane's fancy portrait of the great lady whom she
imagined as Rochester's wife.

Emily turned her haggard head and across her dying face
went a flash of indulgent, scornful amusement. The puppet-
Shirley withdrew, was whisked out of sight.

One other figure joined Emily in the uttermost moment:
Heathcliff, coming to her at a quiet, unhurried stride, to stand
at her shoulder. The two gaunt and terrible faces turned to one
another. Heathcliff was smiling: the *"unnatural appearance of
joy under his black brows."* . . . In the ecstasy of his own willed
dying, as the lost Cathy claimed him, only he could stand before
Emily as she waited for her own agony to make an end. He
took her hand and led her to that unyielding parlour sofa placed
at one side of the stage, and stood over her as she slowly sat
down, stiff and erect against the hard back, and so sitting, died.

. . . There were clipped yew hedges of cardboard splashed
blue and green with the peacock colours of a Cézanne painting
and cut into battlements and birds with spread tails. The male
figures in sober dark coats and narrow pantaloons paced from
the alleys between the crude hedges; Rochester, and Robert
Moore, dark-faced, black-browed and lowering, Louis Moore, a
grave student, John Bretton, handsome, urbane, with bright
head and chestnut side-whiskers and a suggestion of frilled shirt.
They went into a mazurka, forming couples, and the dark
Moore brothers moved as though they were one figure or
Siamese twins, Rochester danced like a Cossack, John Bretton
was nimble and easy with a side-glance of amused disdain for
Rochester's stampings and leapings. A short figure in a flying
greatcoat darted from a path and spun into a dance in the centre
of the stage while the tall, imposing figures of the other men
went on with their measured, agile movements, passing and re-
passing the frenzied spinning-top. John Bretton pointed to
Paul Emanuel with a shrug and a smile, and nodded his handsome head in tolerant salute to an old acquaintance. Paul
Carlos dealt him a furious scowl. Rochester's wide shoulders

lifted in a silent laugh. The Moore brothers stopped dancing and stood against the harsh blue hedge, gravely watching the little man. Paul Carlos pranced up to them, arms spread and head cocked; these men were of his race; they clapped their palms together in soundless applause, and shook hands with him.

From the walled side-paths the women came. Jane, with her russet head and small pointed face, holding her grey skirts wide, skimming and swooping madly as a dragon-fly. Shirley in her purple silk and rainbow scarf, her dark ringlets flowing. Caroline, her face half-hidden by those profuse brown curls, gliding and drooping, a flower in the wind. Paulina, a white swan, in a gauzy crinoline with white roses in her hair. And Lucy, tight, folded face and ruthlessly smooth braids, strutting sedately as though she marshalled the school crocodile for a walk. A tiny child, with eyes too big in a minute face, crept from the side and approached her, catching in one hand a fold of the pink cotton gown that was Lucy's one concession to frivolity. Lucy turned her head stiffly, looked down at the child-Paulina, and withdrew her dress from the fingers.

The men linked arms; the girls laid an arm about one another's waists; the two lines stood at opposite sides of the stage, facing one another. There was as palpable a sense of enmity, of battle, as though they were two opposing armies. Advance, retire; bows, curtsys; it might have been the start of a gavotte as Rochester made an elegant leg and John Bretton all but swept the floor with a flourish of the hand and snowy cuff-frill, while Shirley's pigeon-breast silks spread and sank and Caroline's head dropped till the long curls were a veil for her hidden face and her knee touched the ground under her soft muslins; were it not for antagonism like a bared blade, between the two supple ranks of figures. And Jane's green-hazel eyes were slits under the lowered lids as she raised her head. And Lucy's white, pinched face had the look of a small adder ready for the strike.

A puppet joined the men's ranks, stiffly, from where he stood aloof at the end of the linked line. A rigid figure, but the cold beauty of St. John Rivers' face and head gleamed suddenly, and there was life. He did not join the dance; he paced slowly upon Jane, his hands held out, and she shrank from him, swayed towards him, put her hands suddenly to her face. Rochester took a sharp step forward, and the men who were arm-in-arm with him held him back.

The sober-gowned Charlotte crept to Jane's side, put an arm round her, urged her towards the man who stood like the angel with the flaming sword. Jane stood poised on tip-toe, her body bent backwards, straining from him. The shadows sweeping above the painted hedges rose in a pæan of motion and force that was audible as a storm of sound. Jane flung Charlotte from her, threw up her hands repulsing St. John and slipped back into her place. He moved away to one end of the stage and Charlotte moved backwards to the other and the green walls received them.

The lines broke simultaneously. There was a mad rush of onslaught, full skirts flying about black, breeched legs, the girls lifted by their prim waists and whirled above the men's heads. Set down, they caught one another's hands, fled; and came stealing back again. The whirlpool resolved itself as the couples formed and merged in each other's hold: Jane with the arrow-flight of a bird hurling herself into Rochester's arms, Shirley turning her smooth shoulder and folding her scarf about her, not with coquetry but tense, rigid as a statue, until Louis Moore, striding across the boards between them, went to one knee before her, and rising, drew her into the measured, lovely dance of their exit. Lucy whirled to Paul Emanuel, her body in the plain pink dress writhing, racked, and her cold white face flayed with anguish and bitterness. Lucy's dance would have been a less terrible spectacle if she had worn the rags and beads of a gypsy and if her feet were bare and her smooth braided head an unkempt tangle. Paul Carlos caught her wrist, turned her distorted face to his: she sank against his shoulder, and her face was still hidden as he led her out.

Caroline lingered, the fingers of a hand pressed pensively to her cheek under the falling hair. It would all be well with Caroline, in her high-waisted gown and sandals and the festooned scarf drifting from her elbows: presently—any minute now—Robert would return from the pasteboard hedges, assured and purposeful, to claim her. But while she waited, two came stealing to join her: Charlotte, her small face kindled and her great eyes dark with thought; and a graceful puppet-Ellen, hovering and withdrawing. Caroline looked from one to the other and shook her head, and the dense curls wavered and fell, half-hiding the bewilderment in her face: Caroline, the triple-puppet; the tinted ivory miniature of Ellen; the mouth-piece for Charlotte's profound revolt on behalf of women and of her uneasy sense of the wrongs of oppressed workers: and the living girl whose love and whose pain break the framework of the picture to pieces.

. . . Ah, here's Robert. Charlotte the thinker, Ellen the pretty lay-figure, vanished with a flutter of skirts. Caroline was left, smiling and confident, to meet him.

The last surge of the pageant of shadows passed across the scene, and the sound of their vanishing swelled into a crescendo of wind with the voice of the beck in spate echoing through it.

. . . . .

Among the very numerous books which have been written about the Brontës are certain ones which, I must always feel, were written because the persons who wrote them had—possibly, indeed most probably, without realising it—a certain quality of kinship with those of whom they wrote. All of these commentaries or studies were written before the inestimable and unique research-works of Fannie E. Ratchford brought to light the fragments of the Brontës' imaginative writings. One of them at least was written shortly before the publication of Charlotte's letters to Constantin Héger. Nevertheless, they seem to me of particular value.

It would be impossible to exaggerate the gift to posterity of Fannie E. Ratchford's twenty years of indefatigable and indomitable research. But it is possible to let that inchoate mass of childhood writing block the sight to almost everything else in the Brontës' lives. And this, with profound respect for the work achieved, and with apology for my candour, I feel she has done. It is too much to assert that there was no other influence, no personal equation, in Charlotte's life. That no character in a Brontë book owed anything to a living model. That, in spite of the letters, Charlotte's experience in Brussels really counts for very little in comparison with certain Angrian fragments (which are, nevertheless, of immense value); and that May Sinclair, who wrote before they were published, was right in her vehement denial of any influence due to a love-affair. It is too much to dismiss Ellen, who knew a side of Charlotte unknown to anyone else, as "her staid, phlegmatic and unimaginative friend".

The writers of whom I speak here were not research-students. Their work on the Brontës was what I would name intuitive, and in one case quite indirect. I believe that if there should ever emerge an individual equally equipped for psychological study and for using his or her imagination—or, as Phyllis Bentley aptly suggested in one of her Brontë broadcasts, if there could be a task of collaboration between an expert in psychiatry and an outstanding writer of fiction—we should at last have an adequate book written on the Brontës.

May Sinclair was the greatest woman-novelist of her day. I do not, personally, feel that anyone who has come after her has surpassed her. (But before anyone rises to shout me down, I would remind them to look once more at the title to this part of my book.) She was an artist in intense and passionate emotion conveyed with restraint; she was permeated by a sense of humour which had the dryness of a fine, dry sherry. She was a diminutive creature with a soft voice and manner. A very young poet once said to me at a "*précieux*" literary gathering, staring across the room at the little lady, "Is that really May Sinclair? I thought she wrote very fierce books? . . ." And this was one of the many times when she reminded me vividly of Charlotte.

She had something of the indefinable virginity of the spirit which was in Emily. It led her to write her greatest novel, *The Creators*, the study of a woman who falls in love and marries and finds herself wrecked between her love and her work. It was something of an obsession with her. It drove her to write her vehement Preface to *Villette*, in which she poured scorn on the idea that Charlotte had a love for M. Héger . . . "that actual love-story which is supposed to be the base and root of all novels written by women. *Tout talent de femme est un bonheur manqué.*" She says that "if M. Paul Emanuel had been drawn, line for line, from M. Héger, he would never have come before us with vivid, startling indomitable life." But no one, as far as I know, has ever asserted he was. And, soon after this Preface, the letters were made public.

May Sinclair said of Charlotte that she "never attained to a detached and impersonal view of any person or thing." And that is equally true of herself. She was not afraid of words. She could use hyperbole or denunciation without fear. She called Shirley "a mass of glorious, palpitating fragments", and today's reader, strait-jacketed by understatement, winces just a little. But that is exactly what it is: only, you or I speaking of it would call it "unequal" or something colourless of the sort. Fashions change in phraseology as in hats or dresses; but is it conceivable that material-under-review changes as well? And that no one would use such a panegyric today because no one writing today would be worth it. . . .

The Brontës stole into May Sinclair's work. Her *Rector of Wyk* is a painful study of a sadistic old clerical father with frustrated daughters. It is certainly not to be supposed that this is a study of the Haworth household as seen through her eyes. I only mean to imply that it was written when her mind was full of them. She stated that she read Elizabeth Gaskell's life of Charlotte at least twenty times; and Mrs. Gaskell detested Papa, and considered him a selfish, tyrannical, and hypocritical old man. The Rector of Wyk is sensual; and Elizabeth Gaskell disliked the fact that Papa admired her and paid her elaborate, old-fashioned compliments, and showed, in old age, faint stirrings of the embers. It is not always remembered that in his youth he was very good-looking and highly susceptible. Also that, young or old, he was still an Irishman.

May Sinclair wrote one war book. She joined an ambulance-unit in Belgium in the First World War, and her fragile physique and her intense sensitiveness made it a harrowing experience and not a successful one. *The Romantic* is forgotten now; but it was one of the first books written to de-glamorise war and to expose the pitiful and paltry uglinesses which breed in war work. It throbs with pain. And it is an echo of everything which Charlotte memorably expressed of her own feelings about war. They were of one mind there, as often elsewhere.

May Sinclair's extreme sensitiveness and her fearless use of splendid words in enthusiasm make her, at times, a too partial critic. But no one has *interpreted* the Brontës as she could.

Romer Wilson's book on Emily, *All Alone*, was, of course, written with no knowledge of Emily's world of the imagination, and must necessarily suffer from the lack. It may be said to suffer, also, from being written to support a startling theory, namely, that Emily was possessed by a dæmon-lover, was, in fact, a female version of Faust. But really, I find this fantasy more of a tribute to Emily's heights of power than some other theories which have been freely expressed concerning her. . . . Even if it relegates her to the state of Mr. Mantalini. . . . And the writer, even without benefit of knowledge of Emily's secret world, enters into her existence of the imagination as no one else has done.

Romer Wilson was at college with me. I remember her as a pallid girl, thin as a lath, and delicate in health. Even in those pea-green days of ours, she was a poet, a playwright, a remarkable actress. A few of us assembled and published a very slim volume of our poems, and Romer contributed some of her own. But just before the book went to press, she asked me to have coffee in her room, and suddenly asked me to withdraw her poems. It cost her an effort, because we were in a state of jubilee over this, our first production. She said they weren't good enough to be published—which might with perfect truth be said of all of ours, I expect—and I remember that she caught my hand as she made the demand, and that hers was wet and shaking. I thought, She has a temperature; I had no idea that she was to die, as the Brontës died, almost as young as Emily and Anne. But I sensed the truth which she was too great to put into words: that she had an instinctive knowledge of her own real gifts, and did not want a sheaf of undergraduate poetry to get as far as the printed word and be remembered as hers.

She was a north-countrywoman, and the country of the Brontës was in her veins, and, incidentally, she knew it blindfold. She could enter into their teeming imaginations. She is not only remembered for her brilliant works of fiction, written in an idiom ahead of her time—she must be one of the very few novelists of a quarter-century ago whose works, when read today, sound as though they were written today. But for her collections of fairy-tales from all countries of the world, *Red Magic*, *Green Magic*, *Silver Magic*, with her serious, witty notes of interpretation and her dedication "To the Children of England, good, bad, and indifferent". It is a significant fact that all these interpretative writers on the Brontës were well-endowed with humour. Enchanting legends, the fairy-story at its greatest; books to be read with absorbing delight by more than children. And only a mind of deep and intrinsic imaginative power would have run them to earth and brought them together.

She shared one other thing with the Brontës: we knew her as Roma, beautiful and perhaps rather romantic name. A comic error in spelling on the part of some correspondent gave her the version which she chose to use in her writing, because it did not give away the fact that she was a woman-writer. Acton, Ellis, and Currer Bell; Romer Wilson.

A book by Rachel Ferguson has the title *The Brontës Went to Woolworth's*. It is a slightly misleading one; because the Brontës only make the briefest of appearances in the book. But it belongs to Brontë books by virtue of something less direct and far more noteworthy: it is one of the very few studies in fiction of persons given over to a dream-world and a dream-life. The girls in this book have not a trace of morbidity. They are vital young creatures in a delightful household, they have absorbing jobs. They are anything but solitary; they have more friends and acquaintances than they can do with. They are also, in company with their delicious mother, witty—funny, in fact— to a degree. But their world peopled by imagined figures is so much more real than their surrounding one that Deirdre, independent and successful and a well-spring of keen humour, admits that she has refused a man whom she almost married, because at the time she was too much in love with a celebrated figure in fiction to be able to see him clearly. . . .

The Brontës permeate this book more subtly than in their short ghostly-appearance. There is the intensely close bond between the two sisters and their care for the youngest, an endearing child. Their love for their ungainly dog, who is definitely a member of the household. The two pictures of governesses: the one, a frustrated and nerve-ridden maker of trouble, the other a distressingly hearty young woman who lands on any stray evidences of their imaginary existence with both feet and in heavy hockey-boots and insists on trying to "play too". Two brilliant studies, these. But the memorable thing about the book is not just that the writer is impregnated by the Brontës, but that she has made a remarkable picture of persons in thrall to the dreaming-faculty. Something of the same *motif* comes into her later book *Evenfield*, where a woman cannot get away from her childhood. And even more markedly into a book by another writer, *The Unfaithful Wife*, by Naomi Royde-Smith, where a woman, in her husband's long absence at sea, falls in love with a film-hero never seen except in pictures. Here the writer did an ingenious thing in making the film-actor one easily identifiable as the first man in pictures who made himself very generally and sincerely loved for no good looks and certainly for nothing of the Great Lover, but simply through the possession of a personality so attractive that it tore the cheap celluloid to pieces. I loved him myself.

Somewhere in such work as this, I feel, lies part of the answer to the need for a less single-track interpretation, explanation, what-you-will, of the Brontës.